THE *Virgin* GOOD JUNK GUIDE

THE *Virgin* GOOD JUNK GUIDE

David Black

First published in Great Britain in 1993 by
Virgin Books
an imprint of Virgin Publishing Ltd
332 Ladbroke Grove
London W10 5AH

Copyright © David Black 1993

The moral right of the author has been asserted

This book is sold subject to the condition that it shall not, by way of
trade or otherwise, be lent, resold, hired out or otherwise circulated
without the publisher's prior written consent in any form of binding
or cover other than that in which it is published and without a
similar condition including this condition being imposed upon the
subsequent purchaser.

A catalogue record for this book is available from the British Library

ISBN 0 86369 706 2

Edited, designed and typeset by Book Creation Services Ltd, London
Cartography by Neil Hyslop and Talkback International Ltd.

Printed and bound in Great Britain by
Biddles Ltd, Guildford and King's Lynn

With grateful thanks to Angela Palmer and Sheila McNamara of the
Observer Magazine, and also to Nic Andrews, Maria-Luisa Comerma,
Jessica Duncan, Paul Forty, Christina Jansen, Melanie Jessop, Dennis
Joy, Adrienne Thomas, Clint Twist, Justine Willett, Gill Woolcott and
Yvonne Worth for their help in this book's preparation.

Few travel books are without errors and no guidebook can be
completely up to date, for telephone numbers and opening hours
change without warning and businesses may change hands, which
can affect the goods they sell. Although every attempt has been
made to ensure that the information contained in this book is
accurate and any corrections or suggestions for improvements that
can be incorporated in the next edition will be welcome, the
publishers cannot be held responsible for any consequences arising
from the use of this book or from the information published in it.
The entries are for information only and should not be taken as
endorsements, unless this is specifically stated, nor should the
omission of any establishment or trading point be regarded as an
adverse judgement.

CONTENTS

AUTHOR'S PREFACE

'Junk is an attitude of mind'. So, at any rate, suggests one dealer who has handled more than his share of the stuff. He has a point. There are those who adore junk, and are prepared to spend hours of spare time rummaging through market stalls and back street shops. There are also those who cringe at the very idea of putting up with other people's rejects.

The problem, in part, is a semantic one – what exactly is junk?' The general perception is rarely flattering, summoning up visions of cobweb-festooned clutter and dilapidation. Over the past few years, however, there are signs that the pejorative view is changing. This is due, in part, to a general realisation that goods made in the past were often well crafted, well designed and built to last. Added to this, there has been a rise in environmental awareness leading, inevitably, to a reaction against waste.

Buying junk today is no longer a question of self-denial, or a matter of making ends meet. On the contrary, it has become the positive choice for the imaginative homemaker. Part of the fun of junk-hunting is its unpredictability. Plan as you might, you just never know when, or where, you are going to come across those unexpected bargains.

It is, after all, a game with no fixed rules, in which the winner will need luck and intuition, as well as knowledge and judgement. The trick is just to keep on looking.

Many people were involved with the research and production of this book – too many to mention by name. Thanks are due to those at Virgin Publishing, especially Rob Shreeve, for his inspiration and support, and Hal Robinson of Book Creation Services, who provided encouragement and much unstinting effort. Further thanks are due to the contacts throughout Britain who provided additional information.

Above all, my wife, Alison, and children, Hugh and Adam, deserve very special thanks for putting up with my junk-hunting predilections, not only during the preparation of this book but also during the months that went into researching and writing the six-week series on the same subject for the *Observer Magazine*.

David Black, March 1993

INTRODUCTION
IN PRAISE OF JUNK

The challenge that confronts the aspiring junk-hunter is a daunting one; just how do you set about acquiring enough liveable-with furniture and stylish clutter to set up a home without giving the game away? The game being, of course, to deliver the smartest possible look for the least possible cost.

The very word 'junk' means different things to different people. For some, the connotations can be distinctly off-putting. Aren't other people's throw-outs really only good for piling on the dustcart? Junk – the reasoning goes – is for the hard-up, or for those who don't care about keeping up appearances.

This is a perception which, not many years ago, was widely held. Today, it is becoming distinctly unfashionable. We now live in an age in which the philosophy of environmental awareness encourages the maximum re-use of resources, which is precisely what the junk trade has been about for years.

Most people also have individual resources to consider. What is the sense in paying hundreds of pounds for ubiquitous, off-the-peg modern furniture when you can buy durable, well-designed secondhand and antique items at auction for a fraction of the price? Why spend a fortune on new crockery when you can pick up some solid and serviceable hotel clear-outs from Fred's Junk Bazaar for a fiver?

What is junk?

If people do have a problem with the idea of junk it is usually one of definition. Junk can be viewed negatively or positively. The last thing we want to suggest in this book is that anyone should be living with inferior rubbish. On the contrary, our purpose is to help you find useful and unusual items which will be at least as good as, and in many cases better than, their modern mass-produced equivalents.

The scope of *The Virgin Good Junk Guide* is wide ranging. The 'good junk' in our listed entries could be anything from no-nonsense house clearance basics to value-for-money antiques and collectors' items. We include outlets which may, indeed, carry some fairly grim and uninspiring dross, but which might also, occasionally, come up trumps with something irresistible. We also include a number of upmarket outlets where, from time to time, quality goods can be picked up for surprisingly reasonable prices.

The successful junk-hunter will always be the one who keeps an open mind, who won't be put off by the endless detritus of a car boot sale, or be intimidated by the gleaming silver and polished Georgian mahogany of an impeccably ordered antique shop. In either case, you might well find the object you're looking for at the price you're prepared to pay. The lucky few might even set themselves up with the bargain of a lifetime.

Creation of the guide

The Virgin Good Junk Guide aims to be nothing less than the definitive budget-buyer's manual. Whether you are a committed collector after some rare example in your chosen field, a mortgage-strapped young couple in need of a chest of drawers for the spare room, a holidaymaker with a few hours to fill en-route to your next destination, an impecunious student in search of some cheap and cheerful additions to a rented bedsit, a dealer on the look-out for fresh stock, or simply someone who relishes the idea of picking up a bargain, then this is the book for you. If, on the other hand, your idea of fun is to blow £15,000 on a Louis XVI secretaire, then it probably isn't.

In 1992, while I was researching and writing a six-week series on junk-hunting for the *Observer Magazine*, I was particularly struck by two things.

The first was the number of dealers who felt that the antique trade was often handicapped by an upmarket image, which tended to put off many ordinary members of the general public. I had anticipated continual gasps of horror at the mention of the work 'junk', but in the event there were to be no more than two or three objections. The vast majority of dealers were, on the contrary, delighted to be associated with the notion of budget buying.

The second surprise was that general information on mid- to lower-range antique shops was sparse, and certainly not available on a UK-wide basis.

Put both factors together, and the conclusion was inescapable – there was a clear need for a nationally focused reference book on the subject.

The gap in the market was spotted by Rob Shreeve at Virgin Publishing, and I was invited to take the idea that lay behind the *Observer* series and develop it into a directory for the budget buyer. This book is the result.

The scope of *The Virgin Good Junk Guide*

It should be explained at the outset, however, that this is not simply another guide to buying antiques. There are already several publications covering this area, including the excellent *Guide to the Antique Shops of Britain* at £14.95 from The Antique Collectors' Club.

The Virgin Good Junk Guide is concerned with what might loosely be termed the 'affordable end of the market'. Our sources include charity shops, car boot sales, architectural recyclers, antique markets, house clearance shops and country auctions, as well as the more orthodox retail outlets. Where practical, we give brief descriptions of these different outlets, and the sort of goods they usually stock. We have added a few words of background about many of the larger towns and cities, to remind the wandering junk-hunter that there may be additional virtues in a visit, and we have also added a few notes on various areas of collecting.

The majority of entries carry fair quality secondhand goods or moderately priced antique and collectors' items. Some specialise in 'shipping furniture' – the term which normally denotes the sort of solid Victorian to pre-war pieces favoured by antique exporters. Others dabble in bric-a-brac, or the general mix of crockery, ornaments and curiosities which can have particular appeal for the rummager. The information about them all has been carefully culled from a variety of sources, including tourist information centres, council planning officials, libraries, village postmistresses and, above all, from those involved directly in the junk and antique business. They all deserve a special word of thanks. Wherever possible, our observations were based on actual visits, though with some estimates suggesting there could be as many as 50,000 people involved in the antiques and secondhand trade at one level or another, a call on each one was never going to be a practical proposition.

The joy of junk

Looking for junk can be immensely rewarding. At times, it can even pay huge dividends. One lesson learned from this survey is that spectacular finds can still be made. Sometimes it can be a matter of rescuing a part of the heritage. This was the case when one sharp-eyed punter bought an old white-laquered bureau for £200 only minutes before it was due to be immersed in the caustic stripping tank. It turned out to be the work of Glasgow architect and designer Charles Rennie Mackintosh, and it was later sold for £110,000. Sensational discoveries of this magnitude may be rare, but they add a certain piquancy to the otherwise mundane process of sifting through endless junk. The next headline-grabbing find could be the one picked up at a car boot sale, such as the Doulton 'Bunnykins' family that was bought for £4.60 then resold for £3,690. Or it might be lurking in the back room of a cluttered junk shop, like the album of drawings by Swiss artist Henry Fuseli, which realised a cool £750,000 at auction.

It is unlikely, although not altogether impossible, that *The Virgin Good Junk Guide* will help new junk hunters produce results of this order. What we can be sure of, however, is that if the guide is used regularly it will probably pay for itself several times over, not only in terms of money saved but also in new sources found and new discoveries made.

Buying junk can be immensely entertaining. The antique and junk business attracts people who place a high value on independence, and tend to favour an individual approach to life. This individualism comes in all sorts of guises, from the taciturn to the talkative, and all variations in between. There are some given to complaining – often, it has to be said, with fair cause, because of the combined business rate, the lack of a steady supply of stock, and the ever-decreasing margins resulting from the competitive scramble for a diminishing supply of goods. Many of the more traditional dealers lament the passing of the once sedate style of trading, which used to be the norm. Others frankly admit that the cut and thrust of dealing gives them a buzz. They are all agreed on one thing, however, which is that the one certainty in today's antique and junk business is that things are in a continual state of flux. This has never been more true than it is now.

The junk trade today

Times are as tough at the bread-and-butter end of the trade as many can remember. The recession has compounded a problem that many were warning about years ago – the critical shortage of goods. Decades of virtually unrestricted high-volume container shipping, which reached its peak in the 1970s and 1980s, has seriously depleted the stock of good secondhand and budget antique furniture. The gradual loss of so much middle-quality Georgian and Victorian brown-wood furniture has increased competition at the lower end of the market. Once plentiful authentic pine, too, is becoming less easy to find.

In a curious way, it has been the popularity of antiques that has produced this situation. For the antique business to thrive there must be a proportion of the population that wants to get rid of its old clutter as well as a proportion that wants to acquire it. The upland farmer who, 30 years ago, would have happily let a 'knocker' buy an unwanted pine dresser for a few pounds has been succeeded by a son and daughter-in-law who are fully paid-up members of the Laura Ashley generation and now want to hang on to such things. The result? The shortage is exacerbated and the goods become more difficult to find.

Despite this, Britain remains an astonishing treasure house of the antique and collectable. Vast quantities have certainly been shipped out of the country over the last 40 years and a greater number of us may choose to keep our family heir-looms, but if you know where to start searching there is still a great deal of it out there waiting to be discovered.

Caveat emptor

It should, of course, be borne in mind that as with any area of trading there can be pitfalls for the junk hunter. You should always ask for, and keep, a receipt for any article of more than a few pounds' value, giving a full description of your purchase. Where a dispute does arise, the buyer of junk is, in theory at least, entitled to the same level of protection as the customer in a department store or car showroom. In the case of secondhand and antique furniture, however, it will usually be accepted that some signs of wear and tear, or a few time-honoured scars, are part of the deal. In the case of articles bought at auction or from normal retail sources, the three principles enshrined in the Sale of Goods Act are fully applicable. An item should be of merchantable quality, as described, and fit for its intended purpose. Provided the item is taken back to the dealer within a reasonable period of time, you are fully entitled to ask for your money back. In the case of car boot sales, street markets and antique fairs, there can be other problems – including finding the person who sold you the goods in the first place.

Where a dealer is being particularly awkward, a local

authority tradings standards officer might be prepared to help. Much of the legislation relating to the simple act of making a purchase from a shop is complicated, especially when taken in conjunction with other factors, such as EC directives on foam-filled furniture.

In the case of secondhand goods, safety must be a major consideration, especially with potentially high-risk goods such as old toys, push chairs or nursery equipment, second-hand electrical equipment, glass-topped tables, stepladders and secondhand furniture, which should be structurally stable.

Never buy any antique without thoroughly examining it, and watch out for fakes and forgeries, even at the lower end of the market. The most notorious culprits of recent years have included 'bronze' figurines of cold-cast metallic resin, 'carved' Japanese netsuke figures, which started life in a latex mould, decorative scrimshaw articles purporting to be made from ivory, bogus meerschaum pipes, cleverly 'distressed' Eastern icons, supposedly antique oriental vases with their 'Made in China' stamps erased from the base, and that perennial favourite, the Cairo souk version of the ancient Egyptian artefact. Most dealers with a long-term interest in their business have absolutely nothing to do with such things, and auction houses are generally adept at spotting them. Nevertheless such goods do still crop up occasionally.

Many pine dealers now carry a mix of old and new stock – and make no attempt to hide the fact – but even here there can be grey areas, such as cupboards made up from Georgian shutters and architraves. It should also be remembered that while caustic stripping can remove paint from wood, if overdone it can also dissolve the glue in joints, soften gesso relief and buckle plywood drawer bases.

The most effective line of defence for the junk buyer comes down to two words – *caveat emptor* – which, roughly translated, means 'use your common sense and watch out'. However, it also pays to have a basic understanding of your rights as a consumer from the outset. Two particularly helpful publications – *How to Put Things Right* and *Fair Play* (produced in association with BBC Radio 2) are available free from The Office of Fair Trading, Room 306, Field House, Bream's Buildings, London EC4A 1PR.

Future editions

Inspiration and skill are usually the main ingredients of a

successful junk hunt. With a sense of adventure, the knack of spotting an opportunity, and a copy of this book, you should be well on your way to achieving good results. We have tried our best to make our listings information as comprehensive and accurate as possible. However, it should be borne in mind that shops can relocate, change hands, or close down altogether; car boot sales and charity shops often operate under short-term lease arrangements; and auctioneers can alter their sale schedule depending on how much, or how little, they have to dispose of. Inevitably, we will have missed out some outlets that should have been included, and perhaps even listed a few which you feel don't quite come up to scratch.

With your help, we can iron out such anomalies in future editions. We are particularly keen to hear from any reader who has constructive suggestions to offer, or who would like to draw our attention to sources we may have overlooked. Let us know, too, if you come across an outlet which is particularly good.

The address to write to is The Virgin Good Junk Guide, Virgin Publishing, 332 Ladbroke Grove, London W10 5AH.

Good junk-hunting!

Junk-hunting is about many things. Social history; buying on the cheap; the responsible use of existing resources; the pleasure of choosing; the assertion of one's identity.

It also tells us something about the times we live in. While there are still talented craftsmen and craftswomen in Britain who know how to produce quality goods, for the bulk of the population financial restraint means that choice is usually limited to the volume-produced alternative. Mass production should not necessarily equate with blandness, tackiness and poor quality, but all too often it does. At its best, it can produce minor masterpieces – the Thonet bentwood, that classic 'chair from the Vienna wood'; the American Ansonia Clock; and such eminently practical British products as Lloyd Loom and Utility furniture.

Today, for all our state-of-the-art technology and our familiarity with manned space travel, we seem unable to produce good, durable furniture at a low cost for that most important space of all – the home. It is this, as much as anything, which explains the growing appreciation for junk. Buy it while you can.

CLASSIFIED SUBJECT INDEX

To help you in your search, we have targeted a number of outlets which either specialise in certain collectable categories, or at least stock them frequently. The following list is designed to be helpful, rather than definitive, and by no means includes every specialisation. Silver and porcelain are omitted, for example, because they are normally sold by a large proportion of the listed entries in the guide. The same applies to furniture of all kinds, as well as to 'bric-a-brac' and 'collectables', both common catch-alls that many dealers use for their unclassified stock. Pictures and prints are included, although the outlets referred to should be regarded as supplementary to galleries and fine art specialists. Antique centres, fairs and markets have not been classified, nor have auction rooms, since these are self-evidently sources which should be investigated for specialist goods and general antiques alike.

Architectural salvage and lighting

Art deco, art nouveau and aesthetic movement

Militaria and medals

Records and music

Sports and fishing items

Technical and scientific instruments

Textiles and costumes

Toys, dolls and juvenilia

KEY TO REGIONS OF BRITAIN

The geographical divisions used in this guide represent a view of market areas for junk and antique hunting, even though they may not equate with more conventional, regional boundaries.

LONDON
AND TOWNS NEARBY

London's junk-buying potential is in a class of its own.

It would be impossible to calculate the volume of goods that are being turned over at any one time, or even the number of individuals involved in the trading of junk and antiques at the various levels of the market. There is a tremendous

amount of speculative dealing of an indeterminate character, from the hard-pressed unemployed sifting through jumble sale detritus for anything that might turn in a profit of a pound or two, to titled ladies dabbling in interior decoration as a pastime, rather than a business. Between both extremes exists an army of runners, combing the provinces for anything that can be resold to the established London trade, stall renters upholding the ancient traditions of costermongering, collectors off-loading a few acquisitions in order to buy something better, and, increasingly, people in regular jobs who have discovered that their own hobby-based enthusiasms can help to supplement the mortgage by a once-a-month stint at an antiques fair.

The allure of the antique and junk business is not simply a matter of avarice; the thrill of the hunt is very much part of the process. In this respect, London is full of surprises. Low-cost antiques are by no means the sole province of the junk trade. Exceptional buys can also be made at the top end of the market and in the city's numerous auction rooms. Where rental values per square foot are particularly high, it can even be cost-effective for a dealer to sell at a loss, if an item is proving particularly hard to move. Some of the smartest shops are also prepared to cater for buyers on a tight budget – after all, today's penniless student could be tomorrow's captain of industry with a large Georgian house to furnish. The chances of buying junk, per se, in such places are virtually nil, and you should be prepared to accept that quality – even at a discount – deserves to command a reasonable price. The criterion we apply in this book is, essentially, one of good value for money, and if this is available in Bond Street (as it can be) then Bond Street is on our junk trail. Even the gallery that holds the Royal Warrant qualifies for entry here, simply because – as well as the Correggios and Fragonards – they occasionally have good minor British watercolours at prices that compare well with similar ones in ordinary galleries elsewhere.

CENTRAL LONDON
(W1, WC1 & 2, EC 1, 2, 3 & 4)

Stratospheric property values and a quality-led dealing culture leave little scope for the junk hunter in the heart of the West End and the City, but there is another side to the story. With Britain's three leading auction houses within a few minutes' walk of each other, massive quantities of goods are filtered through the rooms every day, and by no means all of it for the cashmere coat and gold Rolex set. Even the smart shops and galleries can come up with the odd inexpensive piece, as can the book and print shops and fairs of Charing Cross Road and Bloomsbury, and some of the established market complexes.

Abbot & Holder
30 Museum Street, WC1
071 637 3981
A comprehensive and browsable range of watercolours, drawings and original illustrations. Popular with collectors whose budgets may not coincide with their tastes – £50 can buy a perfectly respectable, if minor, work.

Thomas Agnew & Sons
43 Old Bond Street, W1
071 629 6176
Junk on Bond Street? Hardly, but Agnew's, as well as supplying the artistically sublime to the world's leading collectors and institutions, often have mini-exhibitions of uncatalogued items – especially watercolours, which can be surprisingly inexpensive.

Apple Market Stalls
Covent Garden Market, WC2
071 836 9136

Operates every Monday, plus one or two Sundays per month. About 40 stalls with a varied mix of antiques and collectables, including jewellery, pottery and porcelain, teddy-bears, boxes, glass, leather items, telephones and radios, some small furniture and clothes and textiles. Geared to the tourist trade, but still with some eye-catching potential as well as the odd bargain.

The Button Queen
19 Marylebone Lane, W1
071 935 1505
Buttons of every description, from the 18th century to the present day and including examples in Wedgwood, horn, glass, gold and silver, semi-precious stone, Dorset thread, white metal and wood and designed for a variety of locations (the battlefield, the hunt, the servants' hall, etc).

Charing Cross Collectors' Market
Northumberland Avenue and Embankment Place, WC2
On Saturday, philately, numismatics and other collecting disciplines.

The Cinema Bookshop
13–14 Great Russell Street, WC1
071 637 0206
For those who like the idea of waking up to the sight of Meryl Streep or Nigel Havers, posters are available from £7.50. Books, magazines, stills and general cinema ephemera also feature on the shelves.

Covent Garden Fleamarket
Jubilee Market, WC2
071 836 2139
A Monday extravaganza, plus

occasional high days and holidays, consisting of around two hundred stallholders selling a wide range of general antiques and collectors' items.

Eldridge's
99–101 Farringdon Road, EC1
071 837 0379
Rarity of rarities, a non-profit-making antique shop. The general view of the antique trade is rarely a benign one, thanks partly to 'Lovejoy' and the naked avarice of 'The Antiques Roadshow'. Brian Eldrige provides the antidote. For 40 years, profits from his shop have helped support academic research into various categories of antiques, particularly those associated with social history and the development of furniture making. Stock is broad-ranging: scientific instruments, telescopes, busts, intaglios, treen, boxes, games, British furniture and Hogarth prints, with everything well-researched and, refreshingly, nothing restored. Discriminating professionals, particularly lawyers and doctors, are the core clientele. Junk, as such, is not stocked, but the 1,200 square feet of showroom space include low cost items (around £15) as well as the occasional dauntingly expensive piece.

J Franks
7 New Oxford Street, WC1
071 405 4274
Long established source of philatelic and postal history items and printed ephemera.

Gray's Antiques Market
58 Davies Street, W1
(also including Gray's Mews)
071 629 6680
Approximately 100 dealers selling a varied assortment of collectors' items and general antiques in a well-organised and well-designed space – a tributary of the River Tyburn being one decorative element. Dealers tend to be professional and standards are generally high; the management even offers a money-back guarantee on goods of up to £1,000 that turn out not to be authentic. Specialisation abounds – even the London Thimble Society is represented – and there are also dealers in golfing antiques, tools, tribal jewellery, walking sticks, watches, treen, militaria, toys, scent bottles, chess sets and countless other collecting disciplines, as well as high-quality jewellery, silver and decorative antiques.

Robert Holt
98 Hatton Garden, EC1
071 405 0197
Well known as dealers in precious stones, which tends to mean an intriguing sideline often passes unnoticed – oriental curios; these can sometimes be relatively inexpensive – quasi-silver Chinese bells at £17.50, for example.

LASSCo
St Michael's Church,
Mark Street, EC2
071 739 0448
A splendid recycled church, where bits of old buildings come to be saved. Absolutely everything in the architectural salvage line, from tiles, towel rails and traditional building material to larger components, like pulpits and complete panelled rooms. A rummager's paradise.

The London Silver Vaults
53–65 Chancery Lane, WC2
071 242 3844
Around 35 dealers in jewellery, silver and precious things. A large wallet helps, but is not essential, especially if you're on the lookout for sedate wedding or anniversary presents of the silver miniature butter knife variety.

The Maas Gallery
15a Clifford Street, W1
071 734 2302
Doyen among dealers in Victorian paintings and fine art, the proprietor will no doubt be perplexed by this inclusion in a junk guide. The reason is simple – junk may never have crossed the threshold, but the occasional clearout sales of surplus stock and folio leftovers can offer exceptional value. With prices for small sketches by known Victorian artists starting at well below £100, those who have always dreamt of forming a collection, but didn't think they could afford it, could start here.

Phillips
Blenstock House,
7 Blenheim Street
071 629 6602
A large throughput of furniture, works of art, pottery and porcelain, collectors' items and specialist lines. The bulk of goods sold caters for mid-market private and trade buyers, with frequent lots in the lower price range.

The Print Room
37 Museum Street, WC1
071 430 0159
A highly eclectic stock of prints, mostly decorative and topographical and ranging in price from £2 to the giddy thousands. In an area long-associated with the scholar-collector, this is one of a handful of print specialists that still maintains the tradition.

The Scripophily Shop
Georgian Arcade, Britannia Hotel, Grosvenor Square, W1
071 495 0580
Original share certificates and bonds, often elaborately engraved vignettes redolent of an age of imperial confidence. Prices start at around a fiver and ascend into the hundreds for the more spectacular examples.

Sotheby's
34–35 New Bond Street, W1
071 493 8080
As with rivals Christie's, less well-regarded lots can often be picked up, if not for a song, then at least for a modest cost. Sale categories are diverse, covering most categories of art and such collecting areas as coins and medals, dolls and teddy bears, stamps, jewellery and books. Mid-range items covering various categories are offered in frequent 'colonnade sales' where prices are likely to settle in the hundreds, rather than the thousands.

Spatz
48 Monmouth Street, WC2
071 379 0703
Collectable clothes, from vintage classics to 1950s chic, plus linen, lace, curtains and other textiles, hats and cravats, as well as costume jewellery. Also at Castlehaven Road, NW1.

Westland Pilkington
St Michael's Church, EC2
071 739 8094

A separate, if complementary, business, adjacent to **LASSCo** (qv); the emphasis is on the decorative end of the recycling business; statuary, marble chimneypieces, signs, burnished steel grates, brass mounted mahogany doors, carved stonework and complete interiors, plus some large items of furniture.

NORTH LONDON
(ALL N POSTAL DISTRICTS)

The mega-market is an established feature of the North London scene, Camden Passage and Pickett's Lock being especially popular. There are also more traditional retail outlets scattered throughout the area, where anything from bottom-line bedsit basics to expensive specialisations can be found.

139 Antiques
139 Green Lanes, N16
071 354 2466
Antiques on occasion, but stock increasingly moving towards secondhand and standard house clearance goods.

After Noah
21 Upper Street, N1
071 359 4281
Essentially solid mid-range furniture, including pine and general antiques.

Anything Goes
83 Bounce's Road, N9
Secondhand furniture and house clearance goods; one of about three in the area.

At the Sign of the Chest of Drawers
281 Upper Street, N1
071 359 5909

A new and old mix of furniture in various woods and at a wide range of prices; principally pine, but also including oak, satinwood and Malayan rubberwood.

Broadway Furniture Co.
52 The Broadway, N8
081 340 7546
General house clearance goods and secondhand furniture, from fridges and beds to old pine, plus some new items.

CA Burns
252 Holloway Road, N7
071 607 8889
Small space, but packed to the gunnels with secondhand furniture and basics.

Camden Passage, Islington
High Street, N1
A mega-complex of shops and stalls based on the famous Wednesday and Saturday antiques markets and the Thursday books, prints and ephemera market. Many of the shops are open throughout the week. **The Fleamarket**, *(7 Pierrepont Arcade)*, has books, pictures, bric-a-brac and specialised collectors' items. Open Wednesday, Saturday and occasionally Friday (*071 226 8211*). With over 200 shops and 150 stalls in the general area, which make it one of the world's largest antique precincts, it takes several visits to cover everything and even then you'll be spoilt for choice. Every specialisation is catered for and there are several good, all-round shops, such as **Sara Lemkow's** at number 12, where antique pine is mixed with metalware, oil lamps and kitchenalia; open daily (*071*

359 0190); **Annie's**, at number 10, offers a range of clothes and accessories, from antique costume for Victorian maidens with hour-glass figures, to well-lived-in Harris Tweed jackets for the Islington countryman. Upstairs you can buy the leather luggage to take it all home in, plus a selection of antique sporting goods and other stylish lifestyle accessories.

Cobwebs
60 Islington Park Street, N1
071 359 8090
Clothes, from the flapper era to the Festival of Britain and associated items.

Cookson's
121 Marton Road, N16
071 254 9941
Secondhand furniture and house clearance gear.

Crouch End Antiques
47 Park Road, N8
081 348 7652
Mid-range furniture, mostly restored Victorian and Edwardian, plus antique and new lighting.

Curios
130c Junction Road, N19
071 272 5603
With prices ranging from 50p for a vase to £5,000 for a period longcase clock, the selection here can best be described as varied. Fortunately, budget lines predominate.

Get Stuffed
105 Essex Road, N1
071 226 1364
Taxidermy and associated items. No creature too great or small, whether grizzly bear or honey bee.

Hamilton's
96 Stoke Newington Church Street, N16
071 254 1703
One of three in the area with an affordable range, mostly Victorian to shipping furniture, plus some new pine.

Hobnobs
29 Fonthill Street, N4
071 263 4720
Mostly pine furniture, some old, some new, plus a few budget general antiques.

Home to Home
355c Archway Road, N6
081 340 8354
Across-the-range furniture, from Victorian brownwood to house clearance basics.

Hornsey Auctions
54–56 High Street, N8
081 340 5334
General sales each Wednesday.

House of Steel
400 Caledonian Road, N1
071 607 5889
A 5,000 square foot warehouse dedicated to metal, with around 400 original firegrates, lamp posts, railings, gates, balconies and anything capable of being foundry-cast. New casting in steel, brass, bronze and aluminium from original patterns also undertaken.

MacGregor, Nash & Co., auctioneers
9–17 Lodge Lane, N12
081 445 9000
General sales every Monday.

The Mall Antiques Arcade
359 Upper Street, N1
071 354 2839
Upwards of 30 dealers with a

mostly mid-market range of furniture, jewellery, porcelain, clocks, pictures, costume, lighting accessories and collectors' items. Closed on Monday.

The Old Tool Chest
41 Cross Street, N1
071 359 9313
Specialist in antique wood-working tools and related items.

Petherton Antiques
124 Petherton Road, N5
071 226 6597
Mid-range furniture, pictures, decorative and collectors' items, boxes and general antiques.

Pickett's Lock Antiques & Collectors' Fair
Picketts Lock Lane, N9
0444 400570 (enquiries)
A 250-stallholder event with a broad range of antiques and collectors' items. Operates on the first Sunday of each month (except July and August).

Piermont Antiques
7 Wade's Hill, N21
081 886 2486
Some mid-range furniture, plus a mix of smaller goods, including jewellery, textiles, bric-a-brac and collectables.

Rochefort Antiques Gallery
32–34 The Green, N21
081 363 0910
A 12-dealer mini market which is strong on the affordable and good on variation, with furniture, pictures, books, lighting accessories, metalware, jewellery, bric-a-brac, textiles, porcelain and pottery, collectors' items and general antiques.

EPHEMERA

Ephemera is, in a sense, the ultimate junk, being more or less the detritus of everyday existence. To the social historian, however, it can be more precious than gold (and academically respectable too, as the new department at Reading University testifies). As categories go, it can be slightly fuzzy at the edges, however. Is an 1891 LNER timetable railwayana, junk, or a book? On the other hand, a platform ticket of the same period would certainly be classified as ephemera. Other overlaps might include, say, a postcard acknowledgement, circa 1901, from a St Pancras Councillor on the subject of drains, where the councillor in question is George Bernard Shaw (Shaviana), or a ticket to a lecture by Ralph Waldo Emerson (Emersonia). Collectors of ephemera are often as individualistic as their subjects. One might collect 1930s tram tickets; another Noel Coward theatre programmes; yet another engraved steelplate headed receipts from Victorian wine merchants. Somewhere, no doubt, there is an avid collector of early parking tickets, poll tax documents, or Habitat receipts. Junk, perhaps, but to future historians, junk with meaning.

The Secondhand Shop
8–10 Stamford Hill, N16
081 806 1749
House clearance goods, including occasional solid pre-war furniture.

The Secondhand Shop
598 Hertford Road, N21
081 805 6988
The full range of house clearance goods and general basics in a shop plus a sizeable warehouse.

Keith Skeel
Antiques & Eccentricities
94–98 Islington High Street, N1
071 359 9894
Adjacent to Camden Passage Antiques Market, this fascinating shop is owned by a celebrated purveyor of the outlandishly decorative. Cheap junk has no place here, where the bizarre and stylishly whimsical predominate. There is a wide repertoire to whet the appetite, but some things just don't make the grade – the proprietor admits to having qualms about stag's horn chandeliers, for example.

Trader Antiques
484 Green Lanes, N13
081 886 9552
Furniture, from Victorian brownwood and stripped pine, to house clearance basics, plus bric-a-brac and general antiques.

Valantique
9 Fortis Green, N2
081 883 7651
An extensive range of furniture, from Victorian to budget, bric-a-brac, collectors' items, pictures, metalware, lighting accessories and general antiques.

Winchmore Antiques
14 The Green,
Winchmore Hill, N21
081 882 4800
A varied selection of general antiques, particularly metalware, including architectural and lighting accessories.

Terry Wogan
265 Hoxton Street, N1
071 739 9681
Selling basic secondhand furniture and house clearance goods, the eponymous owner smiles wearily when telling you that he really is no relation to his famous namesake. Opening hours vary so it's advisable to phone before visiting.

York Arcade
80 Islington High Street, N1
071 833 2640
Open Wednesday and Saturday. A 16-dealer market with mostly mid-range furniture, decorative and collectors' items, textiles, pictures, porcelain and pottery, jewellery and general antiques.

NORTH WEST LONDON
(ALL NW POSTAL DISTRICTS)

Camden Lock and Alfie's Market are among London's best known picking grounds. Many shops were lost in the 1970s and those who kept going have been joined by a few stylish newer ones. On the fringes some real budget buying takes place: even house clearance shops, charity outlets and car boot sales have been known to produce the odd spectacular find.

AA Furniture Shop
135 Fortess Road, NW5
071 485 1784

Secondhand furniture and house clearance basics.

Alfie's Market
13–25 Church Street, NW8
071 723 6066
A five-storey mega-market with a good range of specialists, as well as dealers in furniture and general antiques. With upwards of 350 stands, time and stamina are essential. The mix on offer includes jewellery, costume and textiles, scientific instruments and mechanical antiques, lighting and accessories, ephemera, stamps and coins, kitchenalia, clocks and watches, records and radios, dolls and teddies, general and commemorative bric-a-brac and corkscrews. One stop collecting par excellence.

Camden Lock Market
Chalk Farm Road, NW1
A busy and extensive spread of tarpaulin-covered market stalls, garage warehouse shops and craft centres, and an important first stop for most ardent junk-hunters. Open seven days a week, 9am to 6pm at weekends.

The Corner Cupboard
679 Finchley Road, NW2
071 435 4870
Compact mini-emporium with a varied mix of jewellery, silver, bijouterie and bric-a-brac.

Ian Crispin
95 Lisson Grove, NW8
071 402 6845
Seasoned dealer with a commendably mixed stock of furniture, from humble to high class. Seems determined to suit most pockets and favours a fast throughput, which is usually

good news for the budget conscious.

Ginger's
72 Mill Lane, NW6
071 794 0672
Country furniture, including pine, architectural and decorative items as well as a range of general antiques.

Kilburn Car Boot Sale
Kilburn College,
Carlton Vale, NW6
A Sunday morning event with a degree of management control over content – new tat is discouraged.

McGovern's
221 Belsize Park Road, NW6
071 624 3322
Long-established stockists of superior secondhand and house clearance goods.

MIND Shop
115–117 Chamberlayne Road, NW10
081 968 7394
A charity shop with the space for furniture, when donated.

Relic Antiques Trade Warehouse
127 Pancras Road, NW1
071 387 6039
Mainly deals in picture frames but may also stock furniture and decorative objects, general antiques.

Risky Business
44 Church Street, NW8
071 724 2194
One of the more quirky outlets on a street of modish antique shops. This is the sort of establishment where Waugh's Boot could have had himself suitably equipped for his foreign adventures. Strong

emphasis on imperial and colonial nostalgia in the form of safari gear, wicker furniture, cricket, hockey and tennis – for lazy Edwardian summer afternoons. Committed fogey life-stylists (for this is their nirvana) could ask politely about the further treasures in the warehouse. Tooled American saddles are amongst other lines being developed.

Sue Ryder Shops

98–102 Fore Street, N18.
324 Euston Road, NW1
Small amount of furniture, clothes, trinkets, bric-a-brac and household goods.

Scope Antiques

64–66 Willesden Lane, NW6
071 328 5833
A mid-market assortment of furniture, including reasonably priced pre-war pieces, decorative items, bric-a-brac and general antiques, plus an adjacent gallery where the same owner stocks a comprehensive range of pictures.

Townsend's

81 Abbey Road and
108 Boundary Road, NW8
071 624 4756
An extensive range of decorative and architectural items, including pine fittings and pews, domestic and ecclesiastical stained glass, fireplaces and assorted fittings.

WEST LONDON
(ALL W POSTAL DISTRICTS)

Clearly, Portobello Road is the market leader here, and an essential London browse. Despite the much hyped international reputation, bargains can still be had, **especially for those who start early. Elsewhere in the area buying possibilities cover the entire spectrum from total tat to over-the-top opulence.**

Arbras Gallery

292 Westbourne Grove, W11
071 229 6772
About 20 dealers on two floors crammed with an assortment of antiques and collectables, including furniture, jewellery, porcelain and pottery, books, pictures, textiles, silver and general antiques; also a specialist in reproduction silver photograph frames.

Bainbridge, auctioneers

St John's Parade,
Mattock Lane, W13
081 579 2966
Eight general sales a year.

Briggs Antiques

73 Ledbury Road, W11
071 727 0909
Long-established stockists of mid-range furniture, textiles and general antiques in retail showrooms plus warehouse.

C & A Furniture

232 Westbourne Park Road, W11
071 221 4556
Large premises consisting of double shop and outside area with an extensive selection of budget furniture.

The Corner Portobello Antiques Supermarket

282, 284, 288, 290 Westbourne Grove, W11
071 727 2027
Open Friday pm and all day Saturday. A market of around 150 dealers which concentrates

on jewellery and smaller collectors' items.

Dodo
286 Westbourne Grove, W11
071 229 3132 or 706 1545
Saturday only. Signage, posters, advertising and display materials, labels and decorative packaging of all descriptions. Original posters start at around £15. Premises are shared with three other dealers, offering a variety of collectors' items from tribal sculpture to teddy bears.

Dolphin Arcade
155–157 Portobello Road, W11
071 727 4883

Approximately 30 stallholders with a range of smaller antiques, jewellery, silver, porcelain and collectors' items. Open on Saturday only.

The Good Fairy Open Air Market
100 Portobello Road, W11
Around 80 stallholders with a range of collectors' items, jewellery and general antiques. Open on Saturday only. A good place to spot a bargain.

The Furniture Exchange
42 Shepherd's Bush Road, W6
081 761 7615
Budget furniture and house clearance goods.

PORTOBELLO ROAD

A street name synonymous with antiques since its days as a totter's pitch, it is now the longest street market in Britain, with up to 2,000 dealers trading every Saturday, and a weekly turnover measured in millions. The 'official' street market consists of 40-odd council-licensed stalls at the junction of Westbourne Grove and Colville Terrace, but grafted on to this are an assortment of alfresco operations, market arcades, and a fleamarket at Thorpe Close and Golborne Road, while proceedings under the Westway flyover have an almost gypsy flavour. There is also some trading activity on Friday and several of the shop outlets operate throughout the week. The scene is constantly changing, with new markets opening – The Silver Fox, Spectus, and 'Still Too Few' will be up and running by the summer of 1993, and Hildreth's, long encased in scaffolding, will be revamped as part of a new development. Some believe that the bargain days here are over, and it is now little more than a picturesque fixture on the tourist itinerary. On the street, it's a different story. With so much stock arriving from all over the country every Saturday morning (from 4.30am, when The Good Fairy begins trading) spectacular finds are still being made – a picture bought recently for £30, for example, was quickly re-sold on for £3,000. Around 70% of all transactions take place between dealers, many of them from overseas, while marginally more than one in ten buyers are members of the British public. Trade is frantic and brisk, with few anxieties about the recession.

Green's Antique Gallery
117 Kensington Church Street, W8
071 229 9618
A comprehensive mix of jewellery, costume, toys, bric-a-brac, furniture, leather, pigskin and crocodile cases, boxes, scent bottles and general antiques. Street-wise Sloanes can buy their low-cost secondhand engagement rings here.

Harold's Place
148 South Ealing Road, W5
General antiques, bric-a-brac, miscellanea, crested and commemorative china.

Hildreth Arcade
139–151 Portobello Road, W11
071 724 9797
A thriving market of around 76 stallholders with a comprehensive range of antiques, bric-a-brac, collectors' items and specialist lines. Saturday only.

Hope & Glory
131a Kensington Church Street, W8
071 727 8424
Commemorative items in porcelain and glass; royal, political, military, religious and personal. Closed on Monday.

Junk & Disorderly
4 Uxbridge Road, W7
081 567 6155
An extensive range of secondhand furniture and house clearance goods, including electrical.

Knight's
100 Shepherd's Bush Road, W6
071 603 4232
A large and varied house clearance stock.

The Lacquer Chest
71 and 75 Kensington Church Street, W8
071 937 1306
Furniture, curios, decorative and unusual items and general antiques.

Roger Matthews
307 Portobello Road, W10
081 964 4281
At the 'unfashionable' end of Portobello, north of the flyover, a collection of traders share a shop selling general antiques, some interesting furniture and modern curiosities too. There are several other junk and bric-a-brac outlets nearby.

Maxi's
71 Churchfield Road, W3
081 993 5626
Budget furniture.

The Old Cinema
160 Chiswick High Road, W4
081 995 4166
15-dealer market strong on decorative antiques, plus furniture – period to mid-range and shipping – general antiques and collectors' items.

The Old Dairy
164 Thames Road, W4
081 994 3140
Mid-range furniture, particularly decorative pieces and painted items which compare favourably in price with similar elsewhere in London.

Portobello Antiques Market (The Red Lion)
165–169 Portobello Road, W11
071 221 4964
Established in the same year as the Festival of Britain, since when prices have increased dramatically, this renowned market can still produce the

goods, though the operation has slimmed down to around 50 dealers in recent years. A good selection of paintings and engravings, amongst other things. Saturday only.

Roger's Antiques Gallery
65 Portobello Road, W11
071 351 5353
Around 60 dealers with a wide range of general antiques, pictures, bric-a-brac, jewellery and collectors' items.

Sue Ryder Shops
72 Westbourne Grove, W2
071 221 1444
Donated items, including furniture, bric-a-brac, clothes and household goods.
Also at: *128 Notting Hill Gate, W11.*

Son of St Bernard's Car Boot Sale
Windmill Lane, W7
An attempted follow-on to the highly popular Sunday event which used to take place in the grounds of the nearby Victorian psychiatric hospital. The occasional bargain surfaces, word of which continues to coax the punters out of their beds at dawn. Well, who wouldn't get up early to buy a Lalique clock for £1? In general, the goods on offer range from the fairly basic to the very basic, plus various useful and functional household items, such as potato peelers for 10p.

Southall Market
Southall, W7
General auctions every Friday.

Strand Antiques
166 Thames Road, Chiswick,
081 994 1912

A mini-market of 8 dealers operating seven days a week with a range of furniture, general antiques and collectors' items, including books, bric-a-brac, jewellery, pictures, textiles and clothes, with a good range of Victorian glass.

Vale Antiques
245 Elgin Avenue, W9
071 328 4796
A mid-range mix of furniture, general antiques and collectors' items.

Yesterday's Furniture
30 Station Terrace,
Chamberlain Road, W13
081 960 5425
Secondhand and budget furniture.

SOUTH WEST LONDON
(SW POSTAL DISTRICTS)

Sloane culture is the prevailing mode, with a sphere of influence extending to Battersea, Stockwell and beyond, but ultra-chic by no means enjoys a monopoly. Mid-market trading is strong, even in the bastions of gentrification, and a few pile-it-high junk dealers have discovered that nice young Sloanes brought up with the best Queen Anne walnut furniture sometimes actually believe that a 1960s chipped formica coffee table from the Co-op has a certain novelty value.

The Age of Elegance
61 Sheen Lane, SW14
081 876 0878
Part-time opening – prior telephone call advised, except Fridays and Saturdays. Jewellery, decorative and collectors' items, lace and linen,

antique tableware and general antiques.

Antiquarius
131–141 King's Road, SW3
071 351 5353
Newly expanded and now with around 100 dealers with a portmanteau assortment of everything collectable, including jewellery, clothes, pens, corkscrews, pictures, pipes, cufflinks, fans and books.

Bonham's Chelsea
65–69 Lots Road, SW10
071 351 7111
Intermittent sales held at frequent intervals, particularly specialist and collectors' categories.

Car Boot Sale
Streatham High Road, SW16
Held every Sunday next to the cinema.

The Chase Antiques
298 Kingston Road, SW20
081 542 3363
Furniture, metalware, porcelain, collectors' items and general antiques.

Chelsea Antique Market
245a and 253 Kings Road, SW3
071 352 5689
Now a rather more upmarket and sedate affair than the anarchic rummage of the swinging 60s and with fewer dealers, but still worth a browse.

Chelsea Bric-a-Brac Shop
16 Hartfield Road, SW19
081 946 6894
Furniture, including pine and pre-war, bric-a-brac, metalware and general antiques.

Christie's
8 King Street, SW1
071 839 9060
Much dazzling treasure, with cheaper lots usually being consigned to South Kensington. However, one point should be borne in mind – the 'serious' dealers who buy here are usually after top-quality items, which occasionally allows less august objects to pass through sales at below the published estimate prices.

Cornucopia
12 Upper Tachbrook Street, SW1
071 828 5752
Style on a shoestring, including the best Belgravia cast-offs, plus an interesting choice of jewellery and accessories.

Tony Davis
23 Battersea Rise, SW11
071 228 1370
The ultimate take-your-pick shop – at any rate, Take Your Pick was the way the former barrow-boy proprietor raised the wherewithal to set up almost 40 years ago (for those who remember TV's pioneering quiz game show). Stock is variable, which lends it a certain interest and charm; likewise the customers, ranging from penniless home-nesters to pop stars. Recommended viewing, whatever your buying status.

The Delightful Muddle
11 Upper Tachbrook Street, SW1
Junk shops are hardly SW1's forte, though on the margins budget buying is still possible. Long established (1935) and tucked away behind the Queen Mother Sports Centre, this shop has generous stock in minimal space – textiles, bric-a-brac,

collectors' items, bijouterie and much that is quaint and curious.

Dixon's Antique Centre
471 Upper Richmond Road West, SW14
081 878 6788
Around 15 dealers with a range of furniture, general antiques, bric-a-brac and collectors' items. Closed on Wednesday.

Dowell Lloyd & Co., auctioneers
118 Putney Bridge Road, SW15
081 788 7777
Mixed sales of general goods and antiques twice per week.

The Furniture Cave
533 Kings Road, SW10
071 352 4229
More chic than cheap, an 8-dealer strong mixture of furniture, garden statuary and decorative pieces. Always stylish and sometimes sensational.

The Griffin
911 Garratt Lane, Tooting Broadway, SW17
081 767 6579
Victorian brownwood to secondhand budget furniture and house clearance items.

Hamilton's Corner
407a Kingston Road, SW20
081 540 1744
Furniture, including mid-range, pine and budget, plus general antiques.

Just a Second Antiques
27 Battersea Rise, SW11
071 223 5341
An across-the-range selection of furniture, bric-a-brac, collectors' items and general antiques.

Lots Road Galleries, auctioneers
71 Lots Road, SW10
071 351 7771
A high throughput of antique furniture and collectors' items every week. Sunday viewing has encouraged private bidders, but the size of sales (upwards of 500 lots) usually means plenty for everyone.

Magpies
152 Wandsworth Bridge Road, SW6
071 736 3738
A five-dealer assortment of

GREEN PENGUINS

The old aphorism about books furnishing a room is particularly true in the case of one collector – a lecturer in English literature, as it happens – who spends his spare time looking for old Penguin paperbacks, which he will probably never read. Some have pages missing, other have tatty covers, coffee stains, childish scrawls defacing their title pages, or dog-eared corners. None of this matters, so long as they are green. The collection, even at 5p or 10p a go, must have cost a substantial sum to put together, because he now has more than 500 green Penguins arranged on bookshelves on either side of his study window. Their function is essentially decorative, and it works well. 'The early greens,' he says, 'are particularly restful.'

furniture, bric-a-brac,
kitchenalia, collectors' items
and general antiques.

Richard Maude Tools
22 Parkfields, SW15
Woodworking tools, from the
functional to museum quality
and associated items.

Ann Mays
*80 Wandsworth Bridge Road,
SW6*
071 731 0862
Furniture, general antiques,
bric-a-brac and collectors'
items.

Murray Brothers
122 Replingham Road, SW18
081 874 1694
Secondhand furniture and
house clearance basics,
including electrical.

Len Nash
271 Lillie Road, SW6
071 381 2450
A constantly changing stock of
furniture and house clearance
goods.

Northcote Road Antiques
Market
155a Northcote Road, SW11
071 228 6850
Around 30 dealers with a varied
range of furniture, including
pine, as well as bric-a-brac, art
deco, lighting accessories,
ephemera such as advertising
and decorative packaging
material, textiles, bottles and
general antiques.

The Old Ephemera &
Newspaper Shop
37 Kinnerton Street, SW1
071 235 7788
An enormous social history
archive, with journals and
newspapers.

Oxfam
23 Streatham High Road
081 769 1291
A charity outlet specialising in
low-cost furniture, household
goods, electrical items and the
occasional junk bargain.

The Pine Mine
*100 Wandsworth Bridge Road,
SW6*
071 736 1092
Antique pine, some of high
quality, but much affordable,
plus reproductions from old
wood.

Pine Village
*162 Wandsworth Bridge Road,
SW6*
071 736 2753
Further acreage of pine in all its
variations.

Secondhand Rose
*763-765 Wandsworth Road,
SW8*
071 498 1359
Furniture, including pine,
kitchenalia, bric-a-brac,
collectors' items and general
antiques.

Mr Wandle's Workshop
202 Garratt Lane, SW18
081 870 5873
Fireplaces and accessories,
mostly burnished steel and cast
iron.

Whiteway & Waldron
305 Munster Road, SW6
071 381 3195
Surplus ecclesiastica, from
glittering vestments to glowing
stained glass, plus pews and
pulpits, reredos screen
components, lecterns and other
artefacts of religious
significance. All prices and
denominations, from high to
low.

Christopher Wray's Lighting Emporium
600–606 Kings Road, SW6
071 736 8434
Specialisation plus – stock also includes tangential accessories like decorative metalwork and advertising material. Stock well presented and business highly organised, but not to the detriment of atmosphere. After 30 years, this remains an illuminating browse.

Yesterdays Antiques
315 Upper Richmond Road West, SW14
081 876 7536
Pine furniture, some antique, some made-to-measure repro, plus jugs, bowls, lights, vases and 'anything for the home'.

SOUTH EAST LONDON
(ALL SE POSTAL DISTRICTS)

Still a flourishing and popular buying area, much covered by the London-Brighton trade as well as by continentals on their way from the Channel ports. The Bermondsey phenomenon dominates, while shops throughout the area supply goods of all categories, and in all price ranges, from Bond Street posh via ubiquitous pine to end-of-the-road basics.

A1 House Clearance
115b Anerley Road, SE20
081 778 4409
A comprehensive range of furniture, from occasional Victorian to secondhand basics and general house clearance goods.

Abe's Arcade
31–33 Woolwich Road, SE10
081 858 4719
Flatfillers and household basics, including electrical goods.

Acorn Antiques
111 Rosendale Road, SE21
081 761 3349
A mix of jewellery, metalware, pictures, bric-a-brac, pine furniture and general antiques.

Antique Mini-Market
15 Greenwich Church Street, SE10
17 dealers, 7 days, with a varied mix of furniture, jewellery, bric-a-brac, collectors' items and general antiques.

Antique Warehouse
175d Bermondsey Street, Newham's Row, SE1
Mid-range to shipping furniture.

Austin's
11–23 Peckham Rye, SE15
071 639 2725
Something of an institution after more than 120 years, combines old-fashioned service with old-fashioned furniture on three extensive floors. Maintains a reputation for reasonable quality at reasonable prices.

Badger's Antiques
320–322 Creek Road, SE10
081 853 1394
A varied mix of furniture, mid-range and decorative, general antiques, collectors' items and leather luggage.

Bermondsey Antiques Market
Long Lane, SE1
071 351 5333 (enquiries)
An indoor market near the larger open Friday market, where some 130 dealers in antiques and collectables of all shapes and sizes start trading at around 3.30 a.m. on Friday.

The Bermondsey Market

Municipal car park, Long Lane and Bermondsey Street, SE1

One of the country's most memorable antique and junk fixtures – and still one of the remaining medieval 'open' markets, where special sanction is afforded to the innocent purchaser of stolen goods, as in the notorious recent case of paintings by Reynolds and Gainsborough bought for only a few hundred pounds. The market takes place every Friday from 4am to 2pm. Arrive early and dress warm.

Bermondsey Antique Warehouse

173 Bermondsey Street, SE1
071 407 2040/403 0022

Three dealers with lots of space, most of it crammed with furniture, general antiques and shipping goods.

Black Cat

202 High Street, Penge, SE20

A comprehensive range of furniture, up to 1920s and 1930s and general antiques.

Brownhill Furniture Store

267 Brownhill Road, SE6
081 697 1100

Secondhand domestic and office furniture and effects piled high inside and out, including cheap floor covering.

The Crystal Ball

30 Rotherhithe New Road, SE16
071 231 1846

Flatfillers and house clearance goods, including electrical.

Crystal Palace Collectors' Market

Jasper Road,
Westow Hill, SE19
081 761 3735

Now a mixed market selling both old and new goods, but several of the 36 stallholders still dealing in a range of general antiques, bric-a-brac and militaria. Closed on Wednesday.

Franklin's

161 Camberwell Road, SE15
071 703 8089

Five floors of furniture and general antiques, including mirrors, beds and decorative items.

The Green Parrot

2 Turnpin Lane,
Greenwich Market, SE10
081 858 6690

Some furniture, including stripped pine blanket chests, bric-a-brac, decorative items and general antiques.

Greenwich Antiques Market

Greenwich High Road, SE10

Summer only; around 80 stalls with a varied mix of bric-a-brac, collectors' items and general antiques.

Hillyer's

301 Sydenham Road, SE26
081 778 6361

A good mid-market mix – and some superior secondhand items – including furniture, bric-a-brac, silver, collectables, books and general antiques.

The Junk Shop

9 Greenwich South Street, SE10
081 305 1666

Low-cost off-shoot of Spreadeagle Antiques (below), specialising in lower range goods and cheap clearouts, though by no means all as junky as the shop name implies.

Lamont Antiques
Tunnel Avenue Antique Warehouse, SE10
081 305 1805
Architectural salvage and decorative items, plus mid-range to shipping furniture and general antiques.

Lewisham Auctions
Nightingale Grove, SE13
081 852 3145
Intermittent sales, usually Saturday and Thursday.

Thomas Moore, auctioneers
217–219 Greenwich High Road, SE10
081 858 7848
Weekly general sales, on Thursday mornings.

New Road Bargains
243 Camberwell New Road, SE5
071 708 0551
A wide range of low-cost basics and flatfillers.

Oddiquities
61 Waldram Park Road, SE23
An enormous stock of antique lighting and accessories, oil, gas and electric, plus fireside metalware.

Oola Boola Antiques Warehouse
166 Tower Bridge Road, SE1
071 403 0794
Three floors of furniture and decorative items, from period to some 'modern' antiques of the 1970s.

Relcy Antiques
9 Nelson Road, SE10
081 858 2812
Much mouthwatering quality interspersed with nautical and scientific collectors' items, plus the decorative and unusual.

Rosebery's, auctioneers
The Old Railway Booking Hall, Crystal Palace Station Road, SE19
081 778 4024
Twice-monthly sales which contain a varied and often interesting mix of antiques, collectors' items and household effects.

The Secondhand Shop
85 Coldharbour Lane, SE5
071 737 4379
Basics and house clearance goods.

The Silver Sixpence
14 Catford Hill, SE6
081 690 0046
A large mixed stock of furniture, including pine, metalware, clocks and general antiques.

Spread Eagle Antiques
8 Nevada Street, and 1 Stockwell Street, SE10
An enticing mixture of rummageable goodies, including bric-a-brac, ephemera, pictures, costume and accessories, books and general antiques. Furniture is accommodated in the Stockwell Street shop.

John Tolley
93 Catford Hill, SE6
081 690 4650
Large premises and forecourt crammed with furniture and house clearance goods.

Tower Bridge Antiques Warehouse
159–161 Tower Bridge Road, SE1
071 403 3660
A vast repository of mid-range and shipping furniture and general antiques.

Tower Furniture
63–65 Old Kent Road, SE1
071 231 1278
The cheap and cheerful end of the secondhand furniture business, good for first-time basics.

HT Whitewood & Son
143 Lee Road, SE3
081 852 0467
Household furniture, including quality secondhand.

EAST LONDON
(ALL E POSTAL DISTRICTS)

Much budget buying and secondhand goods from the flimsy and squalid to the serviceable and solid. There are also some hidden gems for clutter-lovers, and a few standard issue antique shops with moderately priced fare.

AA Furniture Shop
1 Offar Mead,
Lindisfarne Way, E9
081 986 2445
Seven days a week secondhand and house clearance.

Antique City
98 Wood Street, E17
081 520 4032
Around 18 dealers with a comprehensive range of furniture, clocks, clothing and textiles, bric-a-brac, collectables and general antiques. Closed on Thursday.

Anything Goes
21 Mare Street, E8
081 807 9399
Secondhand furniture and house clearance goods.

Atkinson's
599 High Road, E10
081 539 4555
Flatfillers and secondhand basics.

Berick Furnishers
826 Romford Road, E12
081 471 0906
Secondhand furniture and most household basics.

Brick Lane Market
Brick Lane, E1
A mixed junk and general market, on Sundays up to 1pm.

Car Boot Sale
Dalston Cross Shopping Centre, Kingston Road, E8
Held on Sundays beside Leo's Supermarket.

Clapton
60 Lower Clapton Road, E5
081 533 5205
General house clearance goods.

A Crow
149 Grove Green Road, E11
081 556 6298
Secondhand furniture and house clearances. Also at *359 Hoe Street, E17, 081 520 1819.*

Curious Grannies
2 Middleton Road, E8
071 254 7074
A well-known trade source for interesting boxes of all types and periods, for snuff, cutlery, writing materials, sewing, tea, lepidoptera, or anything remotely capable of being boxed, plus some smaller musical instruments. Enquiries from serious private buyers are welcome, but an appointment is essential.

Cutler Street
Antique Market
Goulston Street, E1
071 351 5353 (enquiries)
Jewellery, silver and smaller

collectors' items, such as numismatics, philately and postal history and gemstones.

Fiona's Secondhand Shop
97 Burdett Road, E3
081 981 3611
Apart from clothes, the owner insists that anything that can be fitted into the shop is available, from teaspoons and trinkets upwards and including books, bric-a-brac and electrical goods.

Forrest & Co., auctioneers
79–85 Cobbold Road, E11
081 534 2931
Fortnightly general sales.

Furniture for Value
193 Plashet Road, E13
081 470 0620
Secondhand furniture and house clearance goods.

Georgian Village Antiques Market
100 Wood Street, E17
081 520 6638
Mid-range furniture, clocks, bric-a-brac, jewellery and silver, ephemera and philately, metalware and collectors' items.

GH Harris
178 Plashet Grove, E6
081 552 0904
Secondhand furniture and house clearance goods.

Haysom's
617 High Road, E10
House clearance specialists and secondhand furniture dealers.

Jarvis Auctions
Arch 263, Railway Approach, E11
081 539 1941
Established more than a century ago and still doing brisk

business at fortnightly Thursday and weekly Wednesday sales.

M & R Furnishings
65 Plashet Grove, E6
081 470 8380
Secondhand furniture and house clearance items.

Nearly New Furniture
12 Church Street, E15
081 534 4897
Secondhand furniture and household effects.

Nelson's
709 Romford Road, E12
081 478 2587
Quantity of stock varies, but usually has a selection of secondhand furniture and house clearance items.

The Oxfam Shop
570 Kingsland Road, E8
071 923 1532
After a recent fire, reopening with donated furniture and household goods sold in aid of a worthy cause. Since most of the larger items taken in by Oxfam are diverted here, turnover is reasonably constant.

Pickering's
387 Roman Road, Bow, E3
081 981 4515
Browsable secondhand and house clearance goods within earshot of the Bow Bells.

Regency Auction Rooms
62 St James Street, E17
081 520 0255
General sales every Tuesday.

Nicholas Salter Antiques
8 Station Road, E4
081 529 2938
A Chingford phenomenon. A back door onto the railway platform means you can avoid

the parking hassle (frequent trains to Liverpool Street) although if you decide to buy, say, one of the glass cases of stuffed birds presently on offer, you should try to avoid the rush hour. A varied and versatile stock in the former railway buffet; jewellery, toys, decorative items, bric-a-brac, furniture – Victorian to pre-war – textiles and general antiques, plus an upstairs section with costume and accessories. Yet more can be found at 3-4 Station Road, where the rummageable stock of collectors' items includes old records plus vintage valve radios and wind-up gramophones.

San Fairy Ann
110 Salmon Lane, E14
071 987 5771
A mix of antique to post-war collectables, bric-a-brac and glass.

Serendipity Emporium
18a–20 Leytonstone Road, E15
081 534 7883
Mostly smaller goods and collectables, including art nouveau and art deco items.

Simply Seconds
9 Mare Street, E8
081 985 5049
Secondhand furniture and basics.

Turn o' the Century
78 Wood Street, E17
081 521 6811
Mid-range to shipping furniture, bric-a-brac, pewter and general antiques.

Walthamstow Auctions
89 Grange Road, E17
081 520 9878

General sales every Tuesday.

Wingfield's
87 Plashet Road, E13
081 471 5354
Across-the-board secondhand and house clearance furniture, plus limited bric-a-brac.

OUTSIDE LONDON

The distinction between London and its suburbs is notoriously vague. The term Greater London tried to rationalise this, but failed for other reasons. In this guide we have taken the orbital motorway as our greater boundary. In addition to London proper, therefore, this chapter also includes towns and less precise (but nevertheless well-understood) localities that lie between London's postal districts and the M25. These follow, in alphabetical sequence.

BARNET
(HERTFORDSHIRE)

C Bellinger's Antiques
91 Wood Street
081 449 3467
Mid-range furniture, metalware, porcelain and general antiques.

BECKENHAM (KENT)

The Antique Market
Old Council Hall,
Bromley Road,
081 777 6300 (enquiries).
A Wednesday-only market, 8am to 2pm, where around 20 stallholders offer a range of general antiques and collectors' items, including silver and ephemera.

Norman Witham Antiques
2 High Street
081 650 4651

Well-established across-the-board dealer with some small furniture and an assorted collection of smaller antiques and bric-a-brac. Prices, like stock, are very comprehensive.

BROMLEY (KENT)

Antica
Rear of 35–41 High Street
081 464 7661
A wide selection of furniture, from period to shipping, plus some smaller goods.

Bromley Antique Market
Widmore Road
A well-established Thursday market with around 70 stallholders offering a range of collectors' items, ephemera, jewellery, books, bric-a-brac, useful junk and general antiques.

Paraphernalia Antique & Collectors' Market
171 Widmore Road
081 318 2997
Around 10 dealers with a varied stock of furniture, general antiques and collectors' items.

BUSHEY (HERTFORDSHIRE)

Country Life Antiques
33a High Street
081 950 8575
Three floors of mixed antique and reproduction pine furniture, plus bric-a-brac, memorabilia, pictures and general antiques.

CARSHALTON (SURREY)

Carshalton Antiques
5 High Street
081 647 5664

25-year established dealer with 2,000 sq ft of furniture, period to pre-war, pictures, clocks and general antiques.

Cambridge Parade Antiques
229–231 Carshalton Road
081 643 0014
A group of 18 shops occupied by dealers with a range of general antiques, bric-a-brac and collectors' items. Closed on Monday.

Cherub Antiques
312 Carshalton Road
081 643 0028
An eclectic range of furniture, including pine, from period pieces to 1920s, plus clocks, bric-a-brac and general antiques. Another branch of the shop with similar stock operates at 177 Streatham Road, Mitcham.

Justin Antiques
318 Carshalton Road
081 643 3641
Furniture, much of it good secondhand and budget and with some antique, plus a rummageable mix of smaller items.

Marshall's Antiques
314 Carshalton Road
081 642 2108
A comprehensive range of general antiques and collectors' items, including working oil lamps.

Sue Ryder Shop
18 The Market, Wrythe Lane
081 641 2528
Donated furniture and secondhand household items, clothes, bric-a-brac, jewellery and trinkets and useful odds and ends.

CATERHAM (SURREY)

Caterham Clearance Centre
Raglan Precinct
46–8 Chaldon Road
0883 347267
Furniture, secondhand and the occasional antique and a varied mix of house clearance items, from teaspoons upwards, spread over 3,000 sq ft.

CHEAM (SURREY)

Parkin's, auctioneers
18 Malden Road
081 644 6127
Sales held every Monday, mostly of general goods but antiques are sold on the first Monday of the month.

CRAYFORD (KENT)

Albert Andrews Auctions
Farm Buildings, Maiden Lane
0322 528868
Mixed auctions held every Wednesday.

CROYDON (SURREY)

Collectors' Corner Antiques
43 Brighton Road
081 680 7511
Furniture, general antiques, plus diverse collectors' items, including tin-plate and die-cast toys, dolls and bric-a-brac.

McNally Antiques
322 Brighton Road
081 686 8387
Around 2,500 sq ft of period to pre-war furniture and some general antiques.

Miss Ellany
28 Croham Road
081 688 3380
Flatfillers and general house clearance, furniture and effects.

Rosan, Reeves, auctioneers
144–150 London Road
081 688 1123
Mixed sales every Saturday and most Wednesdays.

DAGENHAM (KENT)

The Budget Home
219 Oxlow Lane
081 592 3823
House clearance specialists.

Sue Ryder Shop
289 Heathway
081 595 4124
A mix of donated furniture and smaller household items, bric-a-brac, jewellery, trinkets and clothes. More of the same available at another outlet nearby *(758 Green Lane, Becontree, 081 599 7326)*.

EAST MOLESEY (SURREY)

The Antiques Arcade
77 Bridge Road
081 979 7954
Furniture and general antiques, mostly mid-range and including pictures, lighting accessories, ceramics, silver and collectors' items. Fourteen dealers, catering for a clientele which includes discerning members of the local Japanese community.

The Gooday Shop & Studio
48–50 Bridge Road
081 979 9971
One of the more delightful shops in an interesting street, with its varied assortment of whimsicalities, from children's games to a five-foot high plastic

ice cream cone, art nouveau, art deco, 1950s contemporary, ephemera and collectors' items. Treasures upstairs include textiles and fabrics.

Howard Hope Phonographs & Gramophones
21 Bridge Road
081 941 2472
Another repository of the curious and unusual in the shadow of Hampton Court Palace. Mechanised music of various kinds, plus a range of accessories.

The Sovereign Antique Centre
53 Bridge Road
081 783 0595
Furniture, mostly mid range, pictures, general antiques and collectors' items.

Nicholas Antiques
31 Bridge Road
081 979 0354
Mid-range furniture, especially large items. Prices aren't budget, but generally good value for the quality on offer.

EDGWARE (MIDDLESEX)

Edgware Antiques
19 Whitchurch Lane
081 952 5924
Open Thursday, Friday and Saturday. Furniture, from mid-range to shipping, clocks, metalware, bric-a-brac, pictures, collectors' items and general antiques. A recommended rummage.

ENFIELD (MIDDLESEX)

Enfield Corner Cupboard
59–61 Chase Side
081 363 6493

Furniture, mid-range to pre-war and general antiques.

The Secondhand Shop
598 Hertford Road
081 805 6988
One of about three shops in the vicinity selling a full range of house clearance goods, in this case from a 1,200 square foot shop and warehouse.

HAMPTON (MIDDLESEX)

Hampton Village Antique Centre
76 Station Road
081 979 5871
Six dealers with a mix of furniture, mostly mid-range, general antiques, clocks and collectors' items.

HAMPTON HILL (MIDDLESEX)

Junk & Disorderly
14 Windmill Road
081 783 1009
A varied selection of house clearance goods, bric-a-brac and furniture, including pre-war oak and stripped pine.

Sound Box
10 High Street
081 977 4802
Rather off the beaten track between Hampton Court and Twickenham, which makes its discovery well worth savouring. A repository of almost everything to do with mechanised sound. About 5,000 78s of all categories including such rarities as original Fred Zimmerman takes, plus early TVs, horn gramophones, polyphones, phonographs, wirelesses, an early Wurlitzer radio, picnic portable wind-ups

for courting students, the occasional orchestrion, plus spare parts and repair facilities. Downstairs in **Scrimshire** the owner's wife runs a children's pre-worn clothes shop.

HAREFIELD
(HERTFORDSHIRE)

The Jays Antique Centre
25–29 High Street
0895 824738
Two floors of varied antiques, bric-a-brac and collectors' items, with much at the low-price end of the spectrum. The mix is comprehensive with only one specialist, who deals in Whitefriars glass. A rambling rummage with some potential.

HARROW (MIDDLESEX)

Baxter's
408 Alexandra Avenue
081 423 7587
A varied selection of furniture, including some less expensive pre-war items, plus bric-a-brac and general antiques.

Kathleen Mann Antiques
49 High Street
081 422 1892
Mainly furniture and aimed at the private buyer with a taste for good Victorian darkwoods, plus some scope for inexpensive purchases in the smaller stock of porcelain and pottery, glass, pictures, textiles and decorative pieces.

ICKENHAM
(MIDDLESEX)

Saich & Edwards
61 High Street
0895 632512
House clearance furniture and basics, plus recycled building

materials for practical minded DIY enthusiasts.

ILFORD (ESSEX)

Belgrave Antiques
77 Belgrave Road
081 554 8032
Furniture, pictures, books and ephemera, bric-a-brac and a varied range of collectables.

Furniture Cash Sales
41 Green Lane
081 478 1347
A mix of new and secondhand house clearance furniture from a downturn survivor with laconic views on the changing scene in the junk business.

Goodwin's of Seven Kings
32 Cameron Road
081 590 4560
Established purveyors of secondhand and house clearance goods with a varied and comprehensive range.

Second Chance
637 High Road, Seven Kings
081 597 4514
A full range of basics and house clearance goods.

Second Chance Two
813 High Road
081 590 7395
Secondhand furniture and house clearance goods.

Shambles
31 Goodmays Road
081 590 4511
Anything secondhand, from junk and bric-a-brac to fruit machines and sofas. Owner would like to (and used to) do antiques, but says they've become too expensive, though the occasional interesting piece comes in by chance.

ISLEWORTH
(MIDDLESEX)

Car Boot Sale
Held on Sundays in the
grounds of the local hospital.

Old Isleworth Antiques
South Street (by the Post Office)
Tuesdays and Thursdays only.
A range of general antiques,
useful odds and ends, bric-a-
brac and collectors' items.

Yistelworth Antiques
13 Shrewsbury Walk,
South Street, Old Isleworth
081 560 7978
The owner has revived the
area's Anglo-Saxon name, and
(with no obvious connection)
carries a varied stock of statuary
and general antiques.

KINGSTON UPON THAMES (SURREY)

Chancellor's Auctions
74 London Road
081 541 4139
Four sales a month, three of
mixed goods, one of antiques.

Harpur Dearden
47 High Street, Hampton Wick
081 943 1100
Mostly furniture, with a
comprehensive selection from
period to budget and
secondhand, plus a general
range of pictures, bric-a-brac,
glass and general antiques.

Pharaoh's
135 Richmond Road
081 546 8597
A comprehensive range of
furniture, general antiques and
collectors' items. Stock varies,
depending on what comes in,
but can include advertising
material, coins, bric-a-brac and
items from the 1950s and 1960s.

LETCHMORE HEATH
(HERTFORDSHIRE)

Anne Barlow Antiques
1 Letchmore Cottages
0923 855270
Long-established stockist of
mid-range and country
furniture, clocks, toys, pottery
and assorted collectors' items.

LOUGHTON (ESSEX)

**Black Horse Agencies,
Ambrose, auctioneers**
149 High Road
081 502 3951
Monthly antique and specialised
sales. Standards are maintained
with a loosely applied 1930
dateline on furniture, although
cheaper lots do filter through –
a table at £40, for example. Car
weary London dealers often
arrive by tube – this is the last
stop on the Central Line.

MITCHAM (SURREY)

Cherub Antiques
177 Streatham Road
081 640 7179
A branch of the Carshalton
outlet of the same name.

Luis Furniture
13 New Road
081 640 2596
Secondhand furniture and
house clearance lines.

NORTHWOOD
(MIDDLESEX)

Northwood Antiques
28 High Street
0923 824040
Mid-range furniture, Georgian
to pre-war, including good
secondhand and renovated,

plus upholstered items, bric-a-brac and general antiques.

Matheson's
24 High Street
081 429 0626
A varied mix of furniture, decorative items, collectables, jewellery and general antiques.

Old Lodge Antiques
7 The Parade, Old Lodge Lane
081 668 9717
A mix of furniture, bric-a-brac, jewellery, toys, collectors' items and general antiques.

Antiques Arcade
22 Richmond Hill
081 940 2035
Mid-market range of dealers biased towards good furniture with some prints, porcelain,and pottery and smaller collectables.

Duke's Yard Antiques Market
1a Duke Street
081 332 1051
Large market of some 50 stalls selling a good mix of mid-range antiques and collectables. Closed on Monday.

Mollie Evans
82 Hill Rise
081 948 0182
Stylish antiques, making individual statements, at a quality which doesn't always come cheap, although some of the smaller items are well selected, interesting and won't break the budget buyer's bank – a Welsh milking stool, trivets, coronation mugs, Liberty's

pewter and sycamore bowls, for instance, all meet these criteria.

Peter & Debbie Gooday
20 Richmond Hill
081 940 8652
Specialists in a diverse range of arts & crafts, art nouveau and art deco items, including some furniture, pictures, pewter, jewellery and decorative pieces. Although the quality is consistently high, prices tend to be reasonable for the sort of goods on offer – £20 for a pair of art deco cufflinks, for example. Stock is mainly of British origin, but there are a few outside influences, such as Lalique glass.

Jim's Things
212 Sandycombe Road
081 948 8115
A believer in the portmanteau approach, with diverse goods including a bus ticket machine, bakelite radios, Victorian nursing lamps, ships' lamps and furniture, up to pre-war. Strangely, the least saleable things in one of London's most painted suburbs would seem to be pictures. Proximity to Kew doesn't even guarantee a turnover in botanical prints, says the owner.

Richmond Antiques
28–32 Hill Rise
081 948 4638
Recently expanded and now with around 25 dealers, the stock on offer largely reflects the prosperous tastes of the area, with much mid-range Victorian furniture, British and French and glittering jewellery. Some pine is also available, however, plus a fairly diverse range of pictures, porcelain and collectors' items.

ROMFORD (ESSEX)

ATA Antiques
91 Waterloo Road
0708 749701
Furniture, from Victorian and Edwardian to 'bread and butter' house clearance, plus repro pine and small collectables.

Collectors' Forum
237 South Street
0708 764457
Apart from books and 78s, anything collectable is on offer, including ephemera, stamps, medals, coins, teddies, tin plate and die-cast toys, jewellery, bric-a-brac and an amazing assortment of useful odds and ends.

Easton Express
259 London Road
0708 745651
A full range of house clearance basics from crockery and cutlery to wardrobes and beds.

RUISLIP (MIDDLESEX)

Car Boot Sale
On Sundays in the grounds of Queensmead School.

SIDCUP (KENT)

All Things Considered
1 Marechal Niel Parade
081 309 5717
Secondhand furniture, including some pre-war pieces and house clearance goods.

SUNBURY ON THAMES (MIDDLESEX)

Kempton Park Market
The Racecourse
0932 853593 (enquiries)
A mega-event on the second and last Tuesday of each month, with around 500 stallholders both indoors and outdoors offering a comprehensive range of antiques, collectors' items and bric-a-brac.

DENTAL INSTRUMENTS

In the magnificent variety of collectables, there are inevitably some very unusual subjects which the majority of us might actually go to great lengths to avoid. For instance, it is hard to imagine drooling over a rare collection of 18th and 19th century dental instruments. Nevertheless, there is a retired professor of dentistry who does just that. Certainly some of the examples in his collection are impressive enough – notably gleaming steel hooks and probes with handles of polished lignum vitae, rosewood and ivory, held together by shiny brass rivets, and neatly arranged on baize-lined trays. It has to be admitted, grudgingly perhaps, that they do have a curious aesthetic appeal, as well as considerable historical significance as low-tech scientific instruments. He flatly refuses to tolerate any suggestion that his hobby is eccentric. Collecting stamps, in his view, is a much more questionable activity.

SURBITON (SURREY)

Cockrell Antiques
278 Ewell Road
081 390 8290
An eclectic range of furniture,
period to modern decorative;
better quality items are
displayed in the shop; less
expensive furniture and
shipping goods are kept in a
store elsewhere.

Fagin's
109 Chiltern Drive
081 399 0487
Furniture from Victorian to
1930s, ephemera, bric-a-brac,
metalware, collectors' items,
and general antiques.

Laurence Tauber Antiques
1231 Ewell Road
081 390 0020
Furniture, including mid-range
items, and general antiques.

THAMES DITTON (SURREY)

Fern Cottage Antiques Centre
28–30 High Street
081 398 2281
A mixed market – some craft
products, but mostly antique.
Around nine dealers with a
broad range of furniture,
jewellery, collectors' items, art
deco, Clarice Cliff china and
general antiques.

THORNTON HEATH (SURREY)

The Corner Cabinet
446 Whitehorse Road
081 684 3156
Two adjacent shops with a
varied selection of furniture,
including brass beds, Victorian
and Edwardian brownwood, to
pre-war oak, plus textiles, toys,
bric-a-brac and general
antiques.

TWICKENHAM (MIDDLESEX)

Ailsa Gallery
32 Crown Court
081 891 2345
Mostly select small furniture,
pictures and decorative items,
but also with a range of less
expensive collectables like
ornamental boxes, pens, signet
rings and the like.

Albert Cigarette Card Specialists
113 London Road
081 891 3067
Venerated by aficionados in the
know, this shop has what must
be the largest stock of pre-war
cigarette cards in the world and
the knowledge to match – its
annual guide to cigarette card
collecting has been published
successfully for almost twenty
years and postal auctions are a
feature of the business. Other
collecting lines include toy
soldiers, matchboxes, film
memorabilia and associated
literature and general
ephemera. The only items
missing are stamps and
postcards.

Cheyne Galleries
8 Crown Road
081 892 6932
A shop, a lock-up warehouse
and a yard with a tantalisingly
comprehensive range from
modest house clearance goods
and general junk to the stylishly
decorative. Stock covers
everything from buttons to
bookcases and includes such
variants as busts, gazebos,
jewellery, pictures and old

frames, recycled fitted kitchens, books, doors, garden furniture, architectural and decorative bits and pieces, Victoriana and assorted collectors' items. Room has even been found for pictures by local artists. The perfect example of one stop shopping for junk lovers.

David Morley Antiques
371 Richmond Road
081 892 2986
A well-established dealer with versatile stock of general antiques, including curios, scientific instruments, small furniture and collectables. Also offers film and TV prop hire.

Relics
80 The Green
081 894 2152
Formerly **Rags and Relics**, but has dropped costume to concentrate on pictures, furniture and collectors' items at a range of prices, including budget, with some framed prints at around £10.

Scotia Philately
Unit B, 75 South Western Road, St Margarets
081 892 7935
An office, rather than conventional retail shop, so prior phone call appreciated. Stock includes manuscripts and letters, railway-related items and postcards, plus philatelic and postal history items.

Anthony Palmer Antiques
169 St Marys Lane
0708 226620
Local stockist of traditional mid-range furniture, mostly Victorian and Edwardian, clocks, bric-a-brac, linen,

original light fittings, plus a couple of display cases with collectors' items.

The Antiques Warehouse
34–36 Rockingham Road
0895 256963
An extensive stock of furniture, from period to pre-war shipping and general antiques.

Wallington & Epsom House Clearance
86a Stafford Road
081 761 7615
A fully inclusive stock of house clearance goods in 1,000 square feet of showroom, from furnishing basics to crockery and cutlery. Better-quality goods are hived off to the same company's antique shop: **The Furniture Exchange** *(216 Norwood Road, SE27).*

Workshop Antiques
1–3 Meadow Cottages, Trout Road
0895 422467
A comprehensive stock of furniture, mostly mid-range and mostly restored, with some pre-war oak and cheaper items.

Sue Ryder Shop
4 The Broadway
081 559 0124
Donated furniture, clothes, bric-a-brac, jewellery, collectables and useful bits and pieces.

SOUTH EAST ENGLAND

Brighton's antique trade may be something of a legend, with its dealers expert in the subtle art of winkling out the goodies from the most unlikely corners, yet even here the quick-witted punter can make off with a bargain.

Wits, to be sure, are fairly essential and some specialised knowledge is a distinct advantage. The atmosphere is akin to a seaside casino, with its winners and losers, lacking the more reverential approach found elsewhere. Buying in Brighton is both entertaining and challenging, although even the most glib raconteur-dealer is likely to possess formidable knowledge.

In other towns, the dealing culture is less adrenalin-based. Bognor and Eastbourne are much favoured by the retired. In many cases the fact that they are giving up larger houses elsewhere means that there can be a surplus to dispose of. Buying patterns in Kent are also mixed, with country auctions that lie beyond comfortable reach of London offering some interesting potential. By and large, however, the ground is well covered, and demand for goods is strong, but there remain a few interesting corners – the Isle of Wight has one or two, for instance, while antique markets in towns such as Hythe can repay a rummage.

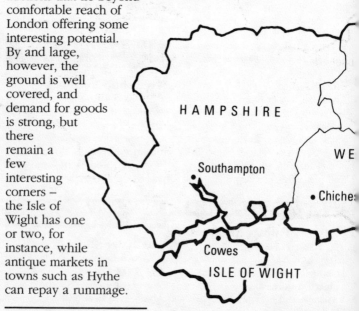

ABINGER HAMMER
(SURREY)

Abinger Bazaar
Guildford Road
0306 730756
Victoriana, bric-a-brac, books, collectors' items and general antiques, to post-war.

Stirling Antiques
Aberdeen House,
Guildford Road
0306 730706
A varied selection of decorative and other architectural items, including stained glass, domestic and ecclesiastical; also general antiques – jewellery, toys, metalware, textiles etc. After 25 years in the business, the owner knows his subject and invariably has some interesting pieces in stock.

ADVERSANE
(SUSSEX)

The Antique Centre
Old House
0403 783594
Around 20 dealers in one location, with a broad range of general antiques, bric-a-brac and collectors' items.

ALDERSHOT
(HAMPSHIRE)

Acorn Furnishings
135 High Street
0252 316211
Shipping and secondhand furniture.

Aldershot Antiques
2a Elms Road
0252 22715
House clearance specialists.

Frantiques
2b Elms Road
0252 341997
Mid-range furniture and general antiques.

ANDOVER *(HAMPSHIRE)*

Andover Saleroom
41a London Street
0264 364820
Fortnightly general sales.

Car Boot Sales
Thruxton motor racing circuit
Held most weekends.

The Globe Galleries
23 High Street
0264 352576
Secondhand furniture and house clearance goods.

Markets
Saturday and Thursday. Some bric-a-brac and general antique stalls.

Second to None
5 Love Lane
0264 355939
Secondhand basics and flatfillers.

ANGMERING *(SUSSEX)*

Bygones
The Square
0903 786152
A selection of mid-range furniture, bric-a-brac, textiles and general antiques.

ARUNDEL *(SUSSEX)*

Dominated by its 11th-century castle, substantially 'improved' during the last century, and its Victorian cathedral, Arundel's upmarket antique shops are complemented by several bric-a-brac centres.

Arundel Bridge Antiques
6 High Street
0903 884164
A market of some 25 dealers in a variety of general antiques, furniture and collectors' items seven days a week.

Tarrant Street Antiques Centre
Nineveh House
0903 884307
A large converted church in a street with a few interesting outlets (such as a walking stick specialist at number 39). Around 15 dealers trade in an eclectic range of mid-market and shipping furniture, jewellery, bric-a-brac, pictures, collectors' items and general antiques, plus some good specialised lines, including cameras, lamps and lace.

Upstairs Downstairs Antique Centre
29 Tarrant Street
0903 883749
Four dealers on three floors with a range of general antiques and furniture at all price levels.

ASHFORD *(KENT)*

Destined to become Britain's gateway to Europe when the Channel Tunnel is complete, the town's expansion has brought brisk business to dealers, especially in the used furniture trade.

Hobbs Parker, auctioneers
Ashford Market, Elwick Road
0233 622222
General sales monthly; antique sales about every six weeks.

Second Time Around
Station Yard
0233 643756

A warehouse containing a large selection of secondhand furniture and house clearance effects.

ASHTEAD (SURREY)

Bumbles
90 The Street
0372 276219
Mixed furniture, clocks, general antiques and a varied stock of decorative items.

Memory Lane Antiques
102 The Street
0372 273436
Former specialist in dolls and toys, now with an expanded repertoire which includes some mid-range furniture and general antiques, plus examples of the local speciality – Ashtead pottery. A factory employing disabled ex-servicemen was established in the 1920s by Lady Weaver, and the pottery made there is now much sought after.

BALCOMBE (SUSSEX)

Pine & Design
Haywards Heath Road
0444 811700
A mix of new and old pine furniture, pictures, sofas, textiles and other lifestyle accessories.

BASINGSTOKE (HAMPSHIRE)

Basingstoke Auction Rooms
82–84 Sarum Hill
0256 840707
Fortnightly general sales.

Longleys
15 Church Street
0256 21290

Budget furniture and house clearance goods; also occasional auctioneers of general goods or antiques.

YMCA Shop
Winchester Street
0256 844104
Secondhand furniture and effects in a former Maples furniture shop.

BEXHILL ON SEA (SUSSEX)

The Old Mint House
High Street, Pevensey
0323 762337
The Warehouse
45 Turkey Road
0424 216056
Two outlets under the same ownership, offering a large selection of mid-range furniture and general antiques, including a selection of less expensive shipping items.

BIDDENDEN (KENT)

Two Maids Antiques
6 High Street
0580 291807
A good all-round mixture, with an emphasis on small decorative stock and interesting collectables, such as bobbins, trivets, kitchenalia, treen and pictures. A few smaller items of furniture are also available.

BISHOPS WALTHAM (HAMPSHIRE)

Julia's Antiques
11 Winchester Road
0489 892474
An extensive range of furniture, including shipping and pre-war, jewellery, bric-a-brac and general antiques.

BLETCHINGLEY
(SURREY)

Quill Antiques
86 High Street
0883 743755
One of a number in town, this shop has particularly good raking potential and much low-cost stock, including old farming items, textiles, bric-a-brac, treen, kitchenalia, metalware and anything old with a vernacular flavour.

Lawrence, auctioneers
80 High Street
0883 743323
About eight mixed sales a year.

BOGNOR REGIS
(SUSSEX)

The Auctionarium
1 Argyle Road
0243 861066 (enquiries)
Hi-tech auction utilising on-screen offer and bid system for the sale of antiques; a variant of racecourse scoreboard technology. Currently seeking new premises.

Ron Hildreth
205 Chichester Road
0243 820082
Furniture, including pine, interesting odds and ends, general antiques.

Magpies
66 and 77 Hawthorn Road
0243 841664
An extensive stock of furniture, mid-range to secondhand and general antiques and reproduction.

Summerley, auctioneer
96 Limmer Lane, Felpham
0243 821212
Monthly general sales.

BOREHAM STREET
(SUSSEX)

Camelot Antiques
Boreham Street, near Hailsham
0323 833460
Mid-range small furniture and general antiques, to pre-war, Victoriana, bric-a-brac, metalware and collectors' items.

BRAMLEY (SURREY)

Memories Antique Shop
High Street
0483 892205
Seven dealers selling mid-range to shipping furniture, including pine and pre-war pieces, bric-a-brac, art deco, kitchenalia and almost anything in the collectable line. Stock varies but there is usually some scope for budget buyers.

BRASTED (KENT)

Brasted Antiques & Interiors
High Street
0959 564863
Among the more affordable shops in this select street, offering a range of decorative items, furniture, bric-a-brac and general antiques.

BRIGHTON (SUSSEX)

Antiques capital of the world, say some, and certainly it is intensively populated with traders and dealers of every description, from humble totters to purveyors of the choicest objets d'art. Few objects, however, are quite as outrageously exotic as the Prince Regent's famous pavilion, which celebrates the wilder shores of Georgian style. The following selection – merely a

taster – should cater for most budget to middle-market interests.

Antiques & Bedsteads
105 Gloucester Road
0273 621434
Mid-range furniture, including pine, brass and iron beds, architectural and decorative items, textiles, bric-a-brac and general antiques.

Ashford Furniture Centre
297 Ditchling Road
0273 556387
Secondhand furniture and house clearance goods.

Ashton's Antiques
1–3 Clyde Road, Preston Circus
0273 605253
Mid-range to shipping furniture, including pine and general antiques.

Bears & Friends
42 Surrey Street
0273 721160
A popular local theme (another bear colony hangs out at number 44) but this is unmistakably teddy country. There are about 750 in stock at any one time, from 90p to £500 for the superior variety. Their friends are the antique dolls who live alongside them.

Car Boot Sale
Trafalgar Street
Sundays in the station car park.

Fleamarket
North Lane
0273 493593
On Saturdays in North Lane.

Inmans, auctioneers
35–40 Temple Street
0273 774777
Monthly general sales.

Jubilee Antique Cellars
Gardner Street
0273 600574
Around 25 stallholders offering a range of general antiques and collectors' items.

Kollect-o-Mania
25 Trafalgar Street
0273 694229
A mini-market of about 10 dealers with a range of antiques and specialist lines, including toys, books, records, doll's houses and associated items as well as varied collectables. A worthwhile speculative browse.

Prinny's
3 Meeting House Lane
0273 204554
About 25 dealers with a range of general antiques, jewellery, pictures, bric-a-brac, books and collectors' items.

BROADSTAIRS (KENT)

Broadstairs Antiques & Collectables
49 Belvedere Road
0843 861965
Some furniture, plus a range of general antiques and collectors' items, including textiles, bric-a-brac and decorative objects.

Michael of The Vale
16 The Vale
0843 867426
Mid-range to secondhand furniture.

BURGESS HILL (SUSSEX)

British Antique Exporters
School Close,
Queen Elizabeth Avenue
0444 245577
Furniture and general antiques, to pre-war and shipping.

BURWASH (SUSSEX)

Chateaubriand Antiques Centre
High Street
0435 882535
Around 15 dealers with a range of furniture, pictures, textiles and collectors' items.

CAMBERLEY (SURREY)

The Treasure Chest
45 London Road
0276 28664
Budget furniture and house clearance goods.

CANTERBURY (KENT)

Ecclesiastical capital of England since the seventh century, and a university town since 1960, Canterbury's relatively small population is dramatically increased by the annual influx of tourists.

Antique & Design
The Old Oast, Hollow Lane
0227 762871
A warehouse and showroom of mid-range furniture, mostly pine, and general antiques.

Antique Market
Sidney Cooper Centre,
St Peters Street
Held every Saturday.

Burgate Antique Centre
10c Burgate
0227 456500
About a dozen dealers with a wide range of furniture, general antiques and collectors' items.

Canterbury Auction Galleries
40 Station Road West
0227 763337
Monthly general sales.

Car Boot Sale
Kingsmead Greyhound Stadium
Held each Sunday.

Coach House Antiques
Duck Lane, Northgate
0227 463117
Furniture, bric-a-brac, textiles, collectors' items and general antiques.

GW Finn & Sons, auctioneers
Brooklands, Fordwich
0227 767751
Quarterly mixed sales at Market Way.

Henley Antiques
37a Broad Street
0227 769055
General antiques and small furniture, plus a specialist line in brass beds.

Nan Leith's Brocanterbury
Errol House, 68 Stour Street
0227 454519
The shop's name often mystifies, but it is explained as a play on the French word *brocante*, meaning broken or junky, which reminds the proprietrix of her time in Belgium. Stock is varied but is strong on decorative metalware, including fireplace accessories, cast-iron doorknockers and brass fittings. Other lines include costume jewellery, bric-a-brac and a variety of collectors' items from the 1950s and earlier. A corner shop with potential.

The Saracen's Lantern
8–9 The Borough
0227 451968
Mid-range furniture, jewellery, porcelain, clocks and watches, curios, unusual items, old

bottles and pot lids as well as general antiques.

Stablegate Antiques
19 The Borough, Palace Street
0227 764086
Mid-range furniture, jewellery, collectors' items and general antiques, with a good selection of glass, porcelain and small objets d'art.

Town & Country Furniture
141 Wincheap
0227 762340
Vernacular furniture and collectables.

CHATHAM (KENT)

Archway Furniture
Luton Road
0634 813911
House clearance specialists.

Past & Present
88–90 Luton Road
0634 811726
Flatfillers and basics.

Walter & Randall, auctioneers
7–13 New Road
0634 841233
Sales at various venues.

CHERTSEY (SURREY)

Chertsey Antiques
8 Windsor Street
0932 563565
Furniture, mid-range to shipping, jewellery, bric-a-brac and general antiques.

Surrey Antiques Centre
10 Windsor Street
0932 563313
Seven dealers with an extensive range of furniture, bric-a-brac, textiles, jewellery, pictures, collectors' items and general antiques.

CHICHESTER (SUSSEX)

Almshouses Arcade
19 The Hornet
0243 528089/776409
Half a dozen dealers with a selection of general antiques and collectors' items, including toys, militaria, furniture and bric-a-brac. Specialist lines include model railways and Dinky toys.

St Pancras Antiques
150 St Pancras
0243 787645
Numismatics, medals, decorations and insignia, bric-a-brac, some furniture and collectors' items.

Stride & Sons, auctioneers
Southdown House, St John Street
0243 780207
Monthly general sales. Phone for details.

CHOBHAM (SURREY)

Penny Farthing Antiques
The Doll's House, 71 High Street
0276 857718
Some mid-range furniture, plus textiles, metalware, bric-a-brac and general antiques. An emphasis on the pretty, including lace-fringed pillow cases and silk flowers.

The Tarrystone
40–42 High Street
0276 857494
Across-the-range furniture, metalware, bric-a-brac, collectors' items and 'good, healthy clutter'.

COBHAM
(SURREY)

Antics
44 Portsmouth Road
0932 865505
An extensive selection of
vernacular furniture and rustic
antiques.

COODEN
(SUSSEX)

Annie's
4 Bixlea Parade,
Little Common Road
04243 6966
A selection of furniture, bric-a-
brac, textiles, clocks, metalware
and general antiques. A small
space, well used, with much at
the lower end of the price
scale.

COPTHORNE
(SUSSEX)

Copthorne Antiques
Copthorne Bank
0342 712802
Furniture, including pine,
jewellery, various collectors'
items, bric-a-brac and local
photographs.

COWES
(ISLE OF WIGHT)

Galerias Segui
75–77 High Street
0983 292148
A range of furniture, including
pine, pictures, bric-a-brac and
some collectables.

CRANBROOK
(KENT)

**Cranbrook Antique
Centre**
15 High Street
0580 712173

Seven dealers under the same
roof, with a good choice of
mid-range furniture, general
antiques and a variety of
collectors' items.

CRAWLEY
(SUSSEX)

**Crawley Antique &
Secondhand Centre**
51 Spencer's Road,
West Green
0293 523325
Approximately 6,000 square
feet filled with secondhand
furniture and house clearance
goods.

DARTFORD
(KENT)

Dartford Antiques
27 East Hill
0322 291350
Furniture, mid-range to
shipping and budget, bric-a-
brac, collectors' items and
'good honest junk'.

DEAL
(KENT)

Quill Antiques
12 Alfred Square
0304 375958
Small furniture and general
antiques, plus some interesting
ephemera, as well as bric-a-
brac and various collectors'
items.

Serendipity
168–170 High Street
A well-orchestrated range of
browseable stock, including
standard collectors' items such
as Staffordshire pottery figures,
as well as general antiques that
can sometimes include lesser
collectables for only a few
pounds.

DORKING (SURREY)

A popular town within the
antique trade, with 28 outlets in
all, and half a dozen of those
being markets. Quality is much
in favour on West Street, which
is dominated by antique shops,
though there are a few
possibilities for the dedicated
bargain hunter.

Antiquaries Antique Centre
56 West Street
0306 743398
Five dealers offering a mid-
market range of furniture,
clocks, pictures and general
antiques.

J & M Coombes
44 West Street
0306 885479
A long-established (30 years)
traditional dealer with an
emphasis on selection rather
than the select, offering
furniture, including mid-range
and shipping, with budget
possibilities such as 1920s
barley-twist dining tables.

Crowe's Auction Galleries
Reigate Road
0306 740382
Weekly general sales.

Dorking Antique Centre
17–18 West Street
0306 740915
Around 30 dealers with
pictures, metalware, bric-a-brac
and collectors' items.

Nostalgia
1 West Street
0306 880022
Specialists in costume and
textiles.

Victoria & Edward Antiques Centre
61 West Street
0306 889645
Approximately 30 dealers
offering a wide range of
furniture, general antiques and
collectors' items.

PF Windibank, auctioneers
18–20 Reigate Road
0306 884556
About 10 antique and fine art
sales per annum.

DOVER (KENT)

Bonnies
18 Bartholomew Street
Collectors' items, bric-a-brac
and general antiques.

J & L Saunders
196–197 London Road
0304 214003
A large selection of furniture,
mid-range to shipping and
general antiques.

Stuff
87 London Road
0304 215405
Furniture, including budget,
bric-a-brac, household goods
and some general antiques.

Wybornes
66 London Road
0304 213940
Mid-range to secondhand
furniture and general antiques.

EASEBOURNE (SUSSEX)

Easebourne Antiques
Easebourne Lane
0730 816240
Furniture and general antiques,
mid-range to budget and
shipping.

EASTBOURNE
(SUSSEX)

A resort town, close to the South Downs and Beachy Head, and retaining its Martello tower as a museum – one of 74 built on the Kent–Sussex coast to repel Napoleon's expected invasion.

The Antiques Market
Leaf Hall, Seaside
0323 727530
Around 16 dealers with a range of furniture, general antiques and collectors' items. Open on Saturday only.

Bygones
24 Willingdon Road, Old Town
0323 737537
Textiles and costume, from Edwardian to 1950s.

Eastbourne Antiques Market
80 Seaside
0323 720128
Around 40 stallholders offering a varied selection of general antiques and bric-a-brac.

Old Town Hall Antique Centre
52 Ocklynge Road
0323 416016
About 20 dealers with a mostly mid-range selection of general antiques and collectors' items.

Timothy Partridge
46 Ocklynge Road
0323 638731
One of about six shops in the area carrying a wide range of furniture, Victorian to pre-war.

Pharaoh's Antiques Centre
28 South Street
0323 738655
Fourteen dealers with a broad selection of furniture, including pine, kitchenalia, books, ephemera, textiles, bric-a-brac, lighting and accessories and a range of collectors' items. Prices are variable but can be low.

EVERSLEY (HAMPSHIRE)

Kingsley Barn Antique Centre
Church Lane
073¾ 328518
An extensive stock of furniture, and general antiques.

FARNBOROUGH
(HAMPSHIRE)

Martin & Parke
97 Lynchford Road
0252 515311
An extensive range of furniture, including shipping, general antiques and books.

FARNHAM (SURREY)

Bits & Pieces
82 West Street
0252 715043
Mid-range to pre-war furniture, and bric-a-brac.

Bourne Mill Antiques
Guildford Road
0252 716663
Established more than 20 years ago and one of the better local sources for those in search of a bargain. Around 75 dealers show a varied and comprehensive stock of furniture, including pine, collectors' items, textiles, pictures, architectural and decorative items, bric-a-brac and general antiques.

Farnham Antique Centre
27 South Street
0252 724475

About a dozen dealers trading in general antiques and collectors' items, including dolls and toys, jewellery, textiles, furniture, bric-a-brac and general antiques.

The Maltings Market
Bridge Square
0252 726234 (enquiries)
Held on the first Saturday of the month, with about half the 170 or so stalls devoted to antiques, bric-a-brac and collectors' items.

FLEET (HAMPSHIRE)

Barnardo's Furniture
279 Fleet Road
0252 624724
Donated secondhand furniture and household effects.

FOLKESTONE (KENT)

Richard Amos Antiques
37 Cheriton High Street
0303 275449
Furniture, mostly shipping.

Alan Lord Antiques
71 Tontine Street
0303 253674
Shop and warehouse with a large selection of furniture, and general antiques.

Newmans
7 Grace Hill
0303 257200
House clearance specialists.

FRESHWATER (ISLE OF WIGHT)

Aladdin's Cave
School Green Road
0983 752934
Furniture, bric-a-brac, metalware, textiles, collectors' items and general antiques for both trade and public. Well worth a forage.

Atticus
146 School Green Road
0983 760148
Furniture, bric-a-brac and general antiques.

GILLINGHAM (KENT)

Dickens Antiques
42 Sturdee Avenue
0634 850950
Furniture, jewellery and general antiques.

FISHING TACKLE

What does an off-season angler do in his spare time? The answer, more likely than not, is shut himself away with memorabilia of anglers past. The lucky ones will be those who started buying old fishing tackle and angling gear, as well as the attendant literature, 30 or more years ago, when a top-class Hardy rod and reel could be picked up for a few pounds at a country auction. Early flies are more of a rarity, except where they have been bound in sample books, which are now much sought after. Flies, after all, can confer immortality: it is unlikely that anyone today bothers to read the sermons of the Reverend Greenwell, but thousands of angling buffs venerate his memory for his 'glory' – the name given to his best-known fly.

GODALMING (SURREY)

The Olde Curiosity Shoppe
99 High Street
0483 415889
Collectors' items, bric-a-brac, jewellery and a range of general antiques.

GOSPORT (HAMPSHIRE)

ET Cooper
20 Stoke Road
0705 585032
Furniture and general antiques, including decorative and fairground items. The proprietor is also reputed to have a passion for mechanical music.

Peter Pan's
105/105c Forton Road
0705 524254
Toys, dolls, collectors' items, jewellery and miniature furniture. Antique photographic equipment and related items are sold at the adjacent Bazaar.

GRAVESEND (KENT)

Furniture Farm
193 Old Road West
0474 537141
Secondhand and budget furniture.

GUILDFORD (SURREY)

The Antiques Centre
22 Haydon Place
0483 67817
Around eight dealers with a comprehensive range of furniture and general antiques, including kitchenalia, textiles, toys and dolls, bric-a-brac and ephemera. Specialisations include topographica, postcards, baby gowns and doll's house furniture.

HASLEMERE (SURREY)

Wood's Wharf Antiques Bazaar
56 High Street
0428 642125
A dozen dealers offer a broad mid-market range of general antiques and collectors' items.

HASTINGS (SUSSEX)

George Street Antiques Centre
47 George Street
0424 813526
Some 20 dealers selling small antiques and collectors' items.

HAYLING ISLAND (HAMPSHIRE)

Mick's
8 Selsmore Road
0705 466149
Secondhand furniture and house clearance goods.

HAYWARDS HEATH (SUSSEX)

Ardingly Antique & Collectors' Fair
The Agricultural Show Ground, Ardingly
0636 702325 (enquiries)
A massive, varied and extremely popular intermittent event in which around 2,000 dealers trade in almost every kind of antique and collectable.

Martins Furnishing World
Queens Road
0444 412058
A large basement premises full of secondhand furniture.

Sussex Auction Galleries
59 Perrymount Road
0444 414935
Intermittent general sales.

HERNE BAY (KENT)

Jeans
22 Charles Street
0227 361544
One of a handful of house
clearance specialists in town.

HINDHEAD (SURREY)

Second Hand Rose
Portsmouth Road,
Bramshott Chase
0428 604880
A large stock of furniture,
period to budget, pictures,
collectables and bric-a-brac.

HORSHAM (SUSSEX)

Denham's, auctioneers
The Auction Galleries,
Warnham
0403 255699
Monthly general sales and
monthly antique and specialist
sales, at a site located two miles
outside town.

HOVE (SUSSEX)

Herriott House
Clearance
69a–69b Church Road
0273 727811
House clearance specialists,
established about four years
ago, offering a varied stock,
which occasionally includes
antiques.

The Sussex
Commemorative Ware
Centre
88 Western Road
0273 773911
A right royal selection of the
sort of dishes, cups, bowls,
glassware and general
memorabilia that began with
jubilee fever last century. Much
mass-production resulted but

there was also some good work
by such as Wedgwood, Doulton
and Parian.

HYTHE (KENT)

Hythe Antique Centre
5 High Street
0303 269643
Located in the former Post
Office, the centre now consists
of about four dealers, with a
comprehensive range of
furniture, period to shipping,
pictures, porcelain, textiles and
general antiques.

Malthouse Arcade
High Street
0303 260103
Around 35 stallholders with a
varied mix of furniture,
collectors' items, bric-a-brac and
general antiques.

Radio Vintage
250 Seabrook Road
0303 230693
Wireless sets of all descriptions,
from mini-Wurlitzer style to
bakelite basics, plus
components and repair service.
Prices vary from a few pounds
to several hundreds. You can
buy a table for your purchase
next door, at number 248.

LAMBERHURST
(KENT)

A Barn Full of Sofas &
Chairs
Lamberhurst
0892 890285
Also several stables, an oast
house and the furnace mill that
used to cast London's iron
railings, all now devoted to the
storage and display of
upholstered goods; many
expensive, but some at
reasonable budget prices.

LEWES *(SUSSEX)*

Birthplace of English parliamentary democracy, after a fashion, in so far as it was the site of Simon de Montfort's rout of Henry III. Today it is perhaps better known for the international festival of opera at nearby Glyndebourne, founded by John Christie in 1934. The Norman castle retains its impressive barbican walls.

Car Boot Sales
Cliffe High Street
In the car park on Sundays.

Cliffe Antiques Centre
47 Cliffe High Street
0273 473266
About 15 dealers with furniture and general antiques.

Cliffe Gallery Antique Centre
39 Cliffe High Street
0273 471877
Across-the-range furniture, jewellery, textiles, collectors' items and general antiques.

The Emporium Antique Centre
42 Cliffe High Street
0273 486866 (enquiries)
A new arrival, with about 40 dealers selling furniture, from period to pre-war, and general antiques, but emphasising arts & craft, art nouveau, art deco, Liberty pewter, Moorcroft ceramics and other late 19th- to early 20th-century specialities.

Felix Gallery
2 Sun Street
0273 472668
Not for the allergic – a treasure-trove of cat-related objects and pictures of all descriptions, plus a bed and breakfast.

The Fifteenth Century Bookshop
99–100 High Street
0273 474160
Antiquarian and secondhand books, plus an intriguing sideline in teddies.

Foundry Lane Antiques Centre
15 Cliffe High Street
0273 475361
Mid-range to pre-war furniture, metalware, textiles, bric-a-brac and general antiques, with a penchant for turn-of-the-century craft and decorative items.

Lewes Antique Centre
20 Cliffe High Street
0273 476148
Around 40 stallholders with a rummageable mix of across-the-range furniture, metalware, bric-a-brac, collectors' items and varied ephemera.

Lewes Auction Rooms
Garden Street
0273 478221
Weekly general sales, plus about eight antique sales a year – the most comprehensive of several auction houses in town. Sales take place in the Old Castle Market, Garden Street.

Roundabout
Unit 8, Cliffe Arcade,
Cliffe High Street
0273 471325
Clothes and costume, including pre-worn designer classics.

The Snowdrop
119 South Street
0273 471018
A pub with some interesting ancillary activities, such as an Indian tepee and two floors to the rear full of rummageable bric-a-brac and collectables.

LINDFIELD (SUSSEX)

The Corner Gallery
99 High Street
0444 482483
Mid-range to budget furniture,
bric-a-brac and general
antiques. Prices start at a few
pounds and rarely exceed two
hundred.

LISS (HAMPSHIRE)

Plestor Barn Antiques
Farnham Road
0730 893922
Furniture, mid-range to pre-war
as well as bric-a-brac and
general antiques.

LITTLEHAMPTON (SUSSEX)

Peter Cheney, auctioneers
Western Road
0903 722264
General sales every three
weeks.

LYMINGTON (HAMPSHIRE)

Lymington Antique Centre
76 High Street
0590 670934
A former garage with around 30
dealers selling a comprehensive
range of furniture, general
antiques and collector's items.
Prices are across the range.

New Forest Auctions
Emsworth Road
0590 677225
Sales every Thursday.

Saturday Market
High Street
Mixed goods on offer, including
some general antiques and bric-
a-brac.

MAIDSTONE (KENT)

An ancient market town, and
centre of the fruit and hop-
growing industry, it retains a
former palace of earlier
Archbishops of Canterbury, and
has a well-known museum of
horse-drawn carriages.

Agricultural Hall Auctions
Hart Street
Large auctions held each
Thursday by different
auctioneers, including Norris
(0622 895515).

Past & Present
60 Union Street
0622 686124
Smaller secondhand goods,
such as collectors' items,
crockery and bric-a-brac.

Sutton Valence Antiques
Unit 4, Haslemere,
Parkwood Estate, Sutton Road
0622 675332
Around 20,000 square feet at
various locations, this being the
one for mid-range to shipping
furniture, bric-a-brac, decorative
items, metalware and general
antiques. More can be seen at
Sutton Valence itself, located on
the A274 travelling towards
Tenterden.

MARGATE (KENT)

Scott's Furniture Warehouse
Bath Place, Grotto Hill
0843 220653
Around 10,000 square feet with
a comprehensive mix of
furniture, from mid-range to
pine and 'old-fashioned
secondhand', plus general
antiques. With prices starting at
around £1, this is a good call-in
for budget buyers.

Wednesday Market
Hartsdown Park
Rummagable bric-a-brac, on
Wednesdays.

MERSTHAM (SURREY)

**The Old Smithy Antique
Centre**
7 High Street
0737 642306
A dozen dealers with a range of
general antiques, bric-a-brac
and collectors' items.

MIDHURST (SUSSEX)

Nationwide, auctioneers
Midhurst Auction Rooms,
Bepton Road
0730 812456
Mixed sales every six weeks.

Midhurst Antiques Market
Knockhundred Row
0730 814231
A strictly mid-market cross
section of furniture, porcelain
and general antiques.

MILLAND (SUSSEX)

The Plough
Maysleith
042 876 323
Rural nostalgia in the form of
old farm implements and
machinery, tools and
equipment, cheese presses,
butter churns, mangles, crow-
scarers and other reminders of
an age when farming was an
active outdoor occupation,
rather than an adjunct of the
accountancy and chemistry
sectors. Appointment required.

NEWHAVEN (SUSSEX)

The Fleamarket
28 South Way
0273 517207

Around 40 dealers with a broad
selection of furniture, bric-a-
brac, collectors' items and
general antiques.

NEWPORT (ISLE OF WIGHT)

**A substantial market town on
the River Medina. Charles I was
imprisoned at nearby
Carisbrooke Castle prior to his
'trial' and execution.**

Castaways
37 Orchard Street
0983 529988
Secondhand furniture.

Mike Heath Antiques
3–4 Holyrood Street
0983 525748
An across-the-range selection of
general antiques, including
metalware, bric-a-brac and
decorative and collectors' items.
Some inventive and imaginative
touches can make this a
pleasant browse.

Lugley Street Antiques
13 Lugley Street
0983 523348
Mid-range furniture, clocks and
general antiques. A mini market
of budget furniture dealers
operates across the road.

**Marilyn Rose Antiques
Centre**
87 Pyle Street
0983 293846/0983 528850
Two dealers with mostly
smaller items, including
jewellery, collectors' items,
costume and textiles,
metalware, bric-a-brac and
general antiques.

Second Time Around
93 Pyle Street
0983 821262

Secondhand furniture and house clearance goods.

Watchbell Antiques
Watchbell Lane
0983 852089
Bric-a-brac, commemorative china, ephemera, collectors' items and general antiques. Prices start low, with postcards at 20p and bric-a-brac from a couple of pounds.

OAKLEY (HAMPSHIRE)

Hutchins Antiques
48 Pardown
0256 780494
Traditional stockists of mid-range to pre-war furniture and general antiques.

OXTED (SURREY)

The Antique Centre
64 Station Road
0883 712806
Around half a dozen dealers with a range of furniture, bric-a-brac and general antiques.

Treasures
151 Station Road
0883 713301
A shop that makes a virtue out of diversity, with a stock consisting of furniture, including pine, metalware, bric-a-brac, toys, collectors' items, books, textiles and general antiques. Can repay a speculative rummage.

PETERSFIELD (HAMPSHIRE)

Folly Market
College Street
0730 264816
Several dealers with mid-range antiques and collectors' items, including jewellery, porcelain, pictures, metalware and textiles.

PETWORTH (SUSSEX)

Petworth Antique Market
East Street
0798 42073
About 35 dealers with a mostly mid- to upper-range selection of general antiques, porcelain, pictures, textiles, books and collectors' items. Much in the style of the town's 20 or so smart antique shops, but some bargains could be available for the truly determined.

PORTSLADE (SUSSEX)

Peter Marks Antique Warehouse
1/11 Church Road
0273 415471
There are three established dealers in town, this one having been in the business almost 30 years as a supplier of a comprehensive range of furniture and general antiques, including shipping goods, from spacious and usually well-stocked premises.

PORTSMOUTH (HAMPSHIRE)

Birthplace of Charles Dickens, and resting place of Nelson's flagship, HMS *Victory*, Portsmouth has some of Hampshire's best junk-buying potential, especially around Fawcett Road, and Albert Road, in the local seaside resort of Southsea.

A & S Antiques
153 Harland Road
0705 736626
A broad range, including budget and house clearance furniture.

Affordable Antiques
130 Highland Road, Southsea
0705 293344
A mix of mid-range and pre-war furniture and general antiques.

Tony Amos
239 Albert Road, Southsea
0705 736818
More mid-market to shipping and budget furniture and general antiques.

Nesbit's, auctioneers
7 Clarendon Road, Southsea
0705 864321
Monthly general sales. Phone for details.

Portsmouth Stamp Shop
184 Chichester Road, North End
0705 663450
Philatelic and numismatic items and general ephemera.

BA Smiffys
195 Albert Road, Southsea
0705 736327
Flatfillers and basics.

RAMSGATE (KENT)

Car Boot Sales
Dumpton Leisure Centre, Pearson Road
On Sundays.

Grange Auctions Ltd
Salmestone Grange, Nash Road
0843 226909
Monthly general sales in quaint surroundings.

Granny's Attic
2 Addington Street
0843 588955
Rummageable bric-a-brac and general antiques, the majority of it low-cost and including items that date up to about the 1950s.

Thanet Antique Trade Centre
45 Albert Street
0843 597336
Large and comprehensive, with everything from period and budget furniture to bric-a-brac and collectors' items.

REDHILL (SURREY)

Home Counties House Clearance
51 High Street, Edenbridge
0732 862785
An extensive range of secondhand furniture and effects.

Second Thoughts
14 Brook Road
0737 762571
House clearance goods.

REIGATE (SURREY)

Bertram Noller
14a London Road
0737 242548
A comprehensive selection of furniture, metalware, fireplaces and accessories and general antiques.

RINGWOOD (HAMPSHIRE)

Barbara Davies Antiques
30a Christchurch Road
0202 872268
A comprehensive mix of porcelain, bric-a-brac, general antiques, collectors' items and some furniture. Prices can be very reasonable, even for some of the better quality pieces of porcelain.

Nesbit, auctioneers
7 Claringdon Road, Southsea
0705 864321
Monthly antiques sales and fine

art auctions. Phone for
information about dates.

The Tennis Bookshop
West Gate, Moyles Court
0425 480518
Books and anything else
remotely connected with tennis
or similar racket games.

ROCHESTER (KENT)

**Dominated by an impressive
Norman castle and cathedral.
The local earl in Charles II's
times had an irrepressible talent
for writing bawdy poems.**

Droods
62 High Street
0634 829000
General antiques, bric-a-brac
and collectors' items.

Memories
128 High Street
0634 811044
General antiques, including
furniture, pictures, collectors'
items and bric-a-brac.

Northgate Antiques
48 High Street
0634 865428
A varied selection of general
antiques including clocks,
textiles, bric-a-brac, clothes,
ephemera and collectors' items,
some quality and mid-market
but much in the cheap-and-
cheerful range, with good
browsing possibilities.

Vince Antiques
18 Crow Lane
0634 815796
Furniture, collectors' items, bric-
a-brac and general antiques
with a reasonable amount in
the budget bracket and usually
with an interesting and varied
stock.

ROLVENDEN (KENT)

Falstaff Antiques
63–67 High Street
0580 241234
Mid-range furniture including
reproduction, bric-a-brac,
metalware, collectors' items,
general antiques as well as a
fascinating museum of
automobiles.

ROMSEY (HAMPSHIRE)

Bell Antiques
8 Bell Street
0794 514719
An extensive selection of
furniture, mid-range to pre-war,
jewellery, bric-a-brac, pictures,
collectables and general
antiques.

Creighton's Antique Centre
23–25 Bell Street
0794 522758
Around 18 dealers with a mix of
general antiques, bric-a-brac
and collectables.

Old Cottage Things
Broxmore Park,
Sherfield English
0794 884538
Furniture, bric-a-brac,
decorative items and recycled
architectural material for both
the house and the garden. The
owner has been in the business
for over 20 years and knows
how to cater for imaginative
DIY home-nesters.

Romsey Medal & Collectors Centre
5 Bell Street
0794 512069
Medals, decorations, insignia,
militaria, crested and
commemorative china and other
collectors' items.

RYDE *(ISLE OF WIGHT)*

Hayters
18–20 Cross Street
0983 563795
An extensive stock of mid-range to pre-war furniture.

Royal Victoria Arcade
Union Street
0983 646651
Around half a dozen dealers with a range of general antiques and collectors' items.

RYE *(SUSSEX)*

Rope Walk Antiques
18–22 Rope Walk
0797 223486
10,000 square feet of furniture, including pine, kitchenalia and general antiques.

Mint Dolls, Toys & Teddies
71 The Mint
0797 222237
Surprisingly enough, specialising in dolls, toys and teddies.

ST LEONARDS *(SUSSEX)*

Arquebus Antiques
46 Norman Road
0424 433267
Established stockists of mid-range to shipping furniture and general antiques, in the business for 35 years. Further browsing of a similar sort is available at **Hanner Antiques**, a few doors away.

Chapel Antiques
1 London Road
0424 440025
An extensive range of furniture, china, pictures and general antiques. Much in the higher price range but a search can reveal some cheaper finds.

The Hastings Antique Centre
59–61 Norman Road
0424 752922
Around two dozen dealers, many strong on specialisation; textiles, kitchenalia, art deco, sporting items, pictures, clocks and general antiques.

SANDGATE *(KENT)*

Antiques Etcetera
93 High Street
0303 249389
Mid-range to pre-war furniture, bric-a-brac, curiosities and collectors' items. Budget-buying appeal is part of the shop's culture although quality can be good.

Churchill Galleries
13–15 High Street
0303 249574
Eight dealers with a comprehensive mix of furniture, mid-range to 1950s, bric-a-brac, collectors' items and general antiques.

Nordens
43–43a High Street
0303 248443
Of the 15 or so antique shops squeezed in Sandgate's High Street, this is the longest established (almost 50 years). It continues to flourish with its traditional mix of mid-range furniture, metalware, collectors' items and bric-a-brac.

Phillips, auctioneers
11 Bayle Parade, Folkestone
0303 245555
Monthly general sales plus about eight specialist and antique sales per annum.

Sandgate Antiques Centre
61–63 High Street
0303 248987
Around half a dozen dealers, mostly with a middle-of-the-road range of general antiques and collectors' items.

SANDWICH (KENT)

The Bargain Shop
68 Dover Road
0304 612260
Secondhand furniture and house clearance goods in 5,000 square feet of showrooms.

Empire Antiques
Old Council Yard, Gazen Salts, Strand Street
0304 614474
Furniture, pine and shipping, and some general antiques.

Halifax Property Services
15 Cattlemarket
0304 611044
General sales held at the Drill Hall, The Quay, approximately every three weeks.

Monken Quay Antiques
62b Strand Street
0304 612345
General antiques.

SEAFORD (SUSSEX)

Courtyard Antiques Market
13–17 High Street
0323 892091
Eight dealers with a range of general antiques, bric-a-brac and collectors' items.

Seaford's Barn Collectors Market
Church Lane
0323 890010
Operates Tuesday, Thursday and Saturday. A varying number of dealers with collectors' and specialist items, including books, philately, buttons and ephemera.

SEDLESCOMBE (SUSSEX)

Mrs Kinloch
Bulmer House, The Green
0424 870364
Dollies, teddies and other childish things.

SELSEY (HAMPSHIRE)

Second Chance
142 High Street
0243 605921
House clearance specialists.

SEVENOAKS (KENT)

The Antiques Centre
120 London Road, Tubs Hill
0732 452104
Mid-market furniture, jewellery, pictures, metalware, porcelain and general antiques, in general catering for up-market tastes but bargains have been known to occur.

Phillips, auctioneers
49 London Road
0732 740310
Monthly general sales.

Sheldon Ward Antiques
57 St John's Hill
0732 455311
Victorian to pre-war furniture, metalware, bric-a-brac and general antiques.

SHANKLIN (ISLE OF WIGHT)

Keith Shotter
81 Regent Street
0983 862334
Jewellery, numismatics, medals

and decorations, pots and bottles and general collectors' items of a fairly variable character but including the odd prize item.

SHEERNESS (KENT)

Times Past
31a St Georges Avenue
0795 660605
Furniture, shipping and budget.

SHERE (SURREY)

Shere Antique Centre
Middle Street
048 641 2846
Fifteen dealers on two floors of a 15th-century house with a comprehensive range of furniture and general antiques.

SHOTTERMILL (SURREY)

Grannies Attic
Checkerboards, Hindhead Road
0428 644572
A rummageable mix of furniture, odds and ends, bric-a-brac and general antiques.

SOUTHAMPTON (HAMPSHIRE)

Cottage Antiques
9 Northam Road
0703 221546
Furniture, period to shipping and general antiques.

Millbank Auctions
72–94 Millbank Street
0703 228179
Monthly general auctions.

The Old Curiosity Shop
280 Shirley Road
0703 774772
Furniture, mid-range to pre-war, jewellery, books, bric-a-brac,

collectors' items and now with an in-house art gallery.

Relics Antiques
54 Northam Road
0703 221635
Across the range furniture and general antiques including competitively priced items.

TENTERDEN (KENT)

The Antique Shop
53a High Street
0580 764491
General mid-range antiques.

Halifax Property Company
53 High Street
0580 763200
Sales every three weeks.

The Lace Basket
1a East Cross
0580 763923
Textiles and associated items.

Lambert & Foster, auctioneers
102 High Street
0580 762083
Monthly general sales.

Tenterden Antiques Centre
66–66a High Street
0580 765885
Sixteen dealers with a mix of furniture, general antiques and collectors' items. Prices are across the range, with some budget-buying possibilities.

TITCHFIELD (HAMPSHIRE)

Gaylords
75 West Street
0329 843402
Furniture, period to shipping, clocks and general antiques.

TONGHAM (SURREY)

Grange Farm Antiques

Grange Farm, Grange Road
0252 782993
General architectural salvage, small items to large scale decorative features.

TUNBRIDGE WELLS
(KENT)

Famed for the curative properties of its Springs, which were discovered in the 17th century, Tunbridge Wells later became a fashionable health resort, and still jealously protects its sedate character. Popularly associated with Queen Victoria, who conferred its 'Royal' status, and 'Disgusted' of *The Times* letters page! Antique shops abound, particularly at the upper end of the market. The main searching areas are around the Pantiles in the old part of town, and the St John's Road and Mount Pleasant areas, where a more mid-market

TUNBRIDGE WARE

The origins of the highly intricate miniature items of inlaid woodware which began to appear in the area around Tunbridge Wells and neighbouring Tonbridge towards the end of the 17th century have never been fully explained. Suggestions for its inspiration have included Dutch marquetry, as popularised by William and Mary, and Italian pietra dura of the kind that grand-tourists were beginning to bring back to Britain at this time. On the other hand, it may have suddenly evolved independently. A local 'inventor' has even been identified: Mr William Burrows, of Gibraltar Cottage. Tunbridge ware was certainly distinctive in one sense: it was used for some of the earliest custom-made souvenirs produced on any commercial scale in the country. By 1697, the tireless traveller Celia Fiennes could declare her astonishment at the large size of the enterprise, and the number of shops and booths engaged in the sale of the product to those in search of good health at the town's fashionable spa. The technique of inlaying wafer-thin veneers of wood to form intricate patterns which could be both geometric and pictorial was relatively straightforward, although the end result could be quite stunning. Boxes and small chests were particularly popular, some being small enough for postage stamps and visiting cards, while others did service as slope-lid travelling desks, tea-caddies and sewing boxes. The scale of production was enormous and items were still being produced shortly before the First World War much as they had been two centuries earlier. As souvenirs, they were eagerly snapped up by tourists who, by the age of the railway, were arriving from all parts of Britain. As a result, Tunbridge ware can often turn up in the most unexpected places, and the quantity in circulation often means that prices can be fairly reasonable.

choice is available. **For a full list of the town's shops, contact the Tourism and Marketing Department of Tunbridge Wells Borough Council, 0892 526171.**

A1 Collectables
53 Colebrook Road,
High Brooms
0892 539085
General antiques, secondhand goods, bric-a-brac and collectors' items.

Aaron Antiques
77 St John's Road
0892 517644
A comprehensive range of furniture, collectors' items, bric-a-brac, ephemera, books, pictures and general antiques.

Bracketts, auctioneers
27–29 High Street
0892 533733
General sales every Friday.

Culverden Antiques
47–49 St John's Road
0892 515264
A well-mixed selection of furniture, bric-a-brac, collectors' items and general antiques in an area that caters for a broadly based buyership and often produces good value.

Fleamarket
The Assembly Hall
0892 515675.(enquiries)
Held on the first Wednesday of each month.

WEYBRIDGE (SURREY)

Jandora
112 Oatlands Drive,
Oatlands Village
0932 851858
General antiques and collectors'

items, including dolls, pictures and decorative pieces. A moderately laid-back option in a town of smart shops catering for well-heeled tastes.

WHITSTABLE (KENT)

The Country Seat
149a Island Wall
Secondhand furniture and house clearance goods.

The Junk Shop
24a Harbour Street
0227 266243
Basics and flatfillers.

Something Old, Something New
2–4 Tankerton Road
0227 265081
An extensive range of budget furniture in several showrooms.

WINCHESTER (HAMPSHIRE)

Phillips, auctioneer
The Red House, Hyde Street
0962 862515
Fortnightly general sales.

The Pine Cellars
39 Jewry Street
0962 867014
Much country-living elegance as well as rustic charm in a vast space, selling everything and anything in pine, from benches to complete wainscotted parlours and including some painted furniture.

Spencers Antiques Emporium
39 Jewry Street
0962 867014
Attached to **The Pine Cellars**, a busy market of around 30 dealers with a broad range of

furniture, bric-a-brac, collectors' items and general antiques. One of several outlets in town with good choice and variation.

WOKING *(SURREY)*

Wych House Antiques
Aberdeen House, Wych Hill
0483 764636
Extensive premises with a broad selection of furniture, including pine, decorative and collectors' items, pictures, kitchenalia. Prices begin at a few pounds and go up to the low- to mid-hundreds.

WOODCHURCH *(KENT)*

Woodchurch Antiques
3 The Green
0233 860249
Furniture, country and pine,

kitchenalia, bric-a-brac and general antiques.

WORTHING *(SUSSEX)*

Ellis, auctioneers
44–46 High Street
0903 238999
Monthly antique auctions.

Gibbins
167–173 Tarring Road
0903 201175
Four shops crammed full of everything to do with house clearance, 'from rubbish to treasures'.

Robert Warner & Son
1–13 South Farm Road
0903 232710
Long-established dealer in extensive premises with a wide range of furniture, general antiques and bric-a-brac.

SOUTH CENTRAL ENGLAND

Proximity to London exerts an influence, particularly in the more comfortable commuting outreaches, but this is not to say that the bargains have all been shaken out – just that you have to work a lttle bit harder to find them.

Antique markets provide the usual opportunities for the knowledgeable buyer, and there are several sources of the cheap-and-cheerful in some of the medium-sized towns like Warminster and Luton. The M4, much traversed by the London–Bath antique trade, means a high dealer profile at many of the local auctions – although according to one auctioneer, the recession's combined effect on the antique business and the housing market has brought good opportunities for the private bidder. The effects of the economic downturn are disparate. One Reading dealer, asked to sum up the state of the trade, did so with a single word: 'devastated'.

In St Alban's, however, where the trade slimmed down substantially about eight

years ago, there were few complaints. One beneficial result would appear to be a general acceptance that goods sell best when price levels are realistic. Nor is it unusual for private buyers to ask for a discount. There are certainly some moderately priced items around in many of the shops, and some exceptionally good buys in large complexes such as the Oxford Antique Trading Company and the Hungerford Arcade, although the real bargains, according to our experienced local source, tend to turn up at auction.

ABBOTS LANGLEY
(HERTFORDSHIRE)

Dobson's Antiques
53 High Street
0923 263186
Traditional outlet with a comprehensive range, from Victorian brownwood furniture to house clearance and shipping goods, bric-a-brac and general antiques.

AMERSHAM
(BUCKINGHAMSHIRE)

The county town, with several picturesque buildings, including a few old inns and a fine 17th-century market hall.

The Antiques & Collectors' Centre
20–22 Whieldon Street
0494 431282
About 25 dealers with a range of furniture, to pre-war, bric-a-brac, jewellery, collectors' items and general antiques.

Auctions
Amersham Auction Rooms
(125 Station Road, 0494 729292) hold weekly general and monthly antique sales.
South Bucks Auctions *(2 School Lane, 0494 722758)* hold fortnightly general sales and monthly antique sales at the British Legion Hall and

above the Conservative Club in Old Amersham.

Sundial Antiques
19 Whieldon Street
0494 727955
Mid-range furniture, lighting accessories, pottery and porcelain, general antiques and collectors' items, including horse brasses.

AMPTHILL
(BEDFORDSHIRE)

Ampthill Antiques Centre
Market Square
0525 403344
Furniture and general antiques, to pre-war, plus a basement with secondhand goods; also pottery, porcelain and collectors' items.

Ampthill Emporium
6 Bedford Street
0525 402131
An extensive stock of across the board furniture, including pine, plus some general antiques and decorative items.

The Old Pine Loft
The Old Slaughter House, 2b Woburn Street
0525 840226
Pine and architectural items, including doors and fireplaces. Closed on Monday. Hours may vary so phone first.

The Pine Parlour
82a Dunstable Road
0525 403030
Specialises in pine furniture,
kitchen items and general
antiques.

Ann Roberts Antiques
1 Kings Arms Yard
0525 403394
Furniture, fireplaces and
accessories, especially original
brass fenders, general antiques
and clocks. Closed on Monday
and Tuesday. Also in King's
Arms Yard is **Pat Bentley
Antiques**, *(7 Kings Arms Yard,
0525 404939)* which has a
large showroom and warehouse
with a comprehensive range of
furniture and general antiques.
Closed on Monday.

BALDOCK
(HERTFORDSHIRE)

Attic
20 Whitehorse Street
0462 893880
Small general antiques,
metalware, bric-a-brac, teddies,
dolls and related items.

The Wheelwright
1 Mansfield Road
0462 893876
Jewellery, bric-a-brac –
especially plates – and
collectors' items.

BANBURY
(OXFORDSHIRE)

Holloways, auctioneer
49 Parsons Street
0295 253197
Intermittent general sales.

Oddlines
3 Cromwell Road
0295 251031
House clearance specialists.

Judy Vedmore Antiques
42 Parsons Street
0295 269626
Across the board furniture, to
pre-war, general antiques,
collectors' items, jewellery and
books.

BARKHAM (BERKSHIRE)

Barkham Antique & Craft Centre
Church Farm, Barkham Street
0734 761355
60 stallholders with a wide
range of goods including
jewellery, porcelain, glass,
kitchenalia and prints. Also
furniture from Georgian to
1930s.

BEACONSFIELD
(BUCKINGHAMSHIRE)

Old Curiosity Shop
47–49 Wycombe End
0494 674473
Furniture and general antiques,
to pre-war, plus porcelain,
metalware and collectors' items.
Closed on Monday.

BEDFORD
(BEDFORDSHIRE)

Better Than New
50 Ampthill Road
0234 349424
Secondhand furniture and
house clearance goods.

New To You
149 Castle Road
0234 341948
House clearance specialists.

Wilson Peacock, auctioneers
26 Newnham Street
0234 266366
Weekly general sales and
monthly antiques sales.

BERKHAMSTED
(HERTFORDSHIRE)

The Auction Rooms
Middle Road
0442 865169
Fortnightly sales of general goods.

Sue Ryder Shop
249 High Street
Furniture, jewellery, trinkets and general secondhand goods.

BICESTER
(OXFORDSHIRE)

All Sorts
10 The Causeway
0869 248847
Specialising in house clearance furniture.

Messengers, auctioneers
27 Sheep Street
0869 252901
Approximately eight mixed sales a year.

BISHOPS STORTFORD
(HERTFORDSHIRE)

Northgate Antiques
21 Northgate End
0279 656957
Collectors' items and general antiques.

Sue Ryder Shop
65 High Street
Some secondhand furniture, bric-a-brac and clothes.

Sworder, auctioneers
15 Northgate End
0279 651388
Weekly general sales and monthly antique sales.

BLEWBURY
(OXFORDSHIRE)

Blewbury Antiques
London Road
0235 850366
An interesting and rummageable range of small furniture and general antiques, bric-a-brac, books and collectors' items. Closed on Tuesday.

BOREHAM WOOD
(HERTFORDSHIRE)

Sue Ryder Shop
269 Shenley Road
Some secondhand furniture, as well as general bric-a-brac, various small collectables and clothes.

BRACKNELL
(BERKSHIRE)

Secondhand City
Scott's Farm,
Amen Corner
0344 868858
A large stock of secondhand basics and house clearance goods.

BUCKINGHAM
(BUCKINGHAMSHIRE)

Flappers
2 High Street
0280 813115
Mid-range furniture, including some stripped pine, plus various textiles and some costume, plus a selection of general antiques.

Johnson & Co., auctioneers
31 West Street
0280 822535
Intermittent general and antique sales.

BURFORD
(OXFORDSHIRE)

Cotswold Gateway Antique Centre
Cheltenham Road
0993 823678
Much typical Cotswolds quality, but also some mid-range smaller goods and decorative objects.

Denver House Antiques & Collectables
Witney Street
0993 822040
Coins, medals and decorations, stamps, militaria, books and general collectors' items.

Jonathan Fyson Antiques
50 High Street
0993 823204
Further mid-range possibilities amongst the gleaming oak, including metalware, porcelain and decorative items.

Robin Shield Antiques
134 High Street
0993 822462
Upper-range furniture and general antiques, with a strong sense of the decorative.

Frank Williams
The Old Post Office,
66 High Street
0993 822128
An extensive selection of furniture, including mid-range, general antiques and decorative items.

CALNE
(WILTSHIRE)

Calne Antiques
2a London Road
0249 816311

Furniture, mid-range to shipping, as well as general antiques and some collectors' items.

CHIPPENHAM
(WILTSHIRE)

Fernleys
21 Park Lane
0249 659701
Secondhand furniture and house clearance goods.

CHIPPING NORTON
(OXFORDSHIRE)

Chipping Norton Antique Centre
1 Middle Row,
Market Square
0608 611212
Around 20 dealers with a comprehensive selection of furniture, bric-a-brac, general antiques and collectors' items.

The Emporium
26 High Street
0608 643103
Collectors' items, some interesting ephemera, pictures and bric-a-brac.

CODFORD (WILTSHIRE)

Tina's Antiques
75 High Street
0985 50828
Mid-range small furniture, jewellery, bric-a-brac, collectors' items and a selection of general antiques.

CROWMARSH GIFFORD
(OXFORDSHIRE)

The Pennyfarthing
49 The Street
0491 37470
Mid-range furniture, mostly

brownwood, with some pine, kitchenalia, bric-a-brac, metalware, textiles and general antiques. Ownership and style recently changed, but still geared towards the middle market buyer. Closed Monday and Tuesday.

DEDDINGTON
(OXFORDSHIRE)

Castle Antiques
Manor Farm, Clifton
An extensive range of furniture, all prices, metalware, kitchenalia, bric-a-brac and decorative items.

The Deddington Antique Centre
Laurel House, Bull Ring, Market Square
0869 38968
16 dealers with a broad selection of furniture, pictures, textiles and collectors' items.

Tucker's Country Store
Market Place
0869 38397
Mid-range furniture, general antiques, linen and collectables.

DONNINGTON
(BERKSHIRE)

Drewatt Neate, auctioneers
Donnington Priory
0635 31234
Fortnightly general sales.

DORCHESTER ON THAMES (OXFORDSHIRE)

Dorchester Galleries
Rotten Row
0865 341116
A mix of pictures, bric-a-brac and collectors' items. Open Thursday to Saturday.

DUNSTABLE
(BEDFORDSHIRE)

Mannucci's
Wood Street
(behind 49 High Street South)
0582 662963
Secondhand furniture and house clearance goods.

GREAT SHEFFORD
(BERKSHIRE)

Ivy House Antiques
Wantage Road
0488 648549
Vernacular and pine furniture and general antiques, kitchenalia and collectors' items.

HARPENDEN
(HERTFORDSHIRE)

Meg Andrews
20 Holly Bush Lane
0582 460107
A seriously comprehensive range of costumes, textiles and related items, from inexpensive pieces to museum quality. Appointment required.

HEATH AND REACH
(BEDFORDSHIRE)

Heath Antique Centre
Woburn Road
052 523 7831
Several dealers trading in a wide range of furniture, general antiques and collectors' items.

Helton Antiques
26a Birds Hill
052 523 474
Recently scaled down operations, but still with a good range, including furniture, metalware, porcelain and general antiques. Opening times vary, so phone first.

HEMEL HEMPSTEAD
(HERTFORDSHIRE)

Aladdin's Cave
6 Lawn Lane
0442 235024
Secondhand furniture and bric-a-brac.

Cherry Antiques
101–103 High Street
0442 64358
Mid-range furniture, including pine, textiles, dolls and toys, jewellery, metalware, bric-a-brac and general antiques.

Wednesday Antique Market
Market Place
071 624 3214 (enquiries)
Around 100 dealers with a varied selection of goods, from bric-a-brac and ephemera to pictures and furniture.

HENLEY ON THAMES
(OXFORDSHIRE)

Friday Street Antique Centre
4 Friday Street
0491 574104
About 15 dealers with a wide range of furniture, to pre-war, general antiques, kitchenalia and collectors' items.

Rhino Antiques
20 Market Place
0491 411162
Collectors' items, bric-a-brac and general antiques.

HERTFORD
(HERTFORDSHIRE)

Village Green Antiques
6–8 Old Cross
0992 587698

A large selection of furniture, porcelain, pictures and decorative antiques, as well as some collectables, with prices from moderate upwards.

HIGH WYCOMBE
(BUCKINGHAMSHIRE)

Burrell Antiques
Unit 2, Kitchener Works, Kitchener Road
0494 523619
Mid-range furniture, up to to pre-war. Appointment recommended.

Martin's Furniture
41–43 Totteridge Road
0494 472200
Specialising in secondhand furniture and a range of household effects.

HITCHIN
(HERTFORDSHIRE)

RJ Perry Antiques
37–38 Bridge Street
0462 434525
Large premises, comprising two shops and upper floors, which are partly let out to about half a dozen other dealers. A comprehensive range of furniture, period to shipping, collectors' items and general antiques.

HUNGERFORD
(BERKSHIRE)

Below Stairs
103 High Street
0488 682317
Mid-range furniture, kitchenalia, architectural and decorative items and collectables.

Hungerford Arcade
26a High Street
0488 683701

Approximately 80 dealers offering a comprehensive range of furniture, bric-a-brac, specialist lines and general antiques.

Victoria's Bedroom
4 Bridge Street
0488 682523
Brass and iron bed specialists. Closed on Monday.

KIMPTON
(HERTFORDSHIRE)

Annick Antiques
28 High Street
0438 832491
Mid-range and vernacular furniture, pictures, bric-a-brac and general antiques.

KINGS LANGLEY
(HERTFORDSHIRE)

Frenches Farm Antiques
Tower Hill,
Chipperfield
0923 265843
A comprehensive range of furniture, metalware, bric-a-brac and general antiques. Located near the Royal Oak pub on the Bovingdon Road.

LANE END
(BUCKINGHAMSHIRE)

Bach Antiques
Essex House, Finings Road
0494 882683
Mid-range furniture, to pre-war and general antiques. Closed on Monday.

LEIGHTON BUZZARD
(BEDFORDSHIRE)

David Ball Antiques
59 North Street
0525 382254

A large and worthwhile selection of furniture, from period to shipping styles, as well as a browseable range of general antiques and some collectors' items.

New Road Households
10a New Road
0525 382960
Specialising in secondhand furniture and household basics, but also offering some low-cost general antiques and a range of small and inexpensive collectables.

BAXTER PRINTS

George Baxter did as much as anyone to add colour to the homes of Britain in the 19th century. His advanced printing techniques enabled him to mass-produce accurate coloured images at a remarkably low price which, in true Victorian style, brought the 'improving' arts to the masses. The most popular subjects usually reflected the prevailing taste for scenes of cloying sentiment, religious devotion or imperialist triumphalism, but the process had other applications, being cheap enough to be used for Christmas cards and the packaging of items such as hat pins and chocolates. Sadly, Baxter's techniques were picked up and exploited by others and he died in relative poverty.

LUTON (BEDFORDSHIRE)

The largest town in the county, and well known in its industrial heyday as a manufacturing centre for lorries and buses. Prior to that, it was a centre for straw-plaiting.

A–Z Stores
Crawley Road
0582 413366
Secondhand furniture and house clearance goods. Closed on Thursday.

Adelaide Auction Rooms
Stuart Place,
82 Wellington Street
0582 423809
General sales every Wednesday.

The Bargain Box
4–6a Adelaide Street
0582 423809
General antiques, bric-a-brac and collectors' items.

Chris & Terry
61 Inkerman Street
0582 412656
A former hat factory, now a shop selling secondhand furniture and house clearance goods.

Denton's Antiques
440 Dunstable Road
0582 582726
Furniture, from mid-range to shipping and budget, bric-a-brac and general antiques.

Luton Multi-Auctions
37 John Street
0582 405281
Weekly Thursday auctions, plus monthly Sunday auctions and monthly Monday auctions where goods are cleared without reserve.

Magpie Corner
99 Selbourne Road
0582 502456
Secondhand furniture and house clearance goods.

MALMESBURY (WILTSHIRE)

One of the county's premier antiques venues, the local abbey has some exceptional 11th-century Saxon carvings. A top-quality range of antiques is available from the town's main antique shops and a number of other outlets provide a more affordable selection of interesting items – and even occasional junk. Two representative shops are listed.

Cross Hayes Antiques
The Antique and Furniture Warehouse, 19 Bristol Street
0666 824260
A large selection of furniture, period to budget, plus some bric-a-brac and general antiques.

Relic Antiques
Brillscote Farm, Lea
0666 822332
Architectural antiques, from doorknobs to complete pub and fairground interiors, plus a range of garden furniture. Appointment required.

MARLBOROUGH (WILTSHIRE)

The Marlborough Parade Antique Centre
The Parade
0672 515331
Upwards of 50 dealers selling mostly mid to upper range furniture, general antiques, porcelain, specialist lines and collectors' items.

Terry's Secondh...
Furniture
2 The Parade
0672 515878
House clearance specia...

Temple Lighting
Stockwell House, Wavendon
0908 583597
Mid-range furniture and
decorative lighting accessories,
Victorian to art deco, to
brighten up the bland
functionalism of the locality.

MINETY (WILTSHIRE)

Sambourne House
Antiques
Sambourne House
0666 860288
A large selection of mid-range
and shipping pine, mostly
antique, with some
reproduction, for trade and
public, plus some porcelain,
kitchenalia and general
antiques. Also with a retail
outlet in nearby Malmesbury.

OLNEY
(BUCKINGHAMSHIRE)

Market Square Antiques
Rose Court
0234 712172
An assortment of general
antiques, including jewellery,
bric-a-brac, textiles, ephemera
and collectors' items.

OXFORD (OXFORDSHIRE)

**Learning and discrimination in
taste might be expected here,
given the seven centuries of
academic tradition. Oxford was
also the Royalist capital during
the Civil War and, in the**

...SOUTH CENTRAL ENGLAND

Phillips, auctioneers
39 Park End Street
0865 723524
Fortnightly general sales,
intermittent specialist s...

The Spinning...
226 Cowley...
0865 246...
Mid-...

...816
...mall antiques, especially
porcelain and bric-a-brac.

The Oxford Antiques
Centre
The Jam Factory,
27 Park End Street
0865 251075
Mid-range to shipping furniture,
metalware, pictures, jewellery,
bric-a-brac, textiles and
costume, rugs, gramophones,
toys and general antiques,
amongst other things.

The Oxford Antique
Trading Co.
40–41 Park End Street
0865 793927
Across-the-range one-stop
shopping with upwards of 50
dealers in 20,000 sq ft offering
everything from period furniture
to cheap-and-cheerful budget
goods.

Oxford Architectural
Antiques
The Old Depot, Nelson Street,
Jericho
0865 53310
Recycled architectural material
and decorative items.

road range of furniture, general antiques, bric-a-brac, lighting and accessories, jewellery and collectors' items.

Honest Ric
Corner of Stanhope Road and Camp Road
Secondhand furniture and household basics.

St Alban's Antique Market
Town Hall, Chequer Street
0727 844957 (enquiries)
A Monday market of about 30 stallholders selling general antiques, bric-a-brac and collectors' items.

Stevens Antiques
41 London Road
0727 857266
Furniture, including pine, bric-a-brac, metalware, collectors' items and general antiques spread around basement, ground and first floor premises. Closed on Thursday.

Wheel
Road
763
nge to budget and ondhand furniture.

READING (BERKSHIRE)

Reading Emporium
1a Merchant's Place
0734 590290
About 10 dealers offering a wide selection of general antiques and collectors' items.

Rod's Discount Shop
441 Oxford Road
0734 508815
Secondhand and house clearance goods.

Thimbleby & Shorland, auctioneers
31 Great Knoll Street
0734 508611
Monthly general auctions.

ST ALBANS
(HERTFORDSHIRE)

Inhabited since the iron age, its largely 13th-century abbey, founded in AD 793, has the second longest nave in Britain. It was promoted to cathedral status in 1877. The Romans left a theatre and some mosaic paving, as well as the town's saint, who served in the ranks until his desertion and martyrdom.

By George Antiques Centre
23 George Street
0727 853032
About a dozen dealers with a

SALISBURY
(WILTSHIRE)

A 13th-century new town which supplanted nearby Old Sarum. The 14th-century cathedral spire, more than 400ft high, is the tallest in the country.

The Antique & Collectors' Market
37 Catherine Street
0722 326033
Three floors of general antiques, bric-a-brac, books, toys, stuffed birds, ephemera and other collectors' items.

The Avonbridge Antiques & Collectors' Market
United Reformed Church Hall, Fisherton Street
About 15 dealers with a range

of general antiques, bric-a-brac and collectors' items. Tuesdays only.

Car Boot Sale
Southampton Road
On Sunday, opposite Tesco's.

Castle Galleries
81 Castle Street
0722 333734
General antiques and collectors' items, including numismatics and militaria.

Woolley & Wallis, auctioneers
Salisbury Salerooms,
51–61 Castle Street
0722 411422
Fortnightly 'shutter' (ie general effects) sales.

SANDHURST
(BERKSHIRE)

Sheila White Antiques
Sandhurst Farm Barn
207 Yorktown Road
College Town
0252 873290
A converted barn at the rear of a 16th-century farmhouse with furniture from period to pre-war, plus occasional antique pine, treen, bric-a-brac, metalware, jewellery and general antiques. Opening times may vary, so phone before visiting.

SAWBRIDGEWORTH
(HERTFORDSHIRE)

The Herts & Essex Antique Centre
The Maltings, Station Road
0279 722044
Around 100 stallholders with a comprehensive range of general antiques, bric-a-brac and collectors' items.

SWANBOURNE
(BUCKINGHAMSHIRE)

Swanbourne Antiques
26–28 Winslow Road
029 672 516
Mid-range to pre-war furniture, general antiques, collectors' items, textiles, pictures and – if that isn't enough – cream teas are sold as well.

SWINDON (WILTSHIRE)

Allen & Harris, auctioneers
The Planks, Old Town
0793 615915
Saturday general sales plus approximately six antique sales a year.

Collectors' Corner
227 King's Hill Road
0793 521545
Numismatics, militaria, toys, buttons, ephemera and general collectors' items tell only part of the story. In fact, the stock includes half a million cigarette cards and 25,000 postcards, among the goldmine of collectables to be found here. Closed on Wednesday.

Old Town Antiques
Wood Street
A mini-market of dealers selling a range of general antiques and collectors' items.

TINGEWICK
(BUCKINGHAMSHIRE)

Tingewick Antiques Centre
Main Street
0280 847922
Furniture, mid-range to pre-war, bric-a-brac, kitchenalia, collectors' items, pictures, clocks and general antiques.

WALLINGFORD
(OXFORDSHIRE)

The Lamb Arcade
63 High Street
0491 35166
About 15 dealers with a range
of furniture, including pine,
general antiques and collectors'
items.

WARFIELD (BERKSHIRE)

Moss End Antique Centre
Moss End Garden Centre
0344 861942
25 dealers with a wide range of
furniture, general antiques, bric-
a-brac and collectors' items.
Closed on Monday.

WARMINSTER
(WILTSHIRE)

The Antique Warehouse
61 East Street
An extensive selection of mid-
range and shipping furniture
and general antiques.

Britannia Antiques
8a Silver Street
0985 217465
Victoriana and custom-made
furniture. At another address
(Furlong House, 61 East Street,
0985 219360) the same
company also has a large and
comprehensive stock of
furniture and general antiques.

Norman Hibbs
166 Boreham Road
0985 846452
A varied range of furniture,
antiques, swords and collectors'
items.

I Browse
10 East Street
0985 846822
'High class junk' and house
clearance lines, including pre-
war budget furniture.

Warminster Warehouse
Station Road
0985 219979
Secondhand furniture and
house clearance goods, plus
some antiques. Closed on
Monday.

K & A Welch
1a Church Street
0985 214687
An across-the-board selection of
furniture, general antiques and
shipping goods for both trade
and private buyers.

WATLINGTON
(OXFORDSHIRE)

Simmons & Son
The Barn, Watcombe Manor
049 161 2810
General auctions held every six
weeks.

WENDOVER
(BUCKINGHAMSHIRE)

Antiques at Wendover
The Old Post Office,
25 High Street
0296 625335
Around 30 dealers with a
comprehensive range of
furniture, general antiques,
textiles, lighting and
accessories, as well as a good
choice of decorative and
collectors' items.

Sally Turner Antiques
Hogarth House, High Street
0296 624402
An extensive selection of
furniture, much of it high-
quality but some more suitable
for mid-range buyers. Also
jewellery, silver and china and
other small antiques.

WINDSOR (BERKSHIRE)

Berkshire Antiques Co.
42 Thames Street
0753 830100
Mid-range furniture and general antiques, ephemera, toys and teddy bears and assorted collectors' items.

WITNEY (OXFORDSHIRE)

Relics
35 Bridge Street
0993 704611
In a town where the local antique ethos is of gleaming oak and mellow marquetry, this outlet cultivates a more budget conscious clientele with mid-range to shipping and secondhand furniture and general antiques.

Secondhand Superstore
45 Bridge Street
House clearance furniture, bric-a-brac, odds and ends and 'the occasional antique'.

WOKINGHAM (BERKSHIRE)

Martin & Pole
12 Milton Road
0734 790460
Monthly auctions of general goods and antiques.

WOODSTOCK (OXFORDSHIRE)

Span Antiques
6 Market Place
0993 811332
A market consisting of 10 dealers offering a comprehensive and interesting range of furniture and general antiques, bric-a-brac, textiles, kitchenalia, rural antiques, pictures and some other collectors' items.

WOOLHAMPTON (BERKSHIRE)

The Old Post House Antiques
Bath Road
0734 713460
Some mid-range furniture, plus metalware, bric-a-brac, collectors' items and general antiques.

WROUGHTON (WILTSHIRE)

Wroughton Antique Centre
23 High Street
0793 813232
Boxes, bric-a-brac, various collectors' items and general antiques. Closed on Wednesday.

SOUTH WEST ENGLAND

South West England provides scenic shopping at its best, particularly for those who enjoy the sound of crashing waves, or the sight of clouds scudding across moorland.

Glorious Bath is obligatory for anyone with a serious interest in antiques (and sublime Georgian architecture), but Bristol and its highly active mid-market antique trade should not be overlooked. The variety on offer in other towns and cities – Bournemouth, Plymouth, St Austell, Exeter and Falmouth, for example – can be mind-boggling. The same applies to the occasional out-of-the-way discovery, as visitors to Long Rock, near Penzance, tend to discover. The budget buyer is generally well catered for, the result in part of the long-standing popularity of weekend and holiday cottages. Much of the pleasure of the bargain-chase in this area is in the travelling, from the rolling hills of Thomas Hardy's Dorset to the artists' havens of Newlyn and St Ives; and a hard day's raking can always be rounded off with a cool glass of cider and some Falmouth oysters.

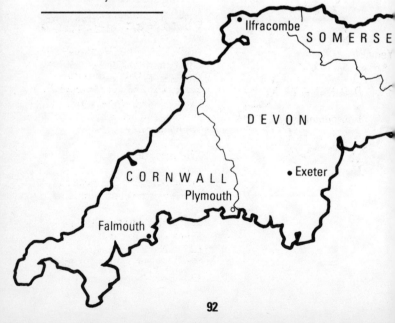

92

ASH PRIORS
(SOMERSET)

The Granary Galleries
Court House
0823 432816
Mostly mid-range and quality items but with some shipping goods and general antiques. The high decorative style is in favour, by and large, but simpler country pieces, including pine, are also available. The same building also houses **Hall's Antiques**, where a similar mix is on offer.

ASHBURTON (DEVON)

Ashburton Marbles
Great Hall, North Street
0364 53189
Architectural items, fireplaces, statuary, lighting and a range of furniture.

The Look In
19a North Street
0364 53617
Secondhand goods and budget collectables.

AXBRIDGE (SOMERSET)

The Old Post House
Weare, Bridgewater Road
0934 732372
Country furniture and general antiques.

AXMINSTER (DEVON)

The Warehouse
Castle Gate, Castle Hill
0297 35191
House clearance goods, secondhand furniture and vernacular items.

BAMPTON (DEVON)

Bampton Antiques
9 Castle Street
0398 331658
Mid-range furniture, pictures and general antiques.

Robert Byles
7 Castle Street
0398 331515
Country furniture, including pine, metalware, decorative and architectural items.

BARNSTAPLE (DEVON)

A mound is the only reminder of the town's Norman castle, but it still has the 12th century Taw Bridge and a covered Pannier Market, built in 1854, where antiques and bric-a-brac can still be bought one day a week.

The Arcade
Bear Street
Includes two budget dealers, Colin Pine and Bob Wray .

Sou'West Auctions
South Street, Newport
0271 78858
Monthly general and monthly antique sales.

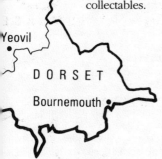

• Bristol

AVON

Yeovil

DORSET

Bournemouth •

BATH (AVON)

The dream city of Augustan England, with ultra-elegant houses, Assembly Rooms, Pump Rooms and the shop-lined Pulteney Bridge, it was much popularised by the ultimate English gentleman, Beau Nash, dandy and gambler as well as an early anti-smoking campaigner.

Aldridge, auctioneers
130–132 Walcot Street
0225 462830
Sales every Tuesday.

Antiques, Linens & Lace
11 Pulteney Bridge
0225 465782
Chic chemises, christening gowns, fine linen and lace from a variety of periods, plus silver and accessories.

Aspidistra
46 St James Parade
0225 461948
Pictures, books, music-related items, and general antiques.

Bartlett Street Antique Centre
7–10 Bartlett Street
0225 466689
Around 50 dealers with a range of antiques and collectables.

Bath Antiques Market
Guinea Lane, Paragon
0225 422510
Around 70 dealers trading in furniture, general antiques, bric-a-brac and collectors' items.

Bath Saturday Antiques Market
by Beaufort Hotel, Walcot Street
Up to 100 dealers with a comprehensive range of antiques, bric-a-brac and collectors' items.

The Galleon
33 Monmouth Street
0225 312330
Mid-range furniture, up to pre-war, general antiques, collectors' items and jewellery.

Gardiner Houlgate, auctioneers
The Old Malthouse, Comfortable Place, Upper Bristol Road
0225 447933
Monthly general sales, quarterly antique and musical instrument sales and irregular jewellery sales.

Great Western Antique Centre
Bartlett Street
0225 424243
Approximately 40 dealers sell here throughout the week, and in addition there is a Wednesday market of about 20 stallholders, selling everything from pine furniture and collectables to period clothes and rare books.

Orlando Jones
10b Monmouth Place, Upper Bristol Road
0225 422750
Brass bedstead specialists.

Junktion
74 Walcot Street
0225 462546
Secondhand furniture, house clearance goods and some budget antiques. An interesting source of eclectic junk in a city more accustomed to the costly and ultra-elegant.

Ann King
38 Belvedere, Lansdown Road
0225 336245
A specialist in textiles, linen, clothes and costume, from historic periods to the 1960s.

Next To
*29 Victoria Buildings, Lower
Bristol Road*
0225 420573
Secondhand furniture and
house clearance goods.

No. 12 Queen Street
12 Queen Street
0225 462363
General antiques and smaller
decorative items, plus samplers,
textiles, needlework and
associated items.

Paragon Market
*3 Bladud Buildings,
The Paragon*
0225 463715
A large Wednesday market with
across-the-board antiques and
collectors' items.

Pennard House Antiques
3/4 Piccadilly, London Road
Around half a dozen dealers
trading in mid-range furniture,
including pine, general antiques
and decorative items.

Phillips, auctioneers
1 Old King Street
0225 310609
Gallery sales every second
Monday, plus regular specialist
and antique sales.

Walcot Reclamation
108 Walcot Street
0225 444404
Pioneering architectural
salvagers, with everything from
doorknobs to porticos and
domes. Stock is extensive and
includes ordinary traditional
building material. A visit here,
and another to **Robert Mills** in
Bristol, would probably be
enough to provide the
complete DIY historic house.
Walcot's sales literature (like
Mills') is professional and

informative and the trading
approach organised and
serious, yet it still retains good
rake-around potential.

BEAMINSTER
(DORSET)

Beaminster Antiques & Pines Gallery
4 Church Street
0308 862591
Jewellery, silver, collectors'
items, boxes, small furniture,
metalware and pictures.

BIDEFORD *(DEVON)*

Acorn Antiques
11 Rope Walk
0237 470177
Furniture, collectors' items and
general antiques.

Bideford Bargains
66b High Street
0237 421255
Secondhand goods and house
clearance lines.

Century Galleries
7 Cooper Street
0237 477245
Jewellery, porcelain and general
antiques.

Scudder's Emporium
Bridge Street
0237 479567
A comprehensive selection of
furniture, general antiques and
collectors' items in generous-
sized premises. The price range
is from less than £10 to over
£1,000 and the period range is
as diverse, ending around 1950.

BODMIN *(CORNWALL)*

Second Chance
Market Street
A variable range of secondhand

furniture and household clearance goods.

BOURNEMOUTH
(DORSET)

With ten miles of beach and a famous symphony orchestra, this is still a popular resort town. Sources of junk and across-the-board antiques are numerous.

Allen's
447–449 Poole Road
0202 763724
An extensive selection of mid-range and shipping furniture.

The Antique Centre
837–839 Christchurch Road, East Boscombe
Furniture, silver, bric-a-brac, clothes and costume, general antiques and collectors' items. Specialisations include arts & crafts to art deco ceramics and decorative items as well as silver and Sheffield plate.

Antiques & Furnishings
339 Charminster Road
0202 527976
Furniture, general antiques, textiles, metalware and pottery.

The Collectables, West Bourne
Seamoor House,
2 Seamoor Road
0202 760720
Around 3,000 square feet of general antiques, bric-a-brac and collectors' items, secondhand and budget antique furniture.

Collectors' Corner
63 Seabourne Road, Southbourne
0202 420945
Furniture, advertising and collectors' items, general antiques and bric-a-brac.

Peter Denver Antiques
36 Calvin Road, Winton
0202 532536
Furniture and general antiques.

Gallery Antiques
835 Christchurch Road
0202 430399
A syndicate of four dealers offering general antiques and collectors' items, including some specialisations, like writing boxes, pens and inkstands.

Georgian House Antiques
110–112 Commercial Road
0202 554175
Furniture, general antiques, jewellery and collectors' items.

The Green Room
796 Christchurch Road, Boscombe
0202 392634
Antique lighting specialists, also with general antiques and decorative items.

HLB Antiques
139 Barrack Road
0202 429252/0202 482388
General antiques and collectors' items.

Hardy's Market
862 Christchurch Road, Boscombe
0202 422407
About 10 dealers offer a range of antiques and collectors' items, including costume and textiles, metalware, art deco and porcelain.

House & Son, auctioneers
Lansdowne House, Christchurch Road
0202 298044

Fortnightly general sales on Tuesdays and Wednesdays.

Kebo's Market
823 Christchurch Road, Boscombe
0202 417052
Around nine dealers trading in a variety of antiques and collectors' items, including linen and lace, jewellery, porcelain, silver and general antiques.

David Mack Antiques
434–437 Poole Road
0202 760005
A large stock of mid-range and shipping furniture and general antiques.

Mussenden Antiques
24 Seamoor Road, Westbourne
0202 764462
Jewellery, silver and collectors' items. Closed on Wednesday.

Riddett's, auctioneers
26 Richmond Hill
0202 555686
Fortnightly general sales on Tuesdays and Wednesdays.

Robin's Antiques
833 Christchurch Road, Boscombe
0202 423049
Four dealers offer a range of furniture and general antiques.

Mike Sandy
790 Christchurch Road, Boscombe
0202 301190
Decorative items, general antiques and shipping goods, to pre-war. Three warehouses and shop.

Steptoe's
907 Christchurch Road, Boscombe
0202 420424

Furniture and house clearance items.

RA Swift & Sons
4b Wolverton Road, Boscombe
0202 394470
Long-established (1904) dealers in furniture and general antiques, mostly mid-range, but with some budget and shipping items.

Victorian Chairman
883 Christchurch Road, Boscombe
0202 420996
Chairs, tables and general mid-range furniture.

Victorian Parlour
874 Christchurch Road, Boscombe
0202 433928
Furniture and country antiques.

Yesterday Tackle & Books
42 Clingan Road, Boscombe
0202 476586
Antique and secondhand fishing related items, including stuffed and mounted fish, books, pictures, reels, tackle and anything associated with angling. Strictly by appointment (the address is private).

BRIDGWATER (SOMERSET)

Blake's Antiques
2 High Street
0278 427131
Jewellery and small collectors' items.

Bridgwater Antiques Market
Marycourt Shopping Mall
0823 451433
Books, small antiques and collectors' items.

Terry Griffiths Antiques
Chapel Road, Pawlett
0278 683846
Mid-range and shipping
furniture, to pre-war.

BRIDPORT (DORSET)

Bridport Antiques Centre
5 West Allington
0308 25885
Around a dozen dealers with a
comprehensive range from
jewellery and lace to garden
statuary and taxidermy.

Hobby Horse Antiques
29 West Allington
0308 22801
Toys, trains and automata, plus
jewellery, general antiques and
collectors' items.

William Morey & Sons,
auctioneers
St Michael's Lane
0308 22078
Antique and general sales held
monthly.

BRISTOL (AVON)

**A city with much to offer,
including a 12th-century
cathedral, the oldest Methodist
chapel in the world, Brunel's
Clifton Suspension Bridge, the
SS *Great Britain*, and Archibald
Leach, who was born there in
1904, and is now remembered as
Cary Grant.**

Allen & Harris,
auctioneers
St John's Place, Apsley Road
0272 737201
General sales every Tuesday.

Better Bargains
49 Raleigh Road
0272 663876
Bric-a-brac, curios and
secondhand goods. Closed on
Wednesday.

Bizarre Antiques
210 Gloucester Road
Bishopston
0272 427888
'Good, clean' secondhand
furniture, bric-a-brac and some
shipping and mid-range
antiques.

Bristol Antique Market
The Exchange, Corn Street
0272 224014
Open on Fridays only. Around
a dozen stallholders dealing in
general antiques and collectors'
items.

Car Boot Sales
Bristol also boasts a number of
car boot sales and further
charity shops.

Carnival Antiques
607 Sixth Avenue, Central
Business Park, Hengrove
0275 892166
General antiques, bric-a-brac,
metalware and furniture,
including mid-range antique,
shipping and budget goods.

Cleeve Antiques
282 Lodge Causeway, Fishponds
0272 658366
General antiques, furniture and
bric-a-brac. Closed on
Wednesday.

Clifton Antiques
Market
26/28 The Mall, Clifton
Around 50 dealers with a wide
selection of general antiques
and collectors' items.

Frocks & Tails
39a Cotham Hill
0272 737461
Standard clothes hire for

weddings etc, plus a sideline in 1920s formal wear and flapper outfits.

Furniture Fayre
522 Filton Avenue
0272 698923
Seven rooms of general basics and flatfillers.

Chris Grimes Militaria
13 Lower Park Row
0272 298205
Military and maritime antiques, scientific instruments and collectors' items.

Hodgson's
26/30 Stapleton Road, Easton
0272 558576
Long-established (75 years) secondhand furniture and house clearance specialists.

Memories
105 Stokes Croft
0272 232213
Six floors of furniture and house clearance goods.

Odds & Todds
210 Whitehall Road
0272 521546
General secondhand and house clearance goods in large premises.

Oldwood's
1 Colston Yard
0272 299023
Stripped pine furniture and architectural items.

Oxfam
61–63 Cotham Hill
0272 735200
Bric-a-brac, jewellery, clothes and secondhand goods.

GLASS

Glass is one area of collecting that almost any budget can cope with. At the top of the range, prices can be fierce – an early piece by George Ravenscroft, who introduced the lead oxide flux process that made the manufacture of clear glass possible, giving 'lead crystal' its name, is strictly for the serious collector. Even more expensive, a Jacobite portrait wine glass could command a king's ransom – one with an air twist stem and a coloured portrait after Sir Robert Strange sold at auction in 1992 for a staggering £28,600. For those of modest means, however, there are other possibilities. The craze for digging up old rubbish dumps, which first caught on in the 1960s and continues to be a popular weekend pastime for some, produces an abundance of bottles of all kinds from the celebrated 'Cod's Wallop' classic, with its integral marble stopper, to wide-necked pre-war milk bottles carrying the names of long-forgotten local dairies. The collector interested in mid-range items is spoilt for choice, with elegant 18th-century wine glasses still available for less than £100, Bristol blue and Bohemian red glass plentiful enough to provide value for money and commemorative pressed glass plates celebrating such events as the Queen's jubilee providing standard stock for shops and stallholders throughout the country.

Potter's Antiques
60 Colston Street
0272 262551
Commemorative and collectors' items, numismatics, glass and smaller general antiques.

Rothschild's Dustbin
157–159 Whitehall Road
0272 558372
A comprehensive range of secondhand furniture, useful junk and house clearance goods.

Saunders
162 Raleigh Road, Bedminster
0272 631268/0272 662637
General antiques, bric-a-brac, metalware and furniture.

Sedan Chair Antiques
17–19 Portland Street, Clifton
0272 734020
Furniture, decorative and general antiques.

John & Sheila Symes
93 Charlton Mead Drive,
Westbury on Trym
0272 501074
Appointment required. Postcards and general ephemera, especially printed items.

Taviner's, auctioneers
Prewett Street, Redcliffe
0272 265996
Weekly general sales on Fridays and monthly antique and fine art sales on Thursdays.

The Vintage Wireless Company Ltd
Tudor House, Cossham Street, Mangotsfield
0272 565472
Valve radios and associated early radio items. Mail order, but with showroom open on Saturday mornings.

Woodstock
103 Stokes Croft
0272 246491
Furniture and house clearance goods.

BRIXHAM (DEVON)

John Prestige Antiques
102 Greenswood Court
0803 856141
A warehouse of mid-range and shipping goods.

BROADSTONE (DORSET)

Galerie Antiques
4/4a Station Approach
0202 695428
Pottery, porcelain, decorative and collectors' items, glass and jewellery. Victorian to present day, including Arts & Craft and art deco periods. Closed on Wednesday.

BUCKFASTLEIGH (DEVON)

Baldrick's Basement
Elliott Plain
0364 43949
Around 3,500 sq feet of secondhand furniture and house clearance goods.

BUDE (CORNWALL)

Kivell & Son, auctioneers
The Strand
0288 352250
Household sales on the third Thursday of each month, at 2pm.

BUDLEIGH SALTERTON (DEVON)

Laces
28 Fore Street
0395 442544

Jewellery, textiles, costume and accessories. Appointment required.

The Old Antique Shop
15 Fore Street
0395 444040
Mid-range furniture, porcelain and general antiques.

BURNHAM ON SEA
(SOMERSET)

Adam Antiques
30 Adam Street
0278 783193
Furniture and general antiques, including shipping goods.

Heape's Antiques
39 Victoria Street
0278 782131
General antiques, pictures, porcelain and collectors' items. Closed on Wednesday.

Palmers, auctioneers
75 High Street
0278 783326
Monthly general sales.

CAMBORNE
(CORNWALL)

Victoria Gallery
28 Cross Street
0209 719268
General antiques, pictures, books and jewellery.

MGA Auctions
West Charles Street
0209 711065
Sales every Thursday at 6pm.

CASTLE CARY
(SOMERSET)

Barrington Antiques
Woodcock Street
0936 51530
Jewellery and military.

Cary Antiques
2 High Street
0963 50437
Mid-range and some cheaper furniture, general antiques, pictures, metalware and bric-a-brac.

Pandora's Box
2 Bailey Hill
0963 50926
Antique pine, linen and lace. Closed on Thursday.

CERNE ABBAS
(DORSET)

Cerne Antiques
2 Duck Street
0300 341490
Furniture, decorative items, silver, porcelain and a selection of general antiques. Closed on Friday.

CHAGFORD (DEVON)

John Meredith
36 The Square
0647 433474
Decorative antiques, furniture and architectural items.

Whiddon's Antiques
6 High Street
0647 433406
Country furniture, pictures, metalware, books and bric-a-brac as well as delicious Devon cream teas.

CHARD (SOMERSET)

The Guildhall Antique Market
The Guildhall
Open on Thursdays. Around 25 stallholders selling general antiques and collectors' items. Further details from The Guildhall Tourist Information Centre *(0460 67463)*.

Mrs Whitehead
The Trading Post, Tytherleigh
0460 21330
Mid-range furniture, general antiques and collectors' items.

CHARMOUTH
(DORSET)

Charmouth Antiques Centre
The Street
0297 60122
Around 15 dealers with general antiques and collectors' items.

CHRISTCHURCH
(DORSET)

Bulstrode, auctioneers
13 Stour Road
0202 482244
Twice-weekly general sales, on Wednesday and Thursday, plus monthly antique sales.

Lankshear Antiques
149 Barrack Road
0202 473091
General antiques and militaria.

The Old Stores
West Road, Bransgore
0425 72616
General antiques, bric-a-brac and collectors' items. Open Thursday to Saturday.

CHUDLEIGH (DEVON)

The Second Hand Shop
30 Fore Street
0626 853309
Incorporating 'Ann's Place'. Furniture, bric-a-brac and house clearance goods.

CLUTTON (AVON)

McCarthy's Antiques
112 Station Road
0761 453188

Specialists in antique lamps and historic lighting equipment and general metalware.

COLYTON (DEVON)

Colyton Antique Centre
Dolphin Street
0297 552339
Opposite White Cottage Hotel. Around 24 traders with a variety of antiques and collectors' items, including musical instruments, textiles, collectors' items, jewellery, books and furniture.

COMBE MARTIN
(DEVON)

Retrospect Antiques
Sunnymede, King Street
0271 882346
General antiques, collectors' items and bric-a-brac.

COXLEY (SOMERSET)

Wells Reclamation Company
The Old Cider Farm
0749 677484
Architectural salvage.

CREWKERNE
(SOMERSET)

Crewkerne Furniture Emporium
Viney Bridge, South Street
0460 75319
Furniture, including budget and shipping, bric-a-brac, collectors' items, agricultural antiques.

Lawrence, auctioneers
South Street
0460 73041
General sales are held weekly, on the second, third and fourth Wednesday of the month at

9.30am. Antiques, fine art and specialist sales are held intermittently.

Oscar's Antiques
13–15 Market Square
0460 72718
Shop and warehouses with a large selection of secondhand, shipping and mid-range antique furniture, bric-a-brac, books, fishing tackle and general antiques. A long-established local rummage.

CULLOMPTON
(DEVON)

Browsaround
Old Forge, Higher Mill Lane
0884 34954
Secondhand and budget furniture, bric-a-brac and household clearance goods. Closed on Thursday.

The Old Tannery
Exeter Road
0884 38476
A syndicate of dealers offering a range of furniture, metalware, decorative items, kitchenalia, bric-a-brac and decorative antiques. Quality in abundance, through all 6,000 square feet, but also some low-cost buyables.

DARTMOUTH (DEVON)

Brock Antiques
32 Lower Street
0803 832615
Furniture, bric-a-brac and general antiques.

Dartmouth Auction Rooms
St Saviour's Square,
off Anzac Street
0803 832224
Monthly general sales.

Fulford's, auctioneers
The Old Sorting Office,
Hauley Street
0803 832223
Monthly general auctions on Thursdays at 11am.

DORCHESTER
(DORSET)

Henry Duke, auctioneer
Weymouth Avenue
0305 265080
Sales every six weeks, on Thursdays.

Dorchester Antiques Market
Hardy Hall
0963 62478 (enquiries)
Around 30 stallholders offering general antiques, bric-a-brac and collectors' items. Open alternate Wednesdays.

Legg of Dorchester
51 High East Street
0305 264964
Mid-range furniture, including pine and general antiques. Established more than 60 years, it puts an emphasis on traditional brownwoods but has the occasional diversion.

DULVERTON
(SOMERSET)

Acorn Antiques & Faded Elegance
39 High Street
0398 23286
Two shops at the same address, selling country furniture, decorative items, textiles, pictures and general antiques.

DUNSTER (SOMERSET)

Westwood Hamil
21 High Street
0643 821212

General antiques, bric-a-brac and collectors' items.

EXETER *(DEVON)*

With a Gothic cathedral that is still architecturally outstanding, despite wartime damage, and a guildhall built in 1330 and said to be the oldest in the country still in municipal use, its fragment of Roman wall is a reminder of an even more ancient past.

The Antique Centre on the Quay
The Quay
0392 214180
Several dealers with general antiques and collectors' items.

Exeter Livestock Centre
Matford Park Road
0392 56847
Car boot sales every Sunday at 8.30am.

Fagin's Antiques
The Old Whiteways Cider Factory, Hele
0392 882062
A treasure trove of furniture – mid-range to budget – bric-a-brac, architectural salvage, taxidermy and general antiques.

Malvern's
128 Buddle Lane
0392 71130
Secondhand furniture and house clearance goods. Closed on Wednesday.

McBain & Sons
Exeter Airport
(follow signs for Westcote)
0392 366261
A trade warehouse – but private buyers are welcome – with mid-range and shipping furniture and general antiques.

Micawber Antiques
New Buildings Lane,
25–26 Gandy Street
0392 52200
Bric-a-brac, collectors' items, lamps and general antiques.

Pennies
Unit 2, Wessex Estate,
Station Road, Exwick
0392 71928
Secondhand basics.

Phillips, auctioneers
Alphin Brook Road
0392 439025
Fortnightly general sales on Thursdays, plus intermittent fine art, antique and specialist sales.

Pirouette
5 West Street
0392 432643
Textiles, lace, linen and period costume, including christening robes and shawls.

The Quay Galleries Antiques Emporium
43 The Quay
0392 213283
Nine dealers with an assortment of furniture, porcelain, silver, decorative pieces and maritime items.

Whitton & Laing, auctioneers
9 Queens Road
0392 59395
Sales every second Wednesday. More upmarket and specialist goods sold at 32 Okehampton Street (0392 52621).

Youll's Antique Centre
Baker's Yard,
Alphin Brook Road
0392 438775
Around 10 stallholders with a range of general antiques and collectors' items. Plans are

being made to move, so phone for information before visiting.

EXMOUTH (DEVON)

Treasures
32–34 Exeter Road
0395 273258
General antiques, bric-a-brac and collectors' items.

FALMOUTH (CORNWALL)

A flourishing resort with good recreational activities. The magnificent harbour is overlooked by 16th-century Pendennis Castle.

Cunningham's Antiques
5 Webber Street
0326 313207
General antiques, jewellery, porcelain and collectors' items.

Brook Street Antiques
Brook Street
0326 211807
Mid-range to pre-war furniture, ceramics and general antiques. Closed on Wednesday.

Fifty-One Antiques
51 Fore Street
0326 40452
Mid-range furniture, some pine.

Fuchsia Antiques
10 High Street
0326 211572
Textiles, rejuvenated curtains, cushions and general antiques.

Old Town Hall
High Street
0326 319437
Furniture and general antiques.

Rosina's
4 High Street
0326 311406
Textiles, costume dolls and toys.

Waterfront Antiques Market
1st Floor, 4 Quay Street
0326 311491
About a dozen dealers with a varied range of furniture, decorative items, collectables, jewellery, books, pictures, clocks, kitchenalia and assorted general antiques.

FEOCK (CORNWALL)

Strickland & Dorling
Come-to-Good
0872 862394
General antiques, silver, pictures, porcelain, collectors' items and anything of local interest. Come-to-Good is a hamlet just outside Feock, about 3½ miles from Truro. This shop is next door to the Quaker Meeting House.

FROME (SOMERSET)

Dores & Rees, auctioneers
32 Vicarage Street
0373 462257
General sales every fortnight, on Wednesday. Another auctioneer in town is **Cooper & Tanner**.

GILLINGHAM (DORSET)

Talisman
The Old Brewery, Wyke
0747 824423
Decorative items, mirrors and furniture. Also architectural antiques, garden ornaments, statuary and fountains. Stock tends to the high decorative manner but there is also some rummageable architectural salvage.

GLASTONBURY
(SOMERSET)

The Antiques Fair
Abbey Car Park.
Summer/winter times vary.
Furniture, general antiques,
collectors' items, jewellery, bric-
a-brac.

Antiques Market
Town Hall
Operates on the first Saturday
of each month. General
antiques, bric-a-brac and
collectors' items.

The Lace & Linen Shop
1 The Monarch, 15 High Street
0458 210021
Period costume and accessories,
textiles, samplers, lace and
linen, quilts and counterpanes,
pictures and general antiques.
Prices right across the board,
with some low-cost buying
possible.

Monarch Antiques
15 High Street
0458 832498
Captures some of the local
mystical flavour, and offers
numismatics, militaria,
ecclesiastica, collectors' items
and general antiques.

GRAMPOUND
(CORNWALL)

Pine & Period
Furniture
Fore Street
0726 883117
Furniture, mostly mid-range.

HELSTON (CORNWALL)

Reg Cann, auctioneer
Office at 43 Lemon Street, Truro
0872 76611
Sales held Trengrouse Way,

Helston, on the first Tuesday of
each month.

HIGHBRIDGE
(SOMERSET)

Terry Dyte Antique
Centre
1 Huntspill Road, Highbridge
0278 786495
A comprehensive selection of
mid-range and shipping
furniture, general antiques,
metalware, pictures and bric-a-
brac. Closed on Saturday.

The Treasure Chest
The Jays, 19 Alstone Lane
0278 787267
Furniture, musical boxes,
collectors' items, metalware.

HONITON (DEVON)

**Famed centre of lacemaking –
examples can be seen in the
town museum – and with some
well-preserved historic
buildings. A thriving antique
trade is now a well established
local feature.**

The Antique Centre
Abingdon House,
138 High Street
0404 42108
Furniture, general antiques,
pictures, tools and collectors'
items. Approximately 15
stallholders.

Auctions
Sales in Honiton are organised
by: **Bonhams (West Country)**,
(Dowell Street, 0404 41879),
who hold intermittent auctions
of up to 700 lots; **Hussey's**
*(Bank House, 66 High Street,
0404 45885),* who hold
frequent general auctions in the
Old Cattle Market; and **Taylor's**
(Honiton Galleries, 205 High

Street, 0404 42404), who hold intermittent specialist and general auctions.

Bramble Cross Antiques
Exeter Road
0404 47085
Retail outlet for McBain's, the Exeter shippers. Mid-range furniture and general antiques.

Fountain Antiques
132 High Street
0404 42074
Pictures, textiles, books, collectors' items and general antiques.

Honiton Junction
159 High Street
0404 43436
Furniture, general antiques and collectors' items.

The Honiton Lace Shop
44 High Street
0404 42416
Dealers in the local speciality, plus other textiles and related materials. This is by no means the only lace town in the country – Nottingham and Darvel, in Scotland, are also renowned – but Honiton had a reputation for fine quality, much of which can be seen here.

Upstairs, Downstairs
12 High Street
0404 44481
Furniture, metalware, pictures and general antiques.

HORRABRIDGE (DEVON)

Ye Olde Saddler's Shoppe
Horrabridge
0822 852109
Furniture, collectors' items and general antiques.

ILFRACOMBE (DEVON)

Ace Bargains
153 High Street
0271 866603
General secondhand and house clearance goods.

Auctions
General sales are organised in the town by **Ilfracombe Auction Rooms** *(2 Wilder Street, 0271 862138)* and by **Skinner & Sons** *(6 – 7 High Street, 0271 863408),* both on an occasional basis.

The Cavern
1 Greenclose Road
0271 865648
Budget furniture and secondhand basics.

ILMINSTER (SOMERSET)

County Antiques Centre
21–23 West Street
0460 54151
Around eight dealers with furniture, general antiques and collectors' items.

KINGSBRIDGE (DEVON)

The Quay Antiques
The Promenade
0548 853718
General antiques and collectables.

C Hawkins Antiques
85 Fore Street
0548 856829
A combined retail and auction operation, selling furniture, bric-a-brac and general antiques in the shop and holding about eight furniture and general auctions a year.

LANGPORT
(SOMERSET)

King's House Antiques
Bow Street
0458 250350
Jewellery, small antiques and collectors' items.

LISKEARD (CORNWALL)

Cleveland Furniture
Cleveland House, St Ive
0579 82383
Secondhand furniture and house clearance goods.

LONG ROCK
(CORNWALL)

Shiver Me Timbers
The Stores, Station Road
0736 711338
Terry 'Trader' Gray's sheds and yards a few miles from Penzance are well known to junk aficionados. Nothing that can be made to serve a purpose should ever be discarded, he claims, with an almost evangelical conviction. A popular sentiment in the era of green consciousness, although Gray does more than most to achieve his aim: the salvageable made rummageable.

LOSTWITHIEL
(CORNWALL)

Old Palace Antiques
Old Palace, Quay Street
0203 872909
Furniture (some pine), general antiques and collectors' items.

LYMPSHAM
(SOMERSET)

Baytree House Antiques
Stevens Lane
0934 750367
Furniture, including pine and general antiques.

LYNTON (DEVON)

Cantabrian Antiques
Park Street
0598 53282
Architectural specialists, with a good range of salvage stock.

LYTCHETT MINSTER
(DORSET)

The Old Button Shop
Dorchester Road
0202 622169
Collectors' items and interesting pieces, metalware, old Dorset buttons. First stop for the would-be button collector has to be Thelma John's delightful little book (£2) describing 'buttony' as an aspect of social history. The buttons themselves are relatively cheap, at £15 upwards for a 'collector's wallet'.

MARAZION
(CORNWALL)

Old Palace Antiques
Marazion
0208 872909
General antiques and collectables.

Wood's Antiques
The Shambles
Ephemera and collectors' items, including commemorative china, glass, postcards and bric-a-brac.

MELBURY OSMOND
(DORSET)

Hardy Country
Holt Mill Farm
0935 873361
Antique and vernacular pine.

MINEHEAD
(SOMERSET)

Gribble, Booth & Taylor
13 The Parade
0643 703646
General sales every third
Thursday.

MODBURY (DEVON)

Wild Goose Antiques
34 Church Street
0548 830715

Furniture from Georgian to
shipping, general antiques, bric-
a-brac, jewellery, light fittings
and pictures. The owners have
another shop nearby (**Bell Inn
Antiques**, *3 Broad Street*) with
similar stock.

Fielden's, auctioneers
*South Hams Auction Rooms,
Poundwell Square*
0548 830494
A mix of house clearance, ex-
hotel goods, shop and office

BUTTONS

Button collecting ranks alongside philately and
numismatics as the perfect pastime for the collector whose
living space is limited. Buttons have a history extending
back thousands of years, and have been used, in one form
or another, throughout the world. For obvious reasons,
they were more common in the northern hemisphere, but
this is not to say they were unappreciated elsewhere – the
African explorer Mungo Park even managed to exchange
his buttons for food. The particular fascination of buttons
is that, as objects of fashion, they were generally well
designed. They could also be adapted for other purposes:
as indicators of rank and status, above all, and, more
recently, as a propaganda and advertising medium.
Occasionally they might even carry political overtones – as
a subtle expression of Jacobite sympathies or a not-so-
subtle celebration of revolutionary zeal, as with the French
button celebrating the storming of the Bastille. Diamond
studded and gold filigree examples excepted, buttons can
be a fairly inexpensive collecting area, and one which also
casts fascinating sidelights on social history. The hand-
stitched Dorset button emerged in the mid-17th century,
after a Cotswold man had seen similar buttons being
produced in Brussels. He then started production in
Britain after settling in Shaftesbury with his local wife. The
story has been published in a book by Thelma Johns,
Buttony: The Dorset Heritage, which is available from The
Old Button Shop in Lytchett Minster. Buttony was a
thriving cottage industry for two centuries and only died
out after Ashton's mechanical button maker was shown at
the 1851 Exhibition. After a lapse of almost a century and a
half, there is now a revival, and an increasing interest in
collecting originals. With good examples selling for
around £15 a pair, it is clearly a collecting area with
potential.

bankruptcy stock. Sales held intermittently.

Fourteen A
14a Broad Street
0548 830732
Jewellery, textiles, tools and kitchenalia, porcelain and small items of furniture.

Tinkers' Corner
3 Modbury Court
0548 831111
Small furniture, bric-a-brac, collectables and some jewellery.

Ye Little Shoppe
1b Broad Street
0548 830732
Collectors' items, oil lamps, small boxes, woodworking tools and interesting or unusual smaller items.

MONKTON (DEVON)

Pugh's Farm Antiques
Pugh's Farm
0404 42860
Agricultural antiques, vernacular furniture, brass and iron beds.

MONTACUTE (SOMERSET)

Montacute Antiques
April Cottage, 12 South Street
0935 824786
Curios and collectors' items, furniture, porcelain, metalware and pictures.

MORETON-HAMPSTEAD (DEVON)

The Old Brass Kettle
2–4 Ford Street
0647 40334
Metalware, porcelain, collectors' items and smaller furniture. Closed on Thursday.

NETHER STOWEY (SOMERSET)

House of Antiquity
St Mary's Street
0278 732426
Ephemera, postcards and collectors' items.

NEWTON ABBOT (DEVON)

Newton Abbot Antique Centre
55 East Street
0626 54074
Around 50 dealers with a range of general antiques, collectables and furniture (from high quality to basic shipping), as well as books, ephemera, bric-a-brac and metalware. Specialisations include textiles and costume, cast toys, porcelain and pottery.

Old Treasures
126a Queen Street
0626 67181
Jewellery, bric-a-brac and collectors' items. Opening times vary, so phone for details.

NORTH PETHERTON (SOMERSET)

Kathleen's Antiques
60 Fore Street
0278 662535
Furniture, pictures, metalware, porcelain collectables and general antiques.

NORTH PETHERWIN (CORNWALL)

Pine & Country Antiques
Petherwingate
056 685 381
Stripped pine furniture and general antiques.

OKEHAMPTON
(DEVON)

Alan Jones Antiques
Fatherford Farm
0837 52970
A large warehouse and showroom with a comprehensive range of furniture – period to shipping – pictures, collectors' items and general antiques.

PADSTOW (CORNWALL)

Mayflower Antiques
15 Duke Street
0841 532308
Jewellery, bric-a-brac, metalware, general antiques and collectors' items.

PAR (CORNWALL)

Phillips, auctioneers
Cornubia Hall
0726 814047
Monthly household auctions, held at 11am on Thursdays.

PARKSTONE (DORSET)

Ashley Antiques
176 Ashley Road
0202 744347
General antiques and collectors' items. Closed on Wednesday.

Wiffen's Antiques
99–101 Bournemouth Road
0202 736567
Mid-range and shipping furniture, garden and decorative items, metalware, pictures, clocks, jewellery, bric-a-brac and general antiques. An eminently eclectic stock from an outlet of more than 30 years' standing.

PENZANCE
(CORNWALL)

Known for its fruit, flowers and ferry to the Scillies, Penzance is also a popular tourist resort, with stunning views of St Michael's Mount.

Ken Ashbrook Antiques
Leskinnick Place
0736 330914
A comprehensive range of furniture – period to shipping – and general antiques.

Catherine & Mary Antiques
2 Old Brewery Yard, Bread Street
0736 51053
Mainly textiles and jewellery, plus some furniture and general antiques.

Brian Humphrys Antiques
1 St Clare Street
0736 65154
Furniture, general antiques, silver, jewellery and clocks.

WH Lane, auctioneers
65 Morrab Road
0736 61447
Monthly antique sales plus intermittent general sales.

David Lay, auctioneer
The Penzance Auction House
0736 61414
Twice-monthly antique sales.

Little Jems
Antron House, 55 Chapel Street
0736 51400
Jewellery and gemstones, textiles and costume, decorative objects, pictures and collectors' items.

New Generation Antique Market
61–62 Chapel Street
0736 63267
Around 10 dealers with a range of furniture, pictures, jewellery, books and general antiques.

The Old Posthouse
9 Chapel Street
0736 60320
Curios, jewellery, bric-a-brac, ephemera and general antiques.

PERRANPORTH
(CORNWALL)

St George's Antiques
33 St George's Hill
0872 572947
Specialists in early 18th- and 19th-century pottery. Also some mid-range furniture, porcelain and pictures. Open Friday and Saturday only, unless by appointment.

PLYMOUTH (DEVON)

Scene of Drake's famous game of bowls ('The Armada can wait', etc.) and for the departure of the Pilgrim Fathers who, on landing in New England in 1620 decided to call their new settlement by the same name.

Anterior Antiques
22 Molesworth Road, Millbridge
0752 558277
Brass and iron beds, decorative items and furniture, including stripped pine. A sense of style predominates and by no means everything is cheap, although mid-market buys at reasonable prices are perfectly possible.

Barbican Antiques Centre
82–84 Vauxhall Street,
Barbican
0752 266927
Upwards of 60 dealers offering a range of general antiques, silver, bric-a-brac, pictures, prints and collectors' items.

Eric Distin, auctioneers
Bretonside
0752 663046
General sales every Friday.

Pete's Emporium
203 Wolseley Road
0752 606855
Basics and flatfillers

Shaun's
230 Albert Road, Devonport
0752 558595
Basics and house clearance goods.

Shobrook & Company, auctioneers
20 Western Approach
0752 663341
General sales every Wednesday. Antique sales every three weeks, on Thursdays.

Brian Taylor Antiques
24 Molesworth Road, Stoke
0752 569061
Vernacular furniture, decorative items, fireplaces, clocks, musical boxes, gramophones and general antiques. A comprehensive stock that seems to include everything from the functional to the exotic.

Upstairs, Downstairs
Camden Street, Greenbank
0752 261015
Textiles, costumes and general antiques.

Woodlands Furnishings
168 Albert Road, Stoke
0752 550866
House clearance goods and flatfillers.

PORTSCATHO
(CORNWALL)

Curiosity Antiques
Portscatho
0872 580411
Closed in winter, except by
appointment. Furniture, general
antiques, bric-a-brac and
collectors' items.

QUEEN CAMEL
(SOMERSET)

Bonnett Antiques
High Street
0935 850724
Mid-range Georgian to
Edwardian brownwood
furniture, plus some pictures,
porcelain and general antiques.
Opening times vary, so phone
before visiting.

REDLAND (AVON)

**Something Old,
Something New**
115 Cold Harbour Road
0272 247479
Furniture and general antiques.

REDRUTH (CORNWALL)

**West End Antiques
Market**
1st Floor, 3 West End
0209 217001
A low-key operation, basically a
bookshop and a single dealer
in furniture and general
antiques, including textiles,
metalware, pictures, porcelain
and collectors' items.

**Richard Winkworth
Antiques**
Unit 6, Station Approach
0209 216631
Mid-range and shipping
furniture, metalware, porcelain
and general antiques.

RUMFORD (CORNWALL)

Henley House Antiques
Rumford
0841 540322
Dolls and dolls' houses, textiles,
bric-a-brac, collectors' items,
some small furniture. Closed
Monday to Wednesday. On
other days, open by
appointment only.

ST AUSTELL
(CORNWALL)

A coastal resort with a long
established china clay industry
as well as a good line in junk
and collectors' items.

Ancient & Modern
32–34 Polkyth Road
0726 73983
Porcelain, pictures, jewellery
and general antiques.

Car Boot Sale
Cattle Market
Every Sunday.

Frank's Used Furniture
42 Penwithick Road
0726 851312
House clearance goods.

**The Furniture Clearance
Centre**
1–3 Clifden Road
0726 63105
A mix of modern and house
clearance secondhand basics.

The Furniture Store
37–39 Truro Road
0726 63178
Upwards of 5,000 square feet of
furniture, from period pieces to
basic shipping, plus a semi-
basement with some
secondhand goods plus general
antiques, books, records and
collectors' items. Vast and

interesting. One core business (Roger Nosworthy) plus outlets on the premises for about 15 other traders.

Junk & Disorderly
The Old Chapel, Chapel Street, Probus
0726 882922
Secondhand furniture and house clearance goods.

ST BLAZEY
(CORNWALL)

The Furniture Circus
The Old Market House
0726 817702
Five dealers with an across-the-board range of furniture, from secondhand to Victorian and general antiques.

SHAFTESBURY
(DORSET)

Antiques & Secondhand
16a Bell Street
0747 55866
General antiques and house clearance goods.

SHERBORNE (DORSET)

With an abbey that was once a cathedral – it was demoted in 1075 but that did not stop them building a spectacular fan vaulted nave four centuries later – this market town is very much on the tourist trail. Several shops, an auction house, and a very busy monthly market cater for the collecting needs of both residents and visitors.

Antique Market
Digby Hall
0258 840224 (enquiries)
One day each month. Around 40 dealers with a range of antiques and collectors' items.

Jasper Burton Antiques
23 Cheap Street
0935 814434
Furniture, period to shipping and general antiques. Closed on Wednesday.

The Nook
South Street
0935 813987
Mid-range furniture, metalware and bric-a-brac. Open Thursday to Saturday from April to October.

Sherborne Antique Centre
Mattar Arcade, 17 Newlands
0935 813464
Jewellery, bric-a-brac, pictures, metalware and some furniture from 12 shop units with a bias towards mid-market and quality but with raking possibilities.

SIDMOUTH (DEVON)

Gainsborough House Antiques
12 Fore Street
0395 514394
Metalware, bric-a-brac, militaria, mid-range furniture and collectors' items. A traditional outlet, established more than 50 years ago, with a comprehensive stock and a diverse price range.

The Lantern Shop
4 New Street
0395 516320
Lamps and lighting accessories, bric-a-brac, pictures, general antiques, mixed with some new goods. Further paintings and prints are available at the gallery upstairs (No 5).

Potbury's, auctioneers
Temple Street Salerooms
0395 515555
Sales of furniture and effects

every two to three weeks.

The Vintage Toy & Train Museum
1st Floor, Field's Department Store, Market Place
0395 515124
Part exhibition, part retail, open in the summer only. Mechanical toys, trains, Meccano, jigsaws and general playroom nostalgia.

SOMERTON
(SOMERSET)

The London Cigarette Card Company
West Street
0458 73452

Specialists in cigarette and decorative trade cards, also with accessories and literature. Prices from about 15p for single cards. Closed on Wednesday and Saturday afternoons.

SOUTH BRENT
(DEVON)

Wootton's Clocks & Watches
2 Church Street
0364 72553
Horology, plus some collectors' items and general antiques. Owner formerly had whole corner block as junk shop, but now semi-retired and the

---

MAPS

Map collecting is something of a specialised field and prices tend to reflect the keen interest of those who pursue it as a hobby, but there is one particular sub-division of the cult that is both fascinating and cheap. For the 18th-century traveller, getting around the British countryside presented a number of problems. The road network was tortuous and archaic, and progress could be cursed by such inconveniences as flooded fords, tolls and lack of signposts. The answer to most if not all of these problems was that primitive predecessor of the AA or RAC route map – a strip map directory. Today such maps are completely obsolete, but in their time they must have been invaluable, with their depiction of landmarks and appended notes on problems such as misplaced milestones. They were usually well used by the coachmen and carters who moved around the countryside and few survive in pristine condition – which therefore means that there are a large number of broken copies and loose plates to be found. Their importance in terms of local history is often crucial, for they were based on detailed practical surveys and so record the positions of important features such as standing stones, ruined churches, estate parklands and old place names, many of which, like some of the roads delineated, may no longer exist. The value of such maps is limited, since each one tends to be of interest only to those who live in its locality, and good examples, even ready mounted, can be found at antiquarian book fairs for as little as £8 or £12 each – which is not a lot to pay for something printed in the 18th-century.

present shop is only open in the mornings. Stock much reduced, but still carries an interesting mix.

SOUTH MOLTON
(DEVON)

Architectural Antiques
West Ley, Alswear Old Road
0769 573342
Architectural salvage, including full interiors, staircases, stone and stained glass. Closed on Monday.

Bond's Bargains
Market Street
0769 572100
Secondhand furniture and house clearance goods.

John D Fleming, auctioneers
North Devon Auction Rooms, Old Savoy Cinema.
also 8 Fore Street, Dulverton
0769 574888
General and antique sales every month.

The Furniture Market
14a Barnstaple Road
0769 573401
Around 20 dealers with a range of furniture, bric-a-brac, collectors' items and general antiques. The selection on offer is usually diverse and prices range across the board.

The Lace Shop
Bay House, 33 East Street
0769 573184
Textiles, especially old lace bridal and christening wear. Closed on Monday in the winter.

Memory Lane Antiques
100 East Street
0769 574288
Furniture, jewellery, metalware, porcelain and general antiques displayed in several showrooms.

JR Tredant
50–50a South Street
0769 573006
Bric-a-brac and general collectables. Closed on Wednesday. Another shop, **Tredantiques** *(19 Broad Street, 0769 573841)* stocks furniture and higher quality general antiques.

STURMINSTER NEWTON (DORSET)

Quarter Jack Antiques
Bridge Street
0258 72558
Specialising in glass and some smaller furniture.

SWANAGE (DORSET)

The Old Forge Antiques
273a High Street
0929 423319
Furniture, including pine, bric-a-brac and general antiques.

TAUNTON (SOMERSET)

An attractive county town with a fine castle dating from the 12th century, the scene of 17th-century Judge Jeffreys' notorious Bloody Assizes. More benign local activities include glove and textile manufacturing, and cider making.

Car Boot Sales
Taunton has several on a regular basis. One at the Albermarle every third Saturday; another at the Creech Castle Hotel and a third on Sundays at Longport, on the A378.

Greenslade Hunt, auctioneers

Magdalene House Saleroom, Church Square
0823 332525
Weekly household sales, and separate monthly sales of general goods and antiques.

Past Perfect

143a East Reach
0823 322667
Small furniture, bric-a-brac and general antiques.

Selwood's

Queen Anne Cottage, Mary Street
0823 272780
Long established (1927) stockists of mostly mid-range furniture, from period to Edwardian brownwood and shipping pieces in extensive showrooms.

Taunton Antiques Market

27–29 Silver Street
0823 289327
Mondays only. Enormous, with over 100 dealers and diverse, with most specialisations.

TAVISTOCK (DEVON)

King Street Curios

King Street
Bric-a-brac, jewellery and collectors' items.

Pendar Antiques

8 Drake Road
0822 617641
A comprehensive stock of Georgian, Victorian, Edwardian and pre-war furniture plus a range of architectural and farm-related items, with both stock and prices in all brackets. Opening times vary, so phone for information.

NAUTICAL ANTIQUES

The collector of seafaring memorabilia enjoys an advantage that is rarely available in other fields – an almost limitless diversity. At the top end of the market, early scientific instruments such as astrolabes or marine chronometers, or decorative items such as an elaborately designed admiral's dress sword, can fetch thousands. But the precise workmanship that produced a sextant or telescope was also lavished on mundane items such as brass cabin locks or window fastenings and these are not likely to be very expensive at all. Maritime trade generated some flamboyant paperwork, whether in charts and maps or bills of lading or inventories. Journals, letters and even naval discharge documents, sometimes detailing entitlement to prize money, are a rich source of historical interest too. Sailors' souvenirs, such as small-scale ship models, possibly bottled, or the carved bone or teeth of whales, known as scrimshaw, provide yet another fruitful field. The area is one where budget buyers can do well, even by beachcombing, and with modern seabed scanning techniques now identifying wreck sites all around the coast, it is one with growing potential.

TEIGNMOUTH
(DEVON)

Lewis & Rowden, auctioneers
24 Brunswick Street
0626 770279
Fortnightly mixed sales.

The Old Passage
13a Bank Street
0626 772634
General antiques and collectors'
items, bric-a-brac, treen, textiles
and silver, with a good choice
for the collector on a budget.
Opening times vary so phone
for details.

TEMPLECOMBE
(SOMERSET)

Yewtree Antiques
17 High Street
0963 70505
Furniture, period to shipping,
antiques and bric-a-brac.

TIVERTON (DEVON)

Chancery Antiques
8–10 Barrington Street
0884 252416
An extensive selection of
furniture, including pine and
shipping. Closed on Thursday.

TORQUAY (DEVON)

Bearne's, auctioneers
Rainbow Avenue Road
0803 296277
'Rainbow' – or mixed antique
and household – sales are held
fortnightly, with other specialist
sales throughout the year.

Hele Road Secondhand Centre
Hele Road
0803 312451
House clearance basics.

Torre Antique Traders
266 Higher Union Street
0803 292184
Furniture, porcelain, glass,
metalware and general antiques
being sold by a syndicate of
dealers in an area with several
other outlets.

West of England Auctions
3 Warren Road
0803 211266
Fortnightly sales, alternating
between household and
antiques with fine art.

TREGONY (CORNWALL)

Clock Tower Antiques
57 Fore Street
087 253 225
The emphasis is on quality
porcelain, metalware, treen and
furniture, but some cheaper
items are available. Opening
times vary so phone for
information.

TRURO (CORNWALL)

The Auction Centre
Calenick Street
0872 260020
Weekly general sales. Antique
sales take place every six to
eight weeks.

Richard Winkworth Antiques
Calenick Street
0872 40901
Also at Redruth. Mid-range to
shipping furniture, metalware,
porcelain and general antiques.

WADEBRIDGE
(CORNWALL)

Victoria Antiques
21 Molesworth Street
0208 814160
Around 10,000 square feet of

furniture, general antiques and decorative items. The range is extensive, from quality period pieces to basic shipping goods.

WAREHAM (DORSET)

Cottees, Bullock & Lees
The Market, East Street
0929 552826
Fortnightly general sales.

WATCHET (SOMERSET)

Clarence House Antiques
41 Swain Street
0984 31389
Mid-range furniture, including pine, metalware, bric-a-brac and general antiques.

WELLINGTON (SOMERSET)

Wellington Salerooms
Clifton House, Mantle Street
0823 664815
General sales held fortnightly, antique sales every six weeks.

WELLS (SOMERSET)

Alcove Antiques
Priest Row
0749 672164
Furniture and general antiques. Opening times vary so phone before visiting.

Courtyard Antiques
The Palace Courtyard,
Priory Road
0749 679533
Furniture and a range of general antiques.

Lovejoy's
5c Queen Street
0749 670706
Decorative antiques, china and some furniture.

Pickwick's Antiques
Broad Street
Furniture, collectors' items and general antiques in shop plus two rear showrooms.

St Thomas Antiques
74 St Thomas Street
0749 672520
Furniture, period to shipping. closed on Wednesday.

WESTON SUPER MARE (AVON)

Martin Capstick, auctioneer
The Auction Rooms,
Station Road
General sales every second Tuesday; about four antique sales per annum.

Harwood West End Antiques
13 West Street
0934 629874
Jewellery, bric-a-brac, collectors' items and general antiques.

Moorland Antiques
134 Moorland Road
0934 632361
Furniture, some secondhand and general antiques.

Toby's Antiques
47 Upper Church Road
0934 623555
Mid-range brownwood furniture, porcelain, pictures and general antiques. Open only on Thursday, with appointment.

Woodspring Auction Rooms
Churchill Road
0934 628419
General sales every second Thursday. Other general sales and occasional antique sales are

arranged by **Martin Capstick**
(*The Auction Rooms, Station Road*).

WEYMOUTH (DORSET)

Henry Duke, auctioneers
Weymouth Furniture Saleroom, St Nicholas Street
0305 761499
Mixed sales every six weeks.

Jandy's
41 Brownlow Street
0305 775499
Secondhand furniture and house clearance items.

Nautical Antique Centre
*Old Harbour Passage
(opposite Brewer's Quay),
3a Hope Square*
0305 777838
A must for collectors with an interest in seafaring. A former bakery with around 2,000 items, the majority nautical, with some army and RAF collectables. The selection is fascinating and diverse – flags, insignia, models, propellers, chronometers, portholes, ships' furniture, wreck salvage, literature and log books, ships' bells, ocean liner memorabilia and sea-related antiques.

North Quay Antique Centre
North Quay
0305 779313
Eight dealers selling a range of general antiques and collectors' items.

Park Antiques
Park Street
0305 787666
Furniture, curios, treen, bric-a-brac, advertising items and general antiques.

The Treasure Chest
29 East Street
0305 772757
Pictures, bric-a-brac, coins, medals, prints, maps, collectors' items and general antiques.

WIDEGATES (CORNWALL)

Pink Cottage Antiques
Main Street
050 34258
Mid-range furniture, Victoriana, metalware, oil lamps, porcelain and general antiques.

WIMBORNE MINSTER (DORSET)

Barnes House Antiques
11 West Row
0202 886275
Four-dealer syndicate selling mostly mid- to upper-range furniture, plus shipping goods.

TW Antiques
12 West Row
0202 888958
Commemorative and collectors' items, furniture and general antiques. Closed on Monday and Wednesday.

Victoriana Antiques
3 Leigh Road
0202 886739
Jewellery, collectors' items and small antiques. Closed on Monday and Wednesday.

WINCANTON (SOMERSET)

Green Dragon Antique Centre
South Street
0963 34111
Around 30 dealers with porcelain, militaria, furniture and general antiques.

North Street Antiques

3 North Street
0963 33954
Furniture, bric-a-brac,
metalware, general antiques.

WIVELISCOMBE (SOMERSET)

Heads 'n' Tails

Bournes House,
41 Church Street
0984 23097
Taxidermy, some antique, some
in process, from trout to tigers,
plus cases and accessories.

Peter Lee Antiques

1 Silver Street
0984 24055
Diversifying estate agent with
section of premises devoted to
sale of porcelain, pictures,
furniture, collectors' items and
general antiques.

WOODBURY (DEVON)

Woodbury Antiques

Church Stile Lane
0395 32727
A large selection of mid-range
furniture and general antiques.
Closed on Wednesday.

YEOVIL (SOMERSET)

Clarke's Furniture

Manor Road,
Hendford
0935 21265
Secondhand furniture and
house clearance items.

Fox & Co.

30 Princes Street
0935 72323
Militaria, weapons, postcards,
ephemera, coins, medals,
banknotes, antiquities and
reference books.

WALES

Junk buying in Wales is largely concentrated on the south coast, notably around Cardiff and Swansea, though the influence of tourism has enabled some dealers to prosper outside the urban centres.

Wales was intensively industrialised throughout the last century, partly to offset the problems of rural poverty. The results have been mixed, but the wrecking of large tracts of landscape was at least accompanied by some spectacular

civic development. Industrialisation encouraged the development of a number of manufacturers, whose output was partly geared to supplying the household needs of those who lived and worked in the urban belt and its surrounding area, all of which has provided good staple fare for today's antique and junk trade. There is much which is distinctively Welsh, such as dressers and quilts, and even the money you spend – the Royal Mint, after all, is now based at Llantrisant.

ABERAERON (DYFED)

Collectomania
Corner Shop, Albert Street
0570 470597
Mid-range selection of furniture, porcelain, metalware and other general antiques. Closed on Thursday.

ABERDARE (MID-GLAMORGAN)

Aberdare Market Antiques
Aberdare Market
0685 870242
Wide range of general antiques and collectors' items.

Steptoe & Sons
56 Bute Street
0685 883588
Mix of secondhand basics and new items. Closed on Thursday.

ABERGAVENNY (GWENT)

Abergavenny Antiques
Market Street
0873 856014
An across-the-board range of furniture, general antiques and collectables.

Straker & Chadwick, auctioneers
Market Street Chambers,
Market Street
0873 852624
Monthly general sales.

Trash & Treasure
2 Merthyr Road
0873 853015
Secondhand household basics.

ABERSOCH (GWYNEDD)

Annteaks
Main Street
0758 712353
A mix of general antiques and shipping furniture, plus garden and architectural items. The owner has a partiality for large furniture and Victorian oak.

ABERSYCHAN (GWENT)

Scenic Secondhand & Antique
High Street
Budget flatfillers.

ABERYSTWYTH (DYFED)

The Furniture Cave
33 Cambrian Street
0970 611234
Up-market early to pre-war furniture and general antiques.

AMMANFORD (DYFED)

Amman Antiques
29 Station Road
0269 592730
General antiques. View by appointment.

BANGOR
(GWYNEDD)

Wellfield Antique Centre
Wellfield Court
0248 361360
A market with about 20 dealers at any one time trading in a range of antiques, furniture, jewellery, costume and other collectors' items. Open from Thursday to Saturday.

BARRY
(SOUTH GLAMORGAN)

Hawkins Brothers Antiques
Romily Buildings,
Woodham Road,
Barry Docks
0446 746561
One of the largest dealers operating anywhere in South Wales with a comprehensive selection of mid-range and shipping goods.

Steptoe's
57 Vere Street
0446 739924
One of a number of outlets for secondhand and basic goods in the town. Opening times vary so phone before visiting.

BEAUMARIS
(GWYNEDD)

Castle Antiques
13 Church Street
0248 810474
Mid-range and general furniture and antiques.

BETWS GARMON
(GWYNEDD)

Revival
Salem Chapel
0286 650397

Mid-range small furniture, to pre-war, bric-a-brac, collectables and general antiques. Appointment advised.

BLAENANNERRCH
(DYFED)

Cross Inn Antiques
Cross Inn
0239 811023
Antique and budget furniture.

BLAENAU FFESTINIOG
(GWYNEDD)

The Antique Shop
74a Manod Road
0766 830629
General antiques, Victorian and Edwardian furniture, clocks, oil lamps and collectors' items.

BOW STREET (DYFED)

Garn House Antiques
Garn House
0970 828562
Furniture, porcelain, glass, jewellery, metalware and general antiques.

BRECON (POWYS)

The Lacelady
Mill House, Defynnog
0874 624844
A committed specialist. Although there is a degree of diversity, the stock shows a clear bias towards textiles, including Welsh quilts, now much prized, and lambswool shawls. 'Quilting' had a social as well as a practical function in rural areas, since it was done communally. Patterns were usually traditional – oak leaves, chains and diamond borders were consistently favoured. Americans, who cherish their

own quilting traditions, are noted enthusiasts. The owner used to operate from a shop but since business rates became so expensive now deals from home, by appointment.

Ship Street Galleries
14 Ship Street
0874 622715
Mid-range furniture and general antiques, including pine and shipping items. View by appointment.

CAERPHILLY
(MID-GLAMORGAN)

Gittins Antiques
10 Clive Street
0222 868835
General antiques, furniture and shipping goods. Closed on Wednesday.

CARDIFF
(SOUTH GLAMORGAN)

The Welsh capital started life as a small Roman fort at the mouth of the River Taff. It was occupied by the Normans, who built its impressive castle, and received its royal charter in 1581. Its most flourishing period, however, was during the late 19th-century, when the Marquis of Bute inaugurated a development scheme that included construction of the port and rebuilding the Norman castle (which now has a magnificent, purely Victorian, Arab hall). The glorious Edwardian city hall, centrepiece of the 'Welsh Washington', was the culmination of this orgy of civic flamboyance. Clearly, in such an impressive setting, rummaging in the city's antique shops can be pleasurable and rewarding.

A1 Bargain Centre
1a Leckwith Road, Canton
0222 227330
Secondhand furniture and house clearance goods.

Abbey Antiques
23 Salisbury Road
0222 224399
Budget antiques and secondhand.

Aladdin's Cave
16 Albany Road
0222 483168
Furniture, bric-a-brac and smaller goods.

Albany Lane Antiques
42 Albany Road
0222 484800
Furniture and general antiques.

Bargain Centre Quality Goods
94 Neville Street, Canton
0222 397842
General secondhand goods and furniture.

Burge Antiques
54 Crwys Road
0222 383268
Clocks and general antiques. Closed on Wednesday.

Charlotte's Wholesale Antiques
129 Woodville Road, Cathays
0222 759809
Large trade shop and warehouse with general antiques, decorative items and shipping furniture. Open to the rummaging public on Saturday.

Cronin Antiques
12 Mackintosh Place, Roath
0222 498929
Antiques, silver, jewellery and general collectors' items.

Glendale
49 Broadway
0222 460391
General household and
secondhand goods.

Grandma's Goodies
31 Mortimer Road, Pontcanna
0222 383142
Bric-a-brac, linen, and general
antiques including some small
furniture. Stock is varied,
diverse and usually
inexpensive, with lots of raking
potential.

Hera Antiques
140 Whitchurch Road
0222 619472
Decided emphasis on mid-
range quality in Georgian to
Edwardian brownwood
furniture but also with some
smaller items including
jewellery, porcelain and clocks.

Heritage Antiques & Pine
83 Pontcanna Street
0222 390097
Furniture and general antiques,
including stripped pine.

Jacob's Antique Centre
West Canal Wharf
0222 390939
Wednesday to Saturday market
of up to 80 dealers offering just
about everything from the
smallest collectables to large
pieces of furniture. A great deal
to choose from and prices can
be competitive. Always good
for a rummage. **Back to the
Wood** *(0222 390939)*, next
door, sells architectural antiques
and pine.

Llanishen Antiques
26 Crwys Road, Cathays
0222 397244
Stock of furniture, porcelain,
silver, collectors' items and
various other general antiques.

Nostalgia
1 Fidlas Road, Llanishen
0222 765122
General antiques, with some
shipping furniture.

Past & Present
242 Whitchurch Road
0222 621443
Furniture, general antiques,
bric-a-brac.

The Stock Exchange
21 Pearl Street, Adamsdown
0222 494766
Secondhand furniture and
household goods.

CARDIGAN (DYFED)

JJ Morris, auctioneers
Cardigan Cattle Market,
also Crymych Village Hall
0239 612343
Sales are held at irregular
intervals.

CARMARTHEN (DYFED)

Cwmgwili Mill
Bronwydd Arms
0267 231500
A spacious showroom with a
large selection of country
furniture, mostly in the mid- to
upper-range. The shop is
renowned for its Welsh
dressers.

Mark's Mart
Colonial Buildings,
Little Water Street
0267 236613
Furniture and secondhand
goods.

Merlin's Antiques
Albion Arcade, Blue Street
0267 237728

Collectors' items, including postcards, ephemera and bric-a-brac.

The Pot Board
30 King Street
0267 236623
Three floors of well-filled showrooms containing a mix of furniture, mostly pine, general antiques, country items and kitchenalia. This is a favourite haunt of young home-makers, because it offers excellent browsing potential and plenty of choice.

CHEPSTOW (GWENT)

Davies Antiques Centre
12 St Mary's Street
0291 625957
A market that offers a comprehensive range of furniture, bric-a-brac, collectors' items and shipping goods.

Plough House Interiors
Upper Church Street
0291 625200
Furniture, general antiques and some shipping goods.

CILIAU AERON (DYFED)

Finlay Antiques
The Forge, Neuaddlwyd
0545 570536
Mid-range furniture and general antiques; an advance telephone call is advised.

CLYNDERWEN (DYFED)

Al's Trading Post
Derwen Garage, Narberth Road
0437 563827
General basics and secondhand.

COLWYN BAY (CLWYD)

North West Antiques
58 Abergele Road
0492 530521
Extensive warehouse premises selling general antiques, mid-range furniture and shipping items.

CONNAH'S QUAY (CLWYD)

North Wales Bargain Centre
264 High Street
0244 830248
Flatfillers and basics.

CONWAY (GWYNEDD)

Black Lion Antiques
11 Castle Street
0492 592470
A mix of furniture, porcelain, metalware, books and collectors' items.

Paul Gibbs Antiques
25 Castle Street
0492 593429
Teapot specialist – probably holds the largest number to be found in any one place – but also sells decorative arts.

Conway Antiques
17 Bangor Road
0492 592461
Pre-war and earlier furniture and general antiques. Closed on Wednesday.

COWBRIDGE (SOUTH GLAMORGAN)

Renaissance Antiques
The Arcade, 49 High Street
0446 773893
Mid-range smaller furniture and collectors' items. One of several

shops in a village with a reputation for good mid- to upper-market antiques. One of these, **Cowbridge Antiques** *(55 Eastgate, 0446 774774)* also specialises in Welsh paintings.

CRICKHOWELL
(POWYS)

Gallop & Rivers Architectural Antiques
Ty'r Ash, Brecon Road
0873 811084
Specialising in country furniture, architectural items and garden furniture.

FISHGUARD (DYFED)

Manor House Antiques
Main Street
0348 873260
Small general antiques and collectors' items from £15. Located inside the Manor House Hotel.

FREYSTOP (DYFED)

This & That
Freystop Cross
0437 890390
Furniture and general basics.

GILWERN (GWENT)

Gilwern Antiques
Main Road
0873 830276
General antiques, clocks, porcelain, glass and jewellery.

GORSLAS (DYFED)

Highfield Stores
Llandeilo Road
0269 843228
General secondhand and household items.

HAVERFORDWEST
(DYFED)

Sylvia & John Davies
2b Dark Street
0437 768550
One of several in town dealing in middle-of-the-road furniture and general antiques. Closed on Thursday.

Dyfed Antiques & Architectural Salvage
Wesleyan Chapel and Schoolhouse, Perrots Road
0437 760496
25 years ago the owner set up as a dealer in his remote country mansion. He has since moved into more accessible premises, where he sells a mix of furniture and architectural items, including stained glass, revamped chapel pews, fireplaces and grates. In addition, he still has a vast amount at home, where serious buyers can view by appointment.

Basil Jones, auctioneer
Clarbeston Memorial Hall
0437 762454
Sales at varying intervals.

Time Was
9 Market Street
0437 767250
Victoriana, pine and general antiques. The former chemist's shop opposite sells secondhand basics.

HAY ON WYE (POWYS)

Antiques Market
6 Market Street
0497 820175
Eighteen dealers trading in a range of general antiques and collectors' items. Hay on Wye is

also renowned for secondhand books, reputedly being the largest single source in Britain and probably also Europe.

HENLLAN *(DYFED)*

Richard Lloyd Antiques
Dolhaidd Mansion
0559 370791
Essentially a trade dealer in pine, decorative furniture, and general antiques. Advance telephone call advised.

KIDWELLY *(DYFED)*

Castle Auction Mart
Unit 4, Station Road
0554 891256
Weekly general sales.

Country Antiques
Old Castle Mill and
31 Bridge Street
Extensive range of vernacular furniture, clocks, metalware, decorative items, carpets and collectables. Some emphasis on quality and middle-market tastes but with some items in the lower price ranges.

KILGETTY *(DYFED)*

Graham H Evans
Auction Sales Centre,
Market Place
0834 811151
Sales on the second and the last Saturday of each month.

LALESTON *(MID-GLAMORGAN)*

Village Antiques
18 Heol Trelales
0656 652468
A shop with additional storage selling general antiques and shipping goods.

LAMPETER *(DYFED)*

Evans Brothers, auctioneers
39 High Street
0570 422395
Lampeter-based, with peripatetic sales at varying intervals. Another auctioneer in town is **King Thomas Lloyd Jones & Co.** *(Victoria Hall, Bryn Road)*, who hold approximately six general sales a year.

Beneibion Troed-y-Rhiw Antiques
Ffordd-y-Gogledd, Llanbedr, Pont Stefan
0570 423625
Also known as Phil Chapman's garage. 4,500 square feet of furniture and general antiques.

LAUGHARNE *(DYFED)*

The Castle House
Laugharne
0994 427645
A mix of crafts and antiques, including silver and furniture. Opening times vary so phone before visiting.

Neil Speed Antiques
The Strand
0994 427412
Country furniture, pottery, treen, items of vernacular interest. Winter/summer opening hours vary. A prior telephone call is advised.

LLANABER *(GWYNEDD)*

Ron Jones Antiques
Tri Brynwcws
0341 280691
General antiques, collectors' items and furniture. Opening times vary so phone before visiting.

LLANDEILO *(DYFED)*

Jim & Pat Ash
The Warehouse, 5 Station Road
0558 823726
Large and varied range of
country furniture and shipping
goods, both Victorian and pine,
including Welsh dressers and
other furniture in a variety of
woods. Opening times vary so
phone before visiting.

Country Branch
Roshman Street
0558 822707
Furniture, general antiques and
collectables.

Jones & Llewelyn, auctioneers
21 New Road
0558 823430
General sales held every three
weeks, antiques sales every
three months.

Prospect Antiques
1 New Road
0558 822138
Furniture, collectors' items,
linens, lace and general
antiques.

LLANDISSILIO *(DYFED)*

Jeremiah Antiques
The Old Saddlery
0437 563848
Sale and restoration of mid- to
upper-range Victorian and
Edwardian furniture. Closed on
Monday.

LLANDOGO *(GWENT)*

Llandogo Antiques
Llandogo
0594 530213
Small antiques, porcelain, glass
and collectors' items. On south
edge of village. Closed on
Tuesday.

LLANDOVERY *(DYFED)*

Dyfri Antiques
11 High Street
0550 20602
Small antiques, dolls, pottery,
porcelain and other collectors'
items. A well-established shop
with an eclectic mix of
affordable items.

LLANDUDNO *(GWYNEDD)*

The Antique Shop
24 Vaughan Street
0492 875575
Specialist in jewellery, silver
and glass.

Collinge Antiques
Wedgwood Building,
Great Orme's Road
0492 870956
A mix of mid-range furniture,
general antiques, and shipping
goods. Also has a warehouse
on Conway Road.

LLANELLI *(DYFED)*

Alice's Antiques
24 Upper Park Street
0554 773045
A mix of smaller antiques,
silver, pictures, porcelain and
metalware, from Victorian to
pre-war. After more than half a
century in the trade, Alice's
continues to offer a varied mix,
much of it reasonably priced.
Closed on Tuesday.

Radnedge Architectural Salvage
41 Pemberton Road
0554 755790
Architectural antiques and

salvage, specialising in fireplaces and decorative items. Opening times vary so phone before visiting.

LLANERCHYMEDD
(GWYNEDD)

Tony Andrews
8 High Street
0248 470204
Shop and warehouse with furniture, pictures and horse-drawn vehicles. Appointment required.

LLANFAIR CAEREINION (POWYS)

Heritage Restorations
Maes y Glydfa
0938 810384
Mid-range country furniture, pine and architectural antiques. The shop is situated just off the A458 two miles from the village.

LLANGATHEN
(DYFED)

Peter Francis, auctioneers
19 King Street
0267 233456
Antique sales held every six weeks.

LLANGOLEN (CLWYD)

M Gallacher (Antiques)
Hall Street
0978 860655
Mid-range and general antiques, including shipping. Open by appointment.

Passers Buy & Victoria House Antiques
Oak Street
0978 860861

Two shops with furniture, metalware, pictures and porcelain.

LLANSADWRN
(DYFED)

Maclean Antiques
Tiradda
0550 777509
Extensive range of pine and country furniture, metalware and general antiques.

LLANTWIT MAJOR
(SOUTH GLAMORGAN)

Argosy Antiques
9 Church Street
0446 796667
Furniture, jewellery and general antiques.

Tomorrow's Antiques
5 Commercial Street
0446 793156
Furniture and secondhand goods.

MAENTWROG
(GWYNEDD)

Harvey Owen Antiques
The Old School
076 685 310
Furniture, general antiques and collectables.

MAESYBONT (DYFED)

Ddygoed Auctions
Maesybont
0269 845274
Monthly sales of general goods.

MILFORD HAVEN
(DYFED)

Milford Haven Antiques
Robert Street
0646 692152
Furniture, bric-a-brac, collectors'

items and general antiques.
Closed on Thursday.

MORRISTON
(WEST GLAMORGAN)

Aaron Antiques
66 Martin Street
0792 773271
Furniture, clocks, general
antiques and shipping goods
from a long-established dealer
usually with a well-varied stock.

MUMBLES
(WEST GLAMORGAN)

Allsorts
46 Newton Road
0792 360749
Furniture and secondhand
basics.

Castle Antiques
58 Newton Road
0792 366363
Mid-range furniture and general
antiques.

NEATH
(WEST GLAMORGAN)

Aladdin's
66 Briton Ferry Road
0639 641703
Bric-a-brac and secondhand
items.

Neath Antiques
6 Alfred Street
0639 645740
Mid-range and cheaper
furniture as well as a selection
of general antiques. Closed on
Thursday.

NEWCASTLE EMLYN (DYFED)

Castle Antiques
Market Square
0239 710420

Mid- to upper-range small
furniture, to pre-war, glass,
porcelain, and kitchenalia.

NEWPORT (GWENT)

Antiques of Newport
418 Chepstow Road
0633 279192
Furniture, pictures, maps,
ceramics, jewellery and
collectors' items. The stock is
mostly mid-market, but
nevertheless diverse, much as it
has been for the past 40 years.

Auctions
Abbey Auctions *(The Maltings
0633 244459)* hold fortnightly
general sales. **Graham** *(Trinity
Hall, Temple Street, 0633
251906)* hold weekly general
sales. **Nuttall & Parker** *(Renoir
Road, St Julian's, 0633 212333)*
hold intermittent sales.

Jim's Bargain Stall
2 Somerton Road
0633 282947
Secondhand furniture and
household goods.

PEMBROKE (DYFED)

Pembroke Antique Centre
The Hall, Hamilton Terrace
0646 687017
A converted chapel with some
30 dealers trading in a range of
furniture, pictures, porcelain,
clocks, collectors' items.
Reasonable diversity in stock
and prices, with good low-cost
possibilities.

**Glyn Jones'
Secondhand-Land**
*11–13 Bush Street,
Pembroke Dock*
0646 621732
Stripped pine, general antiques
and shipping furniture.

PONTNEWWYNYDD
(GWENT)

The Pine Barn
Gillingham House,
Freeholdland
0495 752256
General antiques and pine
furniture.

PONTYPRIDD
(MID-GLAMORGAN)

Pontypridd Antiques
Old Bakery, Shepherd Street,
Pwllgwuan
0443 407616
Stripped pine, Victoriana, bric-
a-brac, collectables and general
antiques.

PORTHCAWL
(MID-GLAMORGAN)

Harlequin Antiques
Dock Street
0656 785910
Furniture, some collectables,
and general antiques.

PORTHYRHYD
(DYFED)

Mark Rowan
Garreg Fawr
05585 478
A specialist in antique hand-
painted and decorated
furniture. Appointment required
for visits to the showroom.

RHOSNEIGR
(GWYNEDD)

Fan-Fayre Antiques
High Street
0407 810580
Silver, jewellery, porcelain, and
collectors' items. Hours vary
from summer to winter and a
telephone call is advisable
before visiting.

ST CLEARS (DYFED)

**Jo & Elsa's Bargain
Warehouse**
The Forge, Pendine Road
0994 230701
Secondhand furniture, bric-a-
brac and household basics. An
abundance of rummagable
secondhand and house
clearance goods of all
descriptions.

SULLY (DYFED)

Car Boot Sales
BP Social Club grounds
Held at weekends.

SWANSEA
(WEST GLAMORGAN)

**The administrative capital of
West Glamorgan, and the second
largest city in Wales, Swansea is
historically a major
manufacturing and exporting
centre. Buying opportunities
are, to say the least, diverse,
ranging from car boot sale
detritus to Victorian mill-
owners' baroque.**

**The Antique
Emporium**
76 St Helen's Road
0792 654697
A small market of about half-a-
dozen dealers offering a range
of general antiques and
collectors' items.

Bygone Antiques
37–39 St Helens Road
0792 468248
Furniture, porcelain, linen and
collectors' items.

Car Boot Sales
There are at least three regular
car boot sales, including one at
Park Tower, Old North Dock,

on Sundays, operated by the city council *(0792 301301)*.

Clydach Antiques
83 High Street, Clydach
0792 843209
General antiques and collectors' items.

David Cornelius, auctioneer
Players Industrial Estate, Clydach
0792 846241
Fortnightly general sales.

Eynon Hughes Antiques
Henrietta Street
0792 651446
Emphasis on up-market antiques, including some good longcase clocks, but also with a line in cheaper brass and cast-iron beds.

John's Shop
101 Clase Road, Morriston
0792 794848
Secondhand furniture and household goods.

Magpie Antiques
57 St Helens Road
0792 648722
Traditional pottery, porcelain and country furniture, with particular emphasis on Welsh-produced goods.

The Rummage Shop
44 Bernard Street, Uplands
0792 473818
General secondhand and budget goods – as the name implies.

Swansea Antique Centre
21 Oxford Street
0792 643085
Around 18 dealers sell a range of furniture, general antiques and collectors' items.

Specialisations include period costume and toys, while several dealers concentrate on jewellery.

SYNOD INN (DYFED)

Forge Antiques
The Old Forge
0545 580707
Furniture, decorative antiques, and textiles, especially Welsh quilts. Opening times vary so phone before visiting.

TENBY (DYFED)

Audrey Bull
15 Upper Frog Street
0834 843114
Country furniture, mid-range antiques, jewellery and silver.

Clareston Antiques
Warren Street
0834 843350
Mid-range furniture, Georgian where possible, plus moderately-priced Victorian and Edwardian pieces. Smaller stock includes silver, memorabilia, musical boxes, advertising material and mechanical models. Closed on Wednesday.

TINTERN (GWENT)

Abbey Antiques
Monkstone Chapel Lane
0291 689233
An extensive stock of mid-range furniture, clocks, bric-a-brac, jewellery, silver, lace and collectables items, with some shipping goods.

TONYPANDY (MID-GLAMORGAN)

Token Antiques
11 Llunpia Road
0443 441299

Smaller antiques and bric-a-brac, with some furniture.

TREDEGAR (GWENT)

Circle Antiques & Nearly New
6 The Circle
0495 254428
General antiques and collectables.

TREORCHY (MID-GLAMORGAN)

Stephen Evans Antiques
Melvyn Wine Cellars,
Regent Street
0443 776410
30,000 square feet of furniture, antiques and shipping goods, in three sites, including a warehouse in nearby Treherbert. Appointment required.

USK (GWENT)

Castle Antiques
41 Old Market Street
0291 672424
Traditional pottery, porcelain, and general antiques. Closed on Thursday, but other times are variable so it is advisable to phone in advance.

WELSHPOOL (POWYS)

Horley Antiques
19 High Street
0938 552421
Small antiques, pictures, bric-a-brac, and collectors' items.
School House Antiques,
nearby, is also worth a browse.

Waterloo Antiques
Salop Road
0938 553999
Furniture, pictures, porcelain and general antiques.

YSTRADGYNLAIS (POWYS)

Margaret's Astoria Antiques
38a Brecon Road
0639 849946
Jewellery, porcelain, general antiques and collectors' items, Victorian to pre-war.

YSTRADMYNACH (MID-GLAMORGAN)

Alan Webb Seth Phillips
5 The Square
0443 813178
Intermittent sales at Blackwood Masonic Hall, about five miles from the village.

WEST OF ENGLAND

West England is, loosely speaking, a rural enclave sandwiched between Offa's Dyke and the M1.

Its dominant characteristic is a mellow feeling of well-being engendered by sleepy Cotswold villages built from golden stone, the half-timbered antiquity of England's garden, the vale of Evesham, and the ebullient and stylish architecture of market towns like Ludlow, in Shropshire. For those who can really afford to indulge themselves, the *sine qua non* is good, well-waxed, period oak. The quantity available might even explain, in part, the disappearance of most of the Forest of Arden, the setting for Shakespeare's *As You Like It*.

The character of the area is not exlusively one of gentrified country living, however. Gloucester, for example, may be dominated by its fine perpendicular cathedral, but it is essentially an industrial city of 100,000 people – more than enough to support a number of budget secondhand shops, as well as a varied antique trade. Shropshire rightly takes pride in its manufacturing past, with the area around Coalbrookdale and Ironbridge being generally recognised as the cradle of England's Industrial Revolution. The ubiquitous cherished oak, with its pewter, brass and silver accessories, is eagerly sought, particularly in quintessential picture-postcard villages such as Broadway, but the market in middle-range and cheaper goods is a flourishing one, especally in the expanding sector of indoor antique markets, where low overheads, a brisk turnover, and a competitive environment can operate to benefit the buyer.

ALCESTER
(WARWICKSHIRE)

High Street Antiques
11a High Street
0789 764009
A mixed assortment of metalware, porcelain, bric-a-brac, small art deco, postcards and collectors' items, many reasonably priced. Appointment advised.

Malthouse Antiques Centre
4–5 Market Place
0789 764032
Fourteen dealers with a range of furniture, pictures, general antiques and collectors' items.

BARNSLEY
(GLOUCESTERSHIRE)

Denzil Verey
Barnsley House
0285 740402
As is usual in the Cotswolds, the emphasis is on quality, but some interesting and unusual smaller items are stocked in addition to period furniture.

BERKELEY
(GLOUCESTERSHIRE)

Berkeley Market
The Market Place
0453 511032
Three dealers in 3,000 square feet with furniture – good Georgian to secondhand – and general antiques. Stock, like prices, is variable but the selection is broad-ranging with some good browsing possible.

Newcombe Antiques
17–19 High Street
0453 810338
Mid-range furniture and general antiques.

Peter & Penny Proudfoot
16–18 High Street
0453 811513
Small furniture, jewellery, bric-a-brac and collectors' items.

BEWDLEY
(HEREFORD & WORCESTER)

Ma's Antiques
89 Welch Gate
0299 403845

Bric-a-brac, including commemorative and souvenir ware, clocks and watches and general antiques.

BIDFORD UPON AVON
(WARWICKSHIRE)

The Antique Centre
194–196 High Street
0789 773680
Now in its tenth year, The Antique Centre accommodates around a dozen dealers with a range of furniture, jewellery, pictures, glass, bric-a-brac, clocks, collectors' items and general antiques.

Bellcourt Auctions
69 High Street
0789 772611
Two auctions a week, on Tuesday and Thursday.

BISLEY
(GLOUCESTERSHIRE)

High Street Antiques
High Street
0452 770153
Small furniture, general antiques, porcelain and rugs.

BRIDGNORTH
(SHROPSHIRE)

Bakehouse Antiques
6 St John Street, Low Town
0746 763227
Metalware, jewellery, country furniture, dolls and toys and general antiques. In process of moving to the adjacent shop *(number 4)*.

English Heritage
2 Whitburn Street, High Town
0746 762097
Jewellery, collectors' items, bric-a-brac, militaria and general antiques.

Northgate Arcade
High Street
0746 764850
Several dealers with a range of furniture, general antiques and collectors' items.

Perry & Phillips, auctioneers
Mew Market Buildings,
Listley Street
0746 762248
Monthly general sales, on the first Tuesday of the month.

Tatters Decorative Antiques
2 West Castle Street
0746 761918
Style sets the tone and stock includes painted furniture and other post-pine alternatives as well as pottery, decorative items, furniture and textiles.

BROADWAY
(HEREFORD & WORCESTER)

Fenwick & Fisher
88–90 High Street
0386 853227
In this picture-postcard village budget buys are relatively rare. This is one shop which carries a reasonably comprehensive range of furniture, collectors' items and general antiques.

Nationwide Fine Art & Furniture
41–43 High Street
0386 852456
Mixed antique and general sales every four months, usually on second Tuesday of the month.

BROMSGROVE
(HEREFORD & WORCESTER)

Strand Antiques
22 The Strand
0527 72686

Furniture and house clearance goods.

CAMBRIDGE
(GLOUCESTERSHIRE)

Bell House Antiques
Bell House
0453 890463
Furniture, including pine and general antiques.

CHARLECOTE
(WARWICKSHIRE)

Country Furniture Antique Centre
Kingsmead Farm
0789 840254
Six dealers offering a broad range of furniture, general antiques, bric-a-brac and collectors' items.

CHELTENHAM
(GLOUCESTERSHIRE)

The atmosphere, still redolent of its fashionable heyday as a Georgian spa town, is livened up on race-days. Its two colleges – actually public schools – educate boys and 'ladies' respectively. The antique trade can be lively and imaginative with a leaning towards the decorative and unusual.

Mark Bailey
16 Suffolk Road
0242 255897
Appointment advised. Architectural fittings, lighting and accessories and advertising items.

Bottles & Bygones
96 Horsefair Street
0242 236393
Stocking furniture, curios, sundry collectors' items, including advertising ephemera, bric-a-brac, architectural pieces and commemorative and crested china and well worth a visit. Open Wednesday to Saturday.

Bruton Knowles, auctioneers
Southam Tithe Barn
0242 245081
Mixed sales on Thursdays, every three or four weeks.

Charlton Kings Antiques Centre
199 London Road
0242 510672
Around a dozen dealers with a comprehensive range of furniture, collectors' items and general antiques.

Cheltenham Antique Market
54 Suffolk Road
0242 529812
Around 30 dealers with a range of furniture, collectors' items and general antiques.

Cocoa
7 Queen's Circus
0242 233588
Textiles, principally historic and bridal christening and lace. There are also approximately 100 Regency and Victorian veils that can be hired. By appointment only on Saturdays.

Heydens Antiques
420 High Street
0242 582466
General antiques, collectors' items and militaria.

Mallams, auctioneers
26 Grosvenor Street
0242 235712
Intermittent antique and general sales on last Thursday of the month.

Patrick Oliver
4 Tivoli Street
0242 513392
Something of a Cheltenham institution and fast approaching its centenary, this shop carries a large stock of furniture, from mid-range and spa-town specials to shipping goods, plus some general antiques. Opening times are irregular, so ring for appointment before visiting.

Sue Ryder Furniture Shop
60–62 Cantay House,
St George's Place
0242 230450
Donated furniture and household items.

John Townsend
2 Oxford Cottages, Ullenwood
0242 870223
Appointment required. About 2,000 square feet of pine and shipping furniture, plus some books.

CHIPPING CAMPDEN
(GLOUCESTERSHIRE)

Pedlars
Lower High Street
0386 840680
Budget secondhand or antique furniture, as well as some collectors' items and bric-a-brac.

School House Antiques
High Street
0386 841474
Across-the-board range of furniture, Georgian to shipping, bric-a-brac and general antiques. One of a number in town; others with a similar range include **Antique**

Heritage and **Stuart House**.

CHURCH STRETTON
(SHROPSHIRE)

Antiques on the Square
2 Sandford Court,
Sandford Avenue
0694 724111
Furniture, general antiques and ceramics, mostly mid-range art deco.

Stretton Antiques & Militaria
7 High Street
0694 723526
Collectors' items, militaria and general antiques.

Stretton Antiques Market
36 Sandford Avenue
0694 723718
Around 50 dealers on three floors with a comprehensive range of furniture, including shipping, general antiques and collectors' items. Prices cover most of the range, from 50p.

CIRENCESTER
(GLOUCESTERSHIRE)

Cirencester Antiques Centre
The Waterloo
0285 644040
Jewellery, furniture from mid-range to shipping, bric-a-brac and general antiques.

Corner Cupboard Curios
2 Church Street
0285 655476
Phonographs, gramophones and general antiques.

Fraser Glennie, auctioneers
The Old Rectory, Siddington
0285 659677

Monthly general sales in the Bingham Hall, usually on Friday.

Moore, Allen & Innocent
33 Castle Street
0285 651831
Mixed mega-sales once or twice a month on an irregular basis; occasional specialist sales.

CLEOBURY MORTIMER
(SHROPSHIRE)

The Antique Centre
Childe Road
0299 270513
Furniture – Georgian to secondhand – general antiques, bric-a-brac and collectors' items. Usually a good range, worth a good rake.

Barnaby's
High Street
When John Carter and his wife are not teaching they operate their Saturday shop of furniture, including stripped pine and ethnographic curios.

COLESHILL
(WARWICKSHIRE)

Geostran Antiques
Middle Lane, Whiteacre Heath
0675 481483
Mid-range furniture, clocks and general antiques, plus some collectors' items.

CRAVEN ARMS
(SHROPSHIRE)

I & S Antiques
Stokesay, Ludlow Road
0588 672263
Furniture, including pine and shipping, vernacular antiques, treen, metalware, books, bric-a-brac and collectors' items. Plenty to rummage through and normally rewarding.

DUNCHURCH
(WARWICKSHIRE)

Dunchurch Antique Centre
16–16a Daventry Road
0788 817147
Around 18 dealers with a comprehensive range of furniture, including shipping and pine, collectors' items, toys, architectural, decorative and general antiques.

ELLESMERE
(SHROPSHIRE)

Wharf Road Antiques
Wharf Road
0691 623652
Furniture, bric-a-brac, collectors' items, books, metalware and general antiques. For the most part an imaginative mix of stock and price levels.

EVESHAM
(HEREFORD & WORCESTER)

Magpie Antiques
2 Port Street and 61 High Street
0386 41631
Jewellery, silver, furniture and general antiques.

Merrivale Farm Antiques
Merrivale Farm
0386 840281
Furniture, mid-range to pine and shipping.

Yesterday
79 Port Street
0386 48068
Costume, jewellery and bric-a-brac.

GLOUCESTER
(GLOUCESTERSHIRE)

With a cathedral which is a *tour de force* of the perpendicular style at its elaborate best – even the monks' lavatorium has an intricate fan vault – this bustling market town is now also known as a manufacturing and administrative centre. Buying opportunities are diverse, ranging from the uncompromisingly basic to the ultra-exotic.

The Gloucester Antique Centre

1 Severn Road
0452 529716
Upwards of 60 dealers with a comprehensive range of furniture, period to shipping, pictures, bric-a-brac, jewellery, collectors' items and general antiques.

Bruton Knowles, auctioneers

Albion Chambers,
111 Eastgate
0452 521267
General sales once a month, usually on a Thursday, at Southam Tithe Barn.

Paul Hayes Architectural Antiques

The Pit, Hare Lane
0452 301145
Decorative architectural salvage, including pulpits, stained glass and elaborate fragments. Particularly noted for ecclesiastical items.

David Kent Antiques

300 Barton Street
0452 304396
Furniture, including shipping stock, general antiques and books.

Military Curios

84 Southgate Street
0452 527716
Militaria, medals and decorations, collectors' items, posters and some jewellery.

Short, Graham & Co, auctioneers

City Chambers,
4–6 Clarence Street
0452 521177
Monthly general sales are held at St Barnabas' Church Hall near the Stroud Road, on Tuesdays.

GREAT MALVERN
(HEREFORD & WORCESTER)

Dennis Atkins

115 Barnard's Green
House clearance basics.

Grays Antiques

Units 24 & 26, Blackmore Park Industrial Estate, Hanley Swan
0684 560038
Furniture, including shipping and general antiques.

Hampton, Pocock & Lar, auctioneers

Barnard's Green Road
Sales on first and third Thursday of each month, some general, some antiques.

Russell Baldwin & Bright, auctioneers

The Portland Room,
Portland Road
0684 893933
Ten sales a year of antiques, fine art and shipping goods.

HEREFORD
(HEREFORD & WORCESTER)

Berrows House Antiques

Bath Street
0432 268822

A former flour mill now with a comprehensive stock of furniture, mid-range to shipping.

Hereford Antiques Centre
128 Widemarsh Street
0432 266242
Around 40 dealers with a range of furniture, general antiques and collectors' items. Prices typically across the board with some low-cost possibilities.

Pickwick's Antiques
9 Barrol Street,
off St Owen's Street
0432 354253
Some mid-range furniture, pottery, porcelain, metalware and general antiques.

Styles Furniture Shop
Cantilupe Street,
off St Owens Street
0432 279242
Secondhand furniture and house clearance goods.

IRONBRIDGE
(SHROPSHIRE)

Ironbridge Antique Centre
Dale End
0952 433784
A former foundry where approximately 30 dealers now trade in 'a little bit of everything'. Although decorative cast iron was a famous local product, unfortunately there is no great abundance here, because it was mostly

UTILITY FURNITURE

Opinions about the merits of Britain's wartime utility systems of production remain a matter of debate, but few would dispute the quality of the furniture that was mass-produced with the logo CC 41 in accordance with strict government specification. More than 40 years after coming off the production line, much of it still survives in excellent order. The philosophy which lay behind the idea was a curious amalgam of socialist collectivism and the romantic ethos of the Victorian arts & crafts movement. Utility's most outspoken champion was the furniture designer Gordon Russell, who headed the Utility Furniture Advisory Committee which had been convened by Hugh Dalton, President of the Board of Trade, in 1941. Bureaucracy being what it is, the first catalogue didn't appear until 1943. There were two styles available – Cotswolds or Chilterns. It didn't matter if you lived in Stromness, or Coleraine, or Grimsby; Cotswolds and Chiltern style were your lot. Furniture manufacturers were outraged, by and large. The rumour was put about that CC stood for 'consumer control', with implications that were particularly sinister at a time when the Gestapo were a mere Channel crossing away. The *Cabinetmaker*, respected organ of the furniture trade, spoke darkly of totalitarian plots. The truth was rather more mundane – CC simply stood for 'civilian clothing', which was also part of the scheme.

despatched to the growing towns of Georgian and Victorian Britain. In general, a well-mixed cross-section of antiques, bric-a-brac and collectables can be browsed through, with no particular specialisations. For the most part the furniture on sale is restricted to a pre-war dateline although there are a few smaller modern reproduction items.

KIDDERMINSTER
(HEREFORD & WORCESTER)

The Antique Centre
5 Lion Street
0562 740389
Approximately 15 dealers with a variety of antiques and collectables. Specialities include fireplaces, beds and a resident artist.

BBM Jewellery & Antiques
8–9 Lion Street
0562 744118
Jewellery, numismatics, silver, porcelain, collectors' items and general antiques are on offer, with a good selection at the cheaper end, plus some quality items.

Phipps & Pritchard, auctioneers
Bank Buildings
0562 822244
Monthly antique, fine art and collectors' sales, at the Village Hall, Hartlebury.

KINETON
(WARWICKSHIRE)

Venables Antiques
The Old Mill, Mill Lane
0295 878160
Large selection of trade and

shipping furniture, Georgian to pre-war.

LEAMINGTON SPA
(WARWICKSHIRE)

Black Horse Agencies, auctioneers
Walton House,
11 The Parade
0926 889100
Weekly general sales and monthly antique sales, on Thursdays.

Drapers Thrift Shop
28 Regent Street
0926 422676
Secondhand goods and house clearance items.

Leamington Antique Centre
20 Regent Street
0926 429679
About a dozen dealers with furniture, including pine and general antiques.

The Trading Post
39 Chandos Street
0926 421857
Jewellery, collectors' items and small general antiques.

LECHLADE
(GLOUCESTERSHIRE)

D'Arcy Antiques
High Street
0367 252471
Mid-range furniture, to pre-war, metalware, bric-a-brac and general antiques. A substantial and comprehensive selection, particularly in furniture, with a broad price range.

Lechlade Antiques Centre
5–7 High Street
0367 252832

Around 40 stallholders with a wide range of antiques and collectors' items, including furniture, metalware, books and bric-a-brac.

Little Barrow Antiques
High Street
0367 253140
Collectors' items, bric-a-brac and small general antiques. What it lacks in space it usually makes up for in sifting potential, with much for the low-budget collector.

Mark Serle
6 Burford Street
0367 253145
Mid-range furniture and collectors' items, including woodworking tools.

LEDBURY
(HEREFORD & WORCESTER)

Alf's Secondhand Shop
Off Southend
Hidden down a lane beside 'Top Brass' *(at number 4)* is the town's main junk and basics supplier.

Coles, Knapp Ltd, auctioneers
The Cattle Market
0531 634455
Intermittent mixed antique and general sales.

LEOMINSTER
(HEREFORD & WORCESTER)

Leominster Antiques Market
14 Broad Street
0568 612189
Around 12 dealers with a wide range of stock, including furniture, from shipping basics and pine to quality period

pieces, jewellery, silver, textiles (including samplers) as well as collectables and general antiques.

Kingsland Auction Services
Shirl Heath
0568 708564
Weekly mega sales, usually with a thousand lots or more, held at a site located about four miles south west of Leominster. Phone for details.

LUDLOW (SHROPSHIRE)

Mitre House Antiques
Corve Bridge
0584 872138
Furniture, including pine and general antiques.

Ludlow Antique Auctions
29 Corve Street
0584 875157
Monthly antique and specialist sales.

MALVERN LINK
(HEREFORD & WORCESTER)

Kimbers Antiques
6–8 Lower Howsell Road
0684 574339
Mid-range furniture and general antiques in a showroom and attached warehouse. The range of furniture on offer is comprehensive and includes some cheaper Edwardian and pre-war items.

MINCHINHAMPTON
(GLOUCESTERSHIRE)

Vospers Antiques
20 High Street
0453 882480
Mid-range furniture, bric-a-brac,

metalware, some collectors'
items and a variety of general
antiques.

MORETON IN THE MARSH
(GLOUCESTERSHIRE)

Windsor House Antiques Centre
High Street
0608 50993
Around 25 dealers with a range
of antiques and collectors'
items. In general this centre
offers a more eclectic selection
than the town's other outlets,
although **The Antique Centre**
at nearby London House can be
worth checking.

NEWPORT
(SHROPSHIRE)

Worth's
34 St Mary's Street
0952 810122
Furniture, mid-range to
shipping, general antiques,
books and some collectors'
items.

NORTHLEACH
(GLOUCESTERSHIRE)

Keith Harding's World of Mechanical Music
The Oak House,
High Street
0451 860181
Established for more than 30
years, and with his enthusiasm
for his subject undiminished,
the proprietor continues to
specialise in musical boxes,
clocks and automata. None of it
junk, perhaps, but no less
fascinating for that. Serious
collectors are welcome.
Opening hours may vary so
telephone in advance.

OSWESTRY
(SHROPSHIRE)

The Antique Shop
King Street
0691 653011
Something of an institution, and
usually with a varied and
comprehensive jumble of
antique and secondhand goods,
bric-a-brac and collectors'
items.

Cambrian House
Gobowen Road
0691 654597
Furniture, including shipping
goods, some collectables and
general antiques.

Doug Morris
Parkers Patch,
27 Whittington Road
0691 653338
Secondhand furniture and
house clearance goods,
occasionally with some small
antiques or collectors' items as
well.

PAINSWICK
(GLOUCESTERSHIRE)

Tibbiwell Antiques
Tibbiwell
0452 813045
Pine, bric-a-brac and general
antiques.

PERSHORE
(HEREFORD & WORCESTER)

The Look In
134b High Street
0386 556776
Furniture, bric-a-brac, pictures,
metalware, collectables and
general antiques. A fair
selection of cheaper items is
commonly available, and there
is usually also some buyable
jewellery.

RODLEY
(GLOUCESTERSHIRE)

Kelly Antiques
Landeck, Goose Lane
0452 760315
Antique pine and vernacular furniture.

ROSS ON WYE
(HEREFORD & WORCESTER)

Bailey's Architectural Antiques
The Engine Shed,
Ashburton Industrial Estate
0989 63015
Architectural salvage, with a strong emphasis on ecclesiastical, residential, commercial and decorative fittings. A well-organised rummage, but remember to bring a tape measure.

Bits & Pieces
23 High Street
0989 62683
Shipping and budget goods as well as some collectables and general antiques.

Fritz Fryer
12 Brookend Street
0989 67416
Antique and decorative lighting and accessories, some spectacular and expensive, some affordable.

The Old Pine Shop
Gloucester Road
0989 64738
Pine furniture and brass and iron beds.

Relics
19 High Street
0989 64539
Jewellery, clocks and watches, textiles, collectors' items and general antiques.

MAKING AN IMPRESSION

One dealer in assorted curios, asked to identify a client with unusual collecting tastes, immediately mentioned the name of a barrister who had started his collecting career with a relatively common subject: signet rings and fob seals. After a time, however, the appeal of these began to fade, so he decided to widen the theme to include anything that could be used in the process of making impressions. Stones with lapidary crests, glass intaglio heraldic seals, and dies made for casting the sort of wax seals that are usually attached to grand documents followed naturally. Soon enough this too ceased to satisfy, so he began to acquire large copper moulds once used in the production of gesso reliefs for Georgian fireplaces, segmental moulds used to manufacture plaster busts, pattern moulds for ornamental brick and tile production, plasterer's cornice moulds, copper confectioner's moulds – in fact, absolutely anything from which another finished product would have been cast. The dealer's verdict? It must have something to do with the wierd workings of the legal mind.

The Secondhand Centre
26 Station Street
0989 67989
House clearance furniture and effects.

RUGBY
(WARWICKSHIRE)

Chris & Jerry
14a Wells Street
0788 536256
Secondhand furniture and house clearance goods.

Rugby Salerooms, auctioneers
16 Albert Street
0788 542367
Weekly general sales on Monday.

Tripontium
Watling Street
0788 860807
Regular weekend indoor car boot sales, usually with about 150 stallholders selling a variety of antiques, collectors' items and general junk. Held at a former riding arena approximately six miles out of town on the A5.

SHREWSBURY
(SHROPSHIRE)

The gateway to Wales, and birthplace of Charles Darwin, Shropshire's administrative capital also supports two antique markets and several collector-friendly mid-range and budget antique or bric-a-brac shops.

Abbey Antiques
Abbey Foregate
0743 231969
Mid-range and secondhand furniture, bric-a-brac, curios, collectables, some general antiques and house clearance items.

Ancient & Modern
186 Monkmoor Road
0743 354667
Budget basics.

Juliette Chiltern Antiques & Interiors
69 Wyle Cop
0743 358699
Mid-range furniture and general antiques, plus occasional collectors' items.

Collectors' Gallery
6–7 Castle Gates
0743 272140
An extensive range covering most areas of collecting: philately, numismatics, militaria, ephemera and books.

Cooper & Green, auctioneers
Rousehill Auction Rooms
0743 232244
Monthly general sales.

Farthingales
3–4 Greyfriars Bridge, Longden Coleham
0743 354800
Mid-range and budget furniture, general antiques, bric-a-brac, metalware, jewellery, textiles, pictures and collectors' items.

Raleigh Antiques
23 Bellevue Road
0743 359552
A broad range of furniture, jewellery, silver, bric-a-brac, clocks and general antiques, from as little as £1 to just over £1,000. The proprietor's knowledge gained much from his years with an auction house and he has an eye for more interesting items.

Shrewsbury Antique Centre
15 Princess House,
The Square
0743 247704
Upwards of 30 dealers with a broad range of furniture, general antiques and collectors' items.

Shrewsbury Antique Market
Frankwell Quay Warehouse
0743 350916
Around 45 stallholders offering a range of general antiques and collectors' items.

STOW ON THE WOLD (GLOUCESTERSHIRE)

Cotswold Antiques Centre
The Square
0451 831585
Around 15 dealers with mostly high-quality jewellery, silver, metalware, porcelain, pictures and decorative items, plus some pine country furniture and art nouveau.

Lillian Middleton's Antique Dolls Shop
Talbot House, The Square
0451 830381
Dolls, teddy bears, dolls houses and related items, plus hospital facilities for wounded or dishevelled dolls and teddies.

Park Street Antiques
2 Park Street
0451 832311
Around 20 dealers with a range of furniture, to pre-war, bric-a-brac, collectors' items and general antiques. Open seven days a week.

Ruskin Antiques
5 Talbot Court
0451 832254
The ethos, rather than the period, is suggested by the name of John Ruskin and it is also pure coincidence that the shop is half owned by one William Morris. Stock is comprehensive, including old cycle lamps and binoculars as well as post-Ruskin specialities such as Clarice Cliffe ware and Whitefriars glass.

STRATFORD UPON AVON (WARWICKSHIRE)

Bigwood, auctioneers
The Old School, Tiddington
0789 269415
Weekly general sales and monthly antique and fine art sales.

Jazz Decorative Arts
Shop 2, Civic Hall, Rother Street
0789 298362
Art deco and art nouveau furniture, general antiques and collectors' items.

The Meer Street Antique Arcade
10 Meer Street
0789 297249
Around 25 dealers trading in a range of smaller antiques, including textiles, toy soldiers, furniture, jewellery, silver, books, art deco and ceramics.

Stratford Antiques Centre
Ely Street
0789 204180
Upwards of 50 dealers with a broad range of furniture, collectors' items and general antiques.

James Wiginton
Stratford upon Avon
0789 293881
General antiques, arms and

149

armour, weaponry and early fishing items. Appointment required. Further fishing-related items are also available at **Burman Antiques** (*Trinity Street*).

STROUD
(GLOUCESTERSHIRE)

Gnome Cottage Antiques
55–57 Middle Street
0453 763669
Furniture, pictures, bric-a-brac and general antiques.

Shabby Tiger
18 Nelson Street
0453 759175
Mid-range furniture, metalware, bric-a-brac, jewellery and general antiques, and can usually be relied upon for a good rummage.

TELFORD (SHROPSHIRE)

Telford Antiques Centre
See **WELLINGTON**

Car Boot Sale
Princess Royal Hospital
Held regularly on Sundays in the hospital grounds.

TETBURY
(GLOUCESTERSHIRE)

Antique Centre
The Old Methodist Chapel,
Church Street
0453 505281
A newly established market complex with a range of furniture, general antiques and collectors' items, operated by the owners of **Country Homes** (*Long Street*).

Elgin House Antiques
1 New Church Street
0666 504068

A comprehensive selection of mid-range furniture, plus brass and iron beds and decorative antiques.

The Old Mill Market Shop
12 Church Street
0666 503127
General antiques, collectors' items and bric-a-brac.

TEWKESBURY
(GLOUCESTERSHIRE)

Abbey Antiques
62 Church Street
0684 292378
Furniture, including shipping, general antiques and bric-a-brac.

Berkeley Antiques
The Wheatsheaf, 132 High Street
0684 292034
Mid-range and period quality furniture and general antiques, plus porcelain, metalware, textiles and costume.

Tewkesbury Antique Centre
Tolsey Hall, Tolsey Lane
0684 294091
Around a dozen dealers with a range of general antiques and collectors' items.

WARWICK
(WARWICKSHIRE)

Goodwins Antiques
Unit F & M,
Budbroke Industrial Estate,
Budbroke Road
0926 491191
An extensive stock of mid-range and shipping furniture. In a town much taken with quality oak and sumptuous elegance, this is one outlet with a broad, if largely conventional, range.

Smith Street Antiques Centre
7 Smith Street
0926 497864
Ten dealers with a mid- to upper-market range of antiques and collectors' items, from cigarette cards to quality silver.

Vintage Antique Market
36 Market Place
0926 491527
Upwards of a dozen dealers with a range of furniture, bric-a-brac, general antiques, jewellery and collectors' items.

Warwick Antiques
16–18 High Street
0926 492482
A large selection of furniture, from period to shipping, bric-a-brac, decorative objects and ornamental garden items.

WELLINGTON
(SHROPSHIRE)

Stubleys Warehouse
Church Street
0952 257610
Secondhand furniture and house clearance goods.

Telford Antiques Centre
High Street
0952 256450
A market of more than 60 dealers with a wide variety of antiques and collectors' items occupies the former Chad Valley toyworks (of fond memory), where pre-war teddy bears, golliwogs, tricycles and pedal-cars were produced before it was requisitioned as an armaments store.

WHITCHURCH
(HEREFORD & WORCESTER)

Oliver's
Farthing Corner, The Square
0600 890662
Furniture, decorative and architectural items, advertising material, metalware, brass and iron beds and collectors' items.

WORCESTER
(HEREFORD & WORCESTER)

The Original Choice
56 The Tithing
0905 613330
Architectural antiques, fireplaces and accessories.

CENTRAL ENGLAND

As with any area dominated by commerce and industry throughout the last century, there is still a great deal around in the way of solid Victorian and Edwardian furniture and general household bits and pieces.

Most of the manufacturing output from the major industrial centres of central England was aimed specifically at the domestic consumer, and some of the best-known items are probably the household ornaments produced in Staffordshire's pottery towns. Birmingham, the second largest city in Britain, had a heavy engineering and metalworking industry which produced well-designed smaller items for the home as well as massive machinery parts. Much of Coventry's wealth came from weaving, while even relatively small towns such as Leek, in Staffordshire, developed their own manufacturing specialities – in Leek's case it was black silk, for which there was a great demand following the death of Prince Albert, consort to Queen Victoria. For those with the financial means to patronise them, the area also had its fashionable watering places. Buxton, in the Peak District, was famous for its mineral waters, which were first discovered by the Romans. Another notable attraction is Buxton's superbly restored Edwardian opera house.

CHESHIRE

• Chester

ABBOTS BROMLEY
(STAFFORDSHIRE)

Birchwood Antiques
Bromley's, Bagot Street
0283 840288
Small furniture, pottery, general antiques and textiles, including samplers, linen and lace. Appointment required.

ALDERLEY EDGE
(CHESHIRE)

Brook Lane Antiques
93 Brook Lane
0625 584896
Furniture, including original and reproduction pine, some shipping goods and general antiques.

ALREWAS
(STAFFORDSHIRE)

Poley Antiques
5 Main Street
0283 791151
A broad selection of furniture,
bric-a-brac and general
antiques, including silver,
metalware and porcelain. Open
Thursday to Saturday.

ALSAGER (CHESHIRE)

Trash 'n' Treasure
48 Sandbach Road South
0270 872972

Furniture, mid-range to
shipping, bric-a-brac, general
antiques and pictures, Victorian
to pre-war with a good mix and
a broad price spectrum. Closed
on Wednesday.

ALTRINCHAM
(CHESHIRE)

Altrincham Antiques
39 Hale Road and
15 Tipping Street
061 941 3554
Upwards of half a dozen
showrooms with everything
from junk to quality furniture.

Cheyne's Antiques

38 Hale Road
061 941 4879
Mid-range Georgian and Victorian, furniture as well as a good selection of general antiques. Two years ago the owner was asked to conduct a fund-raising auction for his local church. He discovered he had a talent for it and so now holds regular quarterly sales at All Saints Church Hall.

Halo Antiques

97 Hale Road
061 941 1800
About 3,000 square feet of furniture, including mostly old pine (plus some repro) and shipping goods. More can be seen at 2a Beech Road. Closed on Monday.

ASHBOURNE
(DERBYSHIRE)

Yvonne Adams Antiques

47 Church Street
0335 46466
Some smaller quality and mid-range furniture, plus decorative items and general antiques. Closed on Wednesday.

Bailey & Hilton's

20 Market Place
0335 43234
Local estate agency which holds about two general sales a year at Osmeston Village Hall.

Pamela Elsom Antiques

5 Church Street
0335 43468
A comprehensive range of stock, mostly mid-market, including furniture, treen, books, bric-a-brac, metalware and general antiques. Closed on Wednesday.

Rose Antiques

37 Church Street
0335 43822
Furniture, jewellery, bric-a-brac and general antiques. Closed on Wednesday.

Mrs Sandall

Off Church Street
Secondhand goods from premises by a builders' yard off Church Street, near Ashbourne's most upmarket antique shop, **Spurrier Smith's**.

BAKEWELL
(DERBYSHIRE)

Cobwebs

Granby Arcade
0629 814676
Furniture, bric-a-brac, textiles, jewellery and general antiques.

BEESTON
(NOTTINGHAMSHIRE)

Elizabeth Bailey

33 Chilwell Road
0602 255685
Furniture, including pine and shipping, plus decorative antiques Closed on Thursday.

BELPER (DERBYSHIRE)

Sweetings

1–1a The Butts
0773 825930
Mid-range and shipping furniture in 11 showrooms.

Neil Wayne, The Razor Man

Old Baptist Chapel, Bridge Street
0773 827910
Knives, razors and virtually anything to do with the Sheffield cutlery industry. Owner is also leading world authority on old English concertinas from 1829 (first

patent) to present day. Around 1500 of these are also displayed on the premises (none for sale). Appointment required.

BIRMINGHAM
(WEST MIDLANDS)

Although no longer the workshop of an empire, and much blitzed by both bombers and planners, England's second city still retains the canal network that brought it prosperity, as well as a fine cathedral, a stupendous art collection, a university, a motorcycle museum, and a vast accumulation of junk and antique shops.

Always Antiques
*285 Vicarage Road,
Kings Heath
021 444 8701*
Antique dolls and associated items, textiles, furniture and general antiques. Open Thursday and Friday.

Architectural Antiques of Moseley
*23a St Mary's Row
021 442 4546*
Architectural antiques and salvaged items in a variety of materials including timber, stone, marble, slate and cast iron. Closed on Monday.

Biddle & Webb
*Ladywood Middleway
021 455 8042*
Weekly general auctions. Lost property from Gatwick airport three times per annum, plus intermittent specialist sales.

Cameo Antiques
*4 Lonsdale Road, Harborne
021 426 6900*
General antiques and bric-a-

brac. Open Thursday and Friday.

Car Boot Sale
*Pershore Street
021 627 3452*
Operated by the city council every Sunday.

City Antique Market
*St Martin's Market,
Edgbaston Street
021 624 3214 (enquiries)*
Several stallholders with an array of general antiques, bric-a-brac and collectables of variable quality and price.

BERLIN IRONWORK

Fashionable Prussian matrons were, perhaps understandably, reluctant to surrender their jewellery when asked to do so in support of the war against the French. Then the authorities hit upon a brilliant solution – Berlin ironwork. Before long, it became the essential fashion accessory for every patriotic woman. Medallion necklaces, earrings and brooches of intricately woven black enamelled wire were exchanged for vulgar diamond and emerald baubles and soon became de rigeur at the opera, particularly when inscribed with the phrase, 'Gold gab ich für Eisen' – I gave gold for iron. Berlin ironwork was still in popular demand at the end of the 19th century and is now collected avidly.

Open Monday mornings from 6.30am. For a good forage an early start is recommended.

Clare's, auctioneers

70 Park Street,
Digbeth
021 643 0226
Mixed household and antique auctions every Tuesday, plus intermittent specialist sales.

The Collectors' Shop

63 Station Street
021 631 2072
Numismatics, militaria, jewellery and collectors' items. Closed on Wednesday.

Flea Market & Rag Market

Edgbaston Street
021 622 3452
Source of secondhand basics, furnlture and household goods. Open Tuesdays, Fridays and Saturdays.

Garratt Antiques

35 Stephenson Street
021 643 9507
Long-established and usually with an interesting assortment of bric-a-brac, metalware, jewellery, toys and dolls and collectors' items.

Holmes & Son

85 Church Road,
South Yardley
021 706 8488
Furniture, up to pre-war.

James Antiques, Canalside

Gas Street Basin
021 643 3131
Decorative antiques and interesting items, including stained glass, tiles, Victoriana, painted furniture, vernacular curiosities and general furniture, nearly all chosen for aesthetic appeal. This family concern is also represented by **Tim James**, and **Sarah James**, below.

Tim James Antiques

47 Dogpool Lane, Stirchley
021 414 0051
Son of Canalside (above) specialising in architectural hardware and fireplaces. Closed on Monday.

Sarah James Antiques

1053 Pershore Road, Stirchley
021 415 4229
Daughter of Canalside (above). Stained glass restoration and design (eg. Birmingham Assay Office) plus antique stained glass for sale.

Johnson's Furnishings

1407 Pershore Road, Stirchley
021 459 4587
A broad range of furniture and household goods.

Kestrel House Auctioneers & Retailers

72 Gravelly Hill North,
Erdington
021 373 2375/7095
The shop stocks shipping furniture, pictures and general antiques. Sales are held fortnightly (usually Fridays) for mixed antiques and household effects, plus intermittent specialist sales.

Noel Furnishings

4 Short Heath Road,
Erdington
021 350 9511
Secondhand furniture and house clearance goods.

Smithsonia

14–16 Piccadilly Arcade
021 643 8405

Jewellery, collectors' items and pictures. Specialists in art deco.

The Treasure Chest
1407 Pershore Road, Stirchley
021 458 3705
Also 636 Bristol Road, Selly Oak
021 414 1544
Furniture, including shipping and general antiques.

The Treasure Trove
Dumphouse Farm,
Lilley Green Road, Alvchurch
021 458 2219
Shipping furniture, secondhand and house clearance goods.

Victoriana Antiques
287 Bearwood Road, Warley
021 429 8661
Jewellery, furniture, including pine and satinwood, fireplaces and accessories, textiles and costume.

Yesterday's Antiques
125 Pottery Road, Oldbury
021 420 3980
Furniture including pre-war and shipping, bric-a-brac and general antiques.

BLOXWICH
(WEST MIDLANDS)

Cobwebs
639 Bloxwich Road
0922 493670
Collectors' items and bric-a-brac. Closed on Monday and Thursday.

BRACKLEY
(NORTHAMPTONSHIRE)

Brackley Antiques
69 High Street
0280 703362
Mid-range furniture, including sofas and armchairs, curios and porcelain.

BRERETON
(STAFFORDSHIRE)

Rugeley Antique Centre
161–163 Main Road
0889 577166
Upwards of two dozen dealers operate here, selling a broad range of furniture, including budget and shipping items, general antiques, textiles, bric-a-brac, treen, glass, pictures and collectables. Prices across the range and the selection on offer is comprehensive.

BRIXWORTH
(NORTHAMPTONSHIRE)

Gunnett's Antiques
128 Northampton Road
0604 880057
Furniture, general antiques and bric-a-brac. Appointment only.

BURTON ON TRENT
(STAFFORDSHIRE)

Brearley's Corner Curios
54 New Street
0283 32600
Bric-a-brac and house clearance items.

Burton Antiques
1–2 Horninglow Road
0283 42331
Comprehensive range of furniture, including shipping, bric-a-brac, metalware and general antiques.

BUXTON
(DERBYSHIRE)

What Now Antiques
Cavendish Arcade, The Crescent
0298 27178
General antiques, textiles, toys, porcelain and pottery, mid-range furniture and collectors' items. The shop is a former

Edwardian hydro-therapy treatment room, still with original tiles, and is in itself an interesting spa-town relic. Space is limited to about 300 square feet, but with further storage elsewhere there are usually around 50 items of furniture plus sundry smaller pieces available or on display at any one time. Prices cover a broad range, from as little as £1 to over £1,000. Other centres in town pursuing a similar policy include **The Antiques Warehouse**, **JW Antiques**, **Past & Present** and **The Penny Post Antiques**.

CARLTON ON TRENT
(NOTTINGHAMSHIRE)

Tudor Rose Antiques
Yew Tree Farm
0636 821841
Appointment required. Mid-range furniture, metalware and decorative items.

CHEDDLETON
(STAFFORDSHIRE)

Jewel Antiques
Whitegates,
63 Basford Bridge Lane
0538 360744
Jewellery, pictures, oil lamps and general antiques. Appointment required.

CHESTER
(CHESHIRE)

A Roman building boom produced, among other things, the largest amphitheatre in Britain. After a lull, construction continued in earnest, producing a cathedral with some fine misericords and a notable lady chapel. Another notable architectural feature is 'The

Rows', an early experiment in pedestrian segregation.

Avalon Postcard & Stamp Shop
1 City Walls
0244 318406
Stamps, ephemera and collectors' items.

Chester Furniture Cave
97a Christleton Road,
Boughton
0244 314798
A warehouse of budget furniture and shipping goods.

Farmhouse Antiques
21–23 Christleton Road,
Boughton
0244 322478
Specialising in long-case and wall clocks, country furniture, pottery, musical boxes and general antiques.

Grosvenor Antiques
22 Watergate Street
0244 315201
Jewellery, bric-a-brac, furniture, from Georgian to shipping, dolls and toys, rugs and general antiques.

Guildhall Fair
22 Watergate Street
Operates on Thursdays. Around 20 dealers with an assortment of general antiques, bric-a-brac and collectors' items.

Harpers Antiques
27 Watergate Row
0244 323004
Rummageable Victoriana, bric-a-brac, metalware, curios, general antiques and collectors' items. A low-price culture is the favoured option for the most part, plus a good range of better collectables.

Robert Hayes & Associates, auctioneers

Hatton Buildings,
Lightfoot Street, Hoole
0244 328941
Weekly general sales and antique and collectors' sale on the first Tuesday of each month.

Made of Honour

11 City Walls
0244 314208
General antiques, textiles, books, 18th- and 19th-century china, especially Staffordshire figures. A good selection of decorative fabric, woolwork and samplers are on offer, all showing in two well-filled rooms.

Mike Melody's Antique Galleries

30–32 City Road
0244 328968
Mid-range furniture, including pine, porcelain, lighting, books, curios, pictures, metalware and decorative antiques. Proprietor and family display an unstinting passion for the trade.

Phillips North West

New House,
150 Christleton Road
0244 313936
Fortnightly gallery sales and intermittent specialist sales.

Roy's Bargain Shop

33 Garden Lane
0244 375139
Secondhand furniture and house clearance items.

CHESTERFIELD
(DERBYSHIRE)

Antique Market

Market Square
Several antique and bric-a-brac stallholders offer a rummageable choice of goods in the market square every Thursday.

CUT STEEL JEWELLERY

Britain's early industrialists had a talent for developing decorative sidelines to their principal output. A producer of clay drainage pipes, for example, would frequently cultivate a repertoire of stunningly designed gardenware, ranging from clay path border tiles with rope-design edges to impeccably classical campagna garden urns, while the ironmaster's girders would be supplemented by a nice line in foliate-pattern benches. Steel, too, could be used for adornment. Facet-cut, it had something of the quality of marcasite, which was often used as a substitute diamond. Being cheap, tough and hard wearing, it could also be fashioned into larger items such as tiaras and waistband clasps which, in more precious gem-set metals, would have been prohibitively expensive. Woodstock, near Oxford, was an early centre for the craft, although it was eclipsed in the mid-18th century by Birmingham, where Matthew Boulton produced steel shoe buckles and sword hilts as well as engine parts.

Langley Fisher's
221 Chatsworth Road
0246 232831
Secondhand and house
clearance basics.

Ian Morris
479 Chatsworth Road
0246 235120
Mid-range and shipping
furniture and general antiques.

**Tilley's Vintage Magazine
Shop**
29–31 South Street
0246 454270
Newspapers, comics, magazines
and general periodicana.

Times Past
13 Chatsworth Road
0246 557077
Mid-range furniture, pictures,
porcelain, some collectables
and general antiques.

COALVILLE
(LEICESTERSHIRE)

Keystone Antiques
9 Ashby Road
0530 835966
Jewellery, silver, collectors'
items, prints, glass and mid-
range general antiques.

Massey's Antiques
26 Hotel Street
0530 832374
Numismatics, bric-a-brac,
collectables and general
antiques. Closed Wednesday.
Nearby is **Anything Old** *(18
Hotel Street)*, which is also
worth a look.

CODSALL
(STAFFORDSHIRE)

Dam Mill Antiques
Birches Road
0902 84 3780

Furniture, collectors' items, and
general antiques. Closed on
Tuesday and Thursday.

CONGLETON
(CHESHIRE)

Congleton Antiques
2 Cross Street
0260 275331
Furniture, mid-range to
shipping, jewellery, bric-a-brac
and general antiques. Closed on
Wednesday.

Little's Collectables
8–10 Little Street
Collectors' items, bric-a-brac
and general antiques.

R & M Antiques
7 Kinsey Street
0260 280404
General antiques and bric-a-
brac, also oil lamps. Closed on
Wednesday.

**Whittaker & Biggs,
auctioneer**
Macclesfield Showroom
0260 273241
Weekly general sales. Phone for
details.

CORBY
(NORTHAMPTONSHIRE)

Spencers Auctions
Unit 3a, Southfold Road
0536 743755
Weekly general sales, on
Wednesdays.

COVENTRY
(WEST MIDLANDS)

Whatever was lost on that night
in 1940, Basil Spence's new
cathedral, built alongside the
shell of the old one, is a
momentous achievement,
thanks in part to the

contributions of Epstein, Piper and Sutherland. A good art gallery and museum also help to attract visitors.

Cobwebs
58 Far Gosford Street
0203 222032
Bric-a-brac, house clearance goods and budget antiques.

Coventry Auction Centre
3 Queen Victoria Road
0203 223377
Weekly general sales.

Earlsdon Antiques
35 Hearsall Lane
0203 675456
Furniture and general antiques.

Horizon Auctions
Gulson Road
0203 220000
Weekly general sales.

Martin's Secondhand
Unit 2,
113 Wheelwright Lane
0203 368254
House clearance items.

Memories Antiques
400a Stoney Stanton Road
0203 687994
Furniture, including mid-range, shipping and pine, jewellery, bric-a-brac, pictures, collectors' items and a good rummage of general antiques. Closed on Wednesday.

Spon End Antiques
115–116 Spon End
0203 228379
Across-the-board furniture, toys, dolls, teddy bears, bric-a-brac, jewellery, textiles, decorative items and costume. An interesting mix and usually plentiful.

CREWE (CHESHIRE)

As Good As New
109 West Street
0270 213653
Secondhand furniture and house clearance items.

CROUGHTON (NORTHAMPTONSHIRE)

Croughton Antiques
29 High Street
0869 810203
Furniture, including shipping and pre-war oak, general antiques and decorative items. Closed on Monday and Tuesday.

DAVENHAM (CHESHIRE)

Davenham Antique Centre
461 London Road
0606 44350
Seven dealers with a range of furniture, bric-a-brac and general antiques. Closed on Wednesday.

Magpie Antiques
4 Church Street
0606 260360
General antiques, curios, bric-a-brac and pictures. A small bookshop occupies the same premises.

DERBY (DERBYSHIRE)

Strangely enough, not the county capital (Matlock has that privilege). The country's first silk mill was set up locally in 1719, and William Duesbury established the famous porcelain works in the 1750s. Between times, it was here that Bonnie Prince Charlie decided the game was up. More recently, railway engineers and Rolls-

Royce aero engines have been key economic areas.

Abbey House
115 Woods Lane
0332 31426
Dolls, toys, teddies and associated items. A dolls' hospital service also available.

All Sorts of Everything
661 London Road
0332 752291
Comprehensive secondhand furniture, collectors' items and house clearance goods. Closed on Wednesday.

Derby Antique Centre
11 Friargate
0332 385002
Fourteen dealers with a range of furniture, period to shipping, bric-a-brac, collectors' items and general antiques.

Mr Micawber's
80 Curzon Street
0332 360350
Saturday only. Bedroom furniture and brass and ironbeds.

The Shardlow Antiques Warehouse
24 The Wharf
0332 792899
Late Victorian and Edwardian furniture, some bric-a-brac. Closed on Friday.

DISLEY *(CHESHIRE)*

Mill Farm Antiques
50 Market Street
0663 764045
Furniture, mid-range to shipping, clocks, musical boxes, decorative items and general antiques.

DRONFIELD *(DERBYSHIRE)*

Bardwell Antiques
51 Chesterfield Road
0246 412183
Directly opposite the railway station, three showrooms of across-the-board furniture, from Victorian to 1930s shipping. The shop also carries some general antiques. Prices range from about £25 to £2,000.

DUFFIELD *(DERBYSHIRE)*

Dragon Antiques
1 Tamworth Street
0332 842332
Victorian and Edwardian furniture, pictures, clocks, Staffordshire pottery and porcelain, books, collectors' items and general antiques.

EMPINGHAM *(LEICESTERSHIRE)*

Churchgate Antiques
13 Church Street
078 086 528
Mid- to upper-range furniture, pictures and general antiques.

Old Bakery Antiques
Church Street
078 086 243
Furniture, mostly mid-range, brass beds, metalware and pottery and general antiques.

FINEDON *(NORTHAMPTONSHIRE)*

Jean Burnett Antiques
37 High Street
0933 681882
A syndicate of about 10 dealers with a range of furniture, including pine, collectors' items, textiles, pictures and general antiques.

Dales of Finedon
1 High Street
0933 680973
Three floors of a 1736 building
filled with a comprehensive
range of furniture, from
Georgian to 1930s, silver and
general antiques. Formerly
Noton Antiques, now under
new ownership.

Finedon Antiques Centre
3 Church Street
0933 681260
Twenty-dealer-strong market
with mainly mid- to upper-
quality antiques, pictures, silver,
porcelain and general antiques.

FOUR OAKS
(WEST MIDLANDS)

Robert Taylor
Windy Ridge, Worcester Lane
021 308 4209
Collectors' toys.

FRODSHAM
(CHESHIRE)

Lothian Antiques
37 High Street
0928 39366
Furniture and general antiques.

GLOSSOP
(DERBYSHIRE)

Glossop Antique Centre
Brookfield
0457 863904
Fourteen dealers with a range
of furniture, collectors' items
and general antiques. Open
Thursday and Friday.

GUILSBOROUGH
(NORTHAMPTONSHIRE)

Nick Goodwin Exports
The Firs, Nortoft
0604 740234
3,000 square feet of furniture
for trade and public, Georgian
brownwood to pine.
Appointment required.

HALESOWEN
(WEST MIDLANDS)

Martyn Brown Antiques
130 Hagley Road, Hayley Green
021 585 5758
Mid-range furniture, pictures,
collectors' items and general
antiques. Closed on
Wednesday.

Rowley Secondhand Centre
294 Long Lane
021 559 3207
House clearance goods and
secondhand basics.

HARPOLE
(NORTHAMPTONSHIRE)

Inglenook Antiques
23 High Street
0604 830007
Furniture, including pine,
jewellery and general antiques.
Closed Wednesday.

HAYFIELD
(DERBYSHIRE)

Michael Allcroft
1 Church Street
0663 742684
Open weekends or by
appointment. Furniture, mostly
pine, and general antiques.

HEANOR
(DERBYSHIRE)

Bygones
23c Derby Road
0773 768503
Mid-range furniture, pictures
and bric-a-brac. Closed Monday
and Wednesday.

HINCKLEY
(LEICESTERSHIRE)

House Things Antiques
Trinity Lane, 44 Mansion Street
0455 618518
Mid-range and shipping furniture, pine, brass and iron beds, fireplaces and associated items and general antiques.

HUCKNALL
(NOTTINGHAMSHIRE)

Curiosity Corner
86 Watnall Road
0602 630789
General antiques, bric-a-brac and collectors' items.

Martins
6 South Street
0602 639837
Furniture and house clearance goods. A further warehouse at Eastwood, near Nottingham and Ilkeston. Closed Wednesday.

IRTHLINGBOROUGH
(NORTHAMPTONSHIRE)

JM Bayes, auctioneers
43b High Street
Twice monthly general sales.

KETTERING
(NORTHAMPTONSHIRE)

Albion Antiques
36 Duke Street
0536 516220
Specialising in caning, rushing and upholstery, with mid-range to budget furniture, bric-a-brac and general antiques. Open Wednesday, Friday and in the morning on Saturday. In general a low-price regime with a number of good budget possibilities.

The Antiques Warehouse
53–56 Havelock Street
0536 510522
Around 7,000 square feet of furniture, including pine, shipping and reproduction plus bric-a-brac and general antiques.

KIBWORTH
(LEICESTERSHIRE)

Vendy Antiques
17 Fleckney Road
0533 796133
Mid-range furniture, general antiques and collectors' items.

KILLAMARSH
(DERBYSHIRE)

Havenplan's Architectural Emporium
The Old Station, Station Road
0742 489972
Architectural salvage, ecclesiastical, domestic and commercial, from doorknobs to staircases. An ambitious selection, including dismantled stone. Closed on Monday.

KINGSTHORPE
(NORTHAMPTONSHIRE)

Laila
25 Welford Road
0604 715277
Stripped pine furniture, beds, fireplaces and general antiques.

KINVER
(STAFFORDSHIRE)

The Antique Centre
128 High Street
0384 877441
Ten dealers with an assortment of furniture, bric-a-brac and general antiques.

KNOWLE
(WEST MIDLANDS)

Chadwick Antiques
Chadwick End
0564 782096
Mid-range furniture, as well as collectors' items and general antiques.

Phillips, auctioneers
The Old House,
Station Road
0564 776151
Weekly sales of antiques and fine art, on Wednesday.

KNUTSFORD
(CHESHIRE)

Car boot sales
At The Red Lion, Pickmere, four miles outside town.

Cranford Galleries
10 King Street
0565 633646
Collectors' items, bric-a-brac, pictures and general mid-range small antiques.

TREEN

The usage of the word 'treen' has evolved over the centuries, and now denotes a small article made from wood, usually for everyday use, and generally of some age. At the time of Shakespeare and Spenser, 'treene' was almost exclusively used in connection with kitchenware of the sort that might be found in households too poor to afford superior products in pewter and silver. For the prospective treen collector, the first hurdle is one of definition. Does a beechwood kitchen roller qualify as treen? And what about a small tea-caddy, or a wooden pattern block as used for printing fabrics? Since the category is not a specific one, the answer can only be subjective. Size is usually an important consideration; the smaller and more intricate, the better. Some collectors also favour unusual, close-grained woods such as laburnum, pear, cherry and apple. Others are quite prepared to admit objects which, in the strict sense, are not wood at all, such as the carved and silver-rimmed coconut cups that were much valued in the 17th century. For the most part, however, it is what treen signifies, rather than what it is, that is important to the collector. A few collectors cultivate very specific fields, collecting items of one period, relating to, say, early textile production, or culinary accessories such as nutmeg graters and butter or shortbread moulds. A few have a penchant for items fashioned out of other objects – a bowl made from the wood of a favourite elm, which blew down 'on the night of the great gale, August 1828; a cigarette box carved by a squaddie in the trenches from part of the blitzed roof of a French cathedral; a turned egg cup fashioned from the fragment of a ship on which its owner had served during the Napoleonic wars – all three are examples from one particular collection of some 20 pieces that was put together for less than £100.

Marshall & Co., auctioneers

Marshall House, Church Hill
0565 653284
About two general, household or specialist sales per month, on Tuesday.

LEEK (STAFFORDSHIRE)

Anvil Antiques

Cross Street Mill
0538 371657
Furniture, including pine, architectural and decorative pieces, bric-a-brac and general antiques, reproduction and original.

Aspley Antiques

Compton Mill, Compton
0538 373396
Furniture, including shipping and pine, bric-a-brac and general antiques. Open seven days a week.

Bury & Hilton, auctioneers

Britannia Street
0538 383344
Intermittent general and antique sales.

Gemini Trading

Limes Mill, Abbots Road
0538 387834
Pine furniture.

Johnson's

Park Works, Park Road, and
1 Clerk Bank
0538 386745
Pine furniture, kitchenalia, country and decorative antiques. Quilts and samplers are a speciality but, strangely, the shop sells none of the black Leek silk and bombazine that proved to be such a lucrative local product after Prince Albert's death plunged his wife, and the nation, into a mourning frenzy.

LEICESTER (LEICESTERSHIRE)

This is the city where the package tour was invented by local publisher, Thomas Cook, in 1841 (strictly no alcohol – it was a Temperance Society excursion to Loughborough). Other notables born in the city include David *'Life on Earth'* Attenborough, cartoonist Bill Tidy, playwright Joe Orton, footballer Gary Lineker, singer Englebert Humperdinck, and *Blue Peter's* Biddy Baxter. Likewise, antique and junk shopping is a bit of a mixed affair. Attractions include a medieval guildhall, and some eight museums, one concentrating on the local speciality, costume and hosiery. An interesting fact: the remains of Richard III were thrown into the river here after the Battle of Bosworth Field.

Able's

191 Melton Road
0533 667666
House clearance lines.

The Antiques Complex

St Nicholas Place
0533 533343
A large selection of furniture, general antiques, jewellery, pictures and collectors' items. About 16,000 square feet in all, with the upper floor operating as a market.

Betty's

9 Knighton Fields Road West
0533 839048
Small furniture, including pine and satinwood, metalware, pictures and general antiques.

Boulevard Antique & Shipping Centre

The Old Dairy,
Western Boulevard
0533 541201
Around 10 dealers with a variety of mid-range to shipping furniture, jewellery, collectors' items and general antiques. A fairly comprehensive mix and usually well worth combing through.

WH Brown, auctioneers

16–18 Halford Street
Fortnightly general sales.

Churchgate Auctions

66 Churchgate
0533 621416
General sales twice per week, on Tuesday and Friday.

Oxford Street Antique Centre

16–26 Oxford Street
0533 553006
Approximately 50 dealers with a broad range of furniture, mid-range to shipping, bric-a-brac, collectors' items and general antiques. A recommended and usually rewarding browse for those with the time and the patience. Open seven days a week.

Reg's Mart

269 Uppingham Road
0533 667826
Secondhand basics and house clearance items.

LICHFIELD
(STAFFORDSHIRE)

Dominated by its graceful, triple-spired cathedral, Lichfield also has a claim to fame as the birthplace of Samuel Johnson, who never tired of London.

Cordelia & Perdy's Antique Junk Shop

53 Tamworth Street
0543 263223
Furniture, general antiques and 'posh junk', which in this shop seems to mean any sort of generally useful clutter or half-way decorative item. Proceedings carried off with stylish aplomb.

Royden Smith

Church View,
Farewell Lane,
Burntwood
0543 682217
Books, bric-a-brac and general antiques, including shipping items. Open Wednesday and Saturday.

Winterton's, auctioneers

Lichfield Auction Centre,
Fradley Park, Fradley
0543 263256
Fortnightly general sales.

LONG BUCKBY
(NORTHAMPTONSHIRE)

Thompson's Antiques

17 Church Street
0327 843487
Furniture, including pine and shipping, plus general antiques and some collectables. Stock extensive and prices cover the range, from a few pounds to several thousands.

LONG CLAWSTON
(LEICESTERSHIRE)

Victoriana Architectural

Old Hall Farm, Hose Lane
0949 60274
Architectural salvage and decorative items, particularly in timber. Stripped pine and pine stripping service.

LONG EATON
(DERBYSHIRE)

Miss Ellany
2 Salisbury Street
0602 734835
Mid-range furniture including pianos and general antiques.

LOUGHBOROUGH
(LEICESTERSHIRE)

Copperfield Antiques
221a Derby Road
0509 232026
Mid-range furniture, porcelain, metalware, pictures and general antiques. Closed Monday and Wednesday.

Freckeltons, auctioneers
1 Leicester Road
0509 214564
Monthly antique sales, on Tuesday.

LOWER KINNERTON
(CHESHIRE)

Brian Edwards Antiques
Gell Farm
0244 660240
A warehouse stocked with a broad range of furniture, from period to shipping and pre-war secondhand, plus general antiques and some bric-a-brac. Mainly for trade but public welcome by appointment.

LUBENHAM
(LEICESTERSHIRE)

Stevens & Son
The Old Post Office,
61 Main Street
0858 463521
Mid-range furniture and some general antiques.

LYE (WEST MIDLANDS)

Retro Products
Antique Warehouse, The Yard, Star Street
0384 894042
Mid-range to shipping furniture, architectural, decorative and garden items and general antiques.

Smithfield Antiques
20 Stourbridge Road
0384 897821
Furniture, general antiques and shipping items.

MACCLESFIELD
(CHESHIRE)

Hidden Gem
3 Chester Road
0625 433884
Small, as the name suggests, but well-stocked with a varied range of general antiques, pictures and collectors' items. Usually worth a potter. Open on Saturday, otherwise only by appointment.

Hills Antiques
Grosvenor Centre
0625 420777
Jewellery, ephemera, numismatics, postal items, small antiques and a range of general collectables. Closed on Monday.

MANSFIELD
(NOTTINGHAMSHIRE)

The Antiques Warehouse
375 Chesterfield Road North, Pleasley
0623 810480
One of a number in town catering for both public and container-export trade, with a large and comprehensively priced selection of furniture, from mid-range to shipping.

MARKET BOSWORTH
(LEICESTERSHIRE)

Corner Cottage Antiques
5 Market Place, The Square
0455 290344
Mid-range furniture, metalware, pictures, porcelain and general antiques.

MARKET HARBOROUGH
(LEICESTERSHIRE)

Abbey Antiques
17 Abbey Street
0858 462282
Mid-range furniture, bric-a-brac, decorative and collectors' items and general antiques.

Gildings, auctioneers
64 Roman Way
0858 410414
Weekly sales, on Tuesday.

MARPLE (CHESHIRE)

Milners Antiques
Lower Fold, Marple Bridge
061 426 0159
Furniture, pictures, bric-a-brac and general antiques. Closed on Wednesday.

MATLOCK
(DERBYSHIRE)

Wheatcrofts, auctioneers
Old English Road
0629 55770
Monthly mixed antique and general sales.

MELTON MOWBRAY
(LEICESTERSHIRE)

Ancient & Modern
2 Elms Road
0664 500889
House clearance goods and bric-a-brac, household goods.

Doreen's Miscellaneous Shop
1 Regent Street
0664 66978
General secondhand goods.

Shouler & Sons, auctioneers
County Chambers, Kings Road
0664 60181
Fortnightly general sales, on Thursdays.

NANTWICH (CHESHIRE)

The Antique Centre
The Old Police Station, Welsh Row
0270 624035
Furniture, mid-range to shipping and budget and general antiques, bric-a-brac and collectors' items.

Tim Armitage
99 Welsh Row
0270 626608
Established 25 years, with a mixed and interesting range including toys, steam engines, advertising material, decorative items and general antiques. Organised but tastefully cluttered and always with much of interest in stock. Opens by request, so phone before visiting.

Stancie Cutler Antique & Collectors' Fair
Civic Hall
0270 624288
A regular fixture on the first Thursday of every month (except May) in the Civic Hall. Usually about 70 stallholders offer a range of antiques, furniture, bric-a-brac and collectors' items.

Lions & Unicorns
Kiltearn House,
33 Hospital Street
0270 628892
Commemorative and crested ware, plus books, ephemera and collectors' items in a diverse and rummageable stock. In the same street can be found other dealers, such as **Farthings Antiques** *(50 Hospital Street, 0270 625117)* and **Terry Richardson** *(89 Hospital Street, 0270 625963)* with similar goods, plus furniture and at Terry Richardson a full restoration service also.

Love Lane Antiques
Love Lane
0270 626239
General antiques and collectors' items to suit most budget to mid-range pockets. Closed on Wednesday.

Peter Wilson, auctioneers
The Victoria Gallery,
Market Street
0270 623878
Weekly general sales, on Thursday.

NEWARK
(NOTTINGHAMSHIRE

An important Midlands antiques fixture, the town retains its fine Norman castle, scene of King John's little-lamented death, and much beseiged during the Civil War. A fleamarket is held every Sunday at Thoresby Park.

Castle Gate Antiques Centre
55 Castle Gate
0636 700076
Around 10 dealers with a range of furniture and general antiques.

D & G Antiques
11 Kings Road
0636 702782
Furniture, pictures, bric-a-brac and Victoriana. Closed on Monday.

International Antiques & Crafts Fair
Newark & Notts Showground,
Winthorpe
0636 702627
Blockbuster fairs, six a year, with literally hundreds of stallholders selling all categories of antiques and collectors' items. Exhibitors come from all over with a multitude of general and specialised lines so that a great amount of inter-trade dealing takes place. Chances of leaving empty-handed are remote.

Newark Antiques Centre
Regent House, Lombard Street
0636 605504
Upwards of 50 stallholders with a comprehensive selection of mid-range furniture, bric-a-brac, textiles, militaria, books and general antiques.

Newark Antique Warehouse
Kelham Road
0636 74869
Around 10 dealers with a range of trade and shipping furniture and general antiques.

Portland Antiques
20 Portland Street
0636 701478
Furniture, including shipping and pine, general antiques and collectors' items. Closed Monday and Thursday.

Jack Spratt Antiques
Unit 5, George Street
0636 707714

A warehouse of mixed furniture, mostly pine and oak.

Richard Watkinson, auctioneers
17 Northgate
0636 77154
Weekly general sales and antique and specialist sales on the first Thursday of each month.

NEWCASTLE
UNDER *LYME*
(STAFFORDSHIRE)

The Antique Market
The Stones
Open on Tuesdays. Around 50 dealers with a range of antiques, bric-a-brac and collectors' items.

NORTHAMPTON
(NORTHAMPTONSHIRE)

A town with a shoe-making tradition and an unusual round 12th-century church, The Holy Sepulchre. Since becoming a designated new town in 1968 its population has expanded considerably. The Kettering Road in particular is a good hunting ground for antique and budget buyers.

Buley Antiques
164 Kettering Road
0604 491577
Furniture, metalware, bric-a-brac, toys, costume and general antiques.

Peter Cooksley Antiques
Poachers Gap,
Hyse Road, Boughton
0604 842705
Furniture, mid-range to shipping, in two shops and a warehouse.

DC Draper
44–46 Barrack Road
0604 39907
Secondhand furniture and house clearance goods spread around three rooms.

Heathcote Ball & Co., auctioneers
Albion Auction Rooms,
Commercial Street
0604 22735
Fortnightly general sales.

Nostalgia Antiques
190 Kettering Road
0604 33823
Furniture, clocks, collectors' items and general antiques.

Penny's Bric-a-Brac
83 Kettering Road
0604 32429
Mid-range, shipping and budget furniture, pictures, metalware, bric-a-brac, interesting collectables and general antiques. Prices, on the whole, are moderate to cheap.

Sue Ryder Charity Shop
193 Kettering Road
0604 602039
Typical charity shop mix of bric-a-brac, jewellery, trinkets, clothes, household bits and pieces and some (usually small) furniture.

Second Hand City
7 Albert Place
0604 21011
House clearance furniture and effects.

Talent Pastimes Ltd
85 Kettering Road
0604 36396
Ephemera, postal history, some numismatics, collectors' reference books, toy soldiers, stamps, models and collectors'

items. Closed on Thursday
afternoon.

NOTTINGHAM
(NOTTINGHAMSHIRE)

**William the Conqueror's castle,
where Charles I raised his
standard at the outbreak of the
Civil War, was over-restored by
the Victorians, but now makes
an interesting museum. Even
more interesting is 'The Trip to
Jerusalem', supposedly the
oldest licensed house (or rather,
cave) in Britain, and a popular
watering hole for pilgrims and
crusaders. Robin Hood, lace,
cigarettes, and DH Lawrence are
some of the better-known local
offspring.**

Actons
221 Radford Road
0602 787571
Secondhand furniture and
house clearance goods.

Barkers
119a Sneinton Dale
0602 582491
House clearance goods and
secondhand basics.

The Golden Cage
99 Derby Road
0602 411600
Period costume, formal evening
wear and associated items,
including stylish rarities such as
beaded dresses and more
practical attire of the tweed coat
variety. The shop also hires out
costume. Phone for further
information

Granny's Attic
308 Carlton Hill
0602 265204
Furniture, bric-a-brac, dolls and
associated items and general
antiques.

Hockley Coins
170 Derby Road
0602 790667
Numismatics, medals and
decorations, toys, ephemera
and collectors' items. Closed on
Thursday.

Johnson's, auctioneers
The Nottingham Auction Centre,
Meadow Lane
0602 869128
Weekly sales on Saturday.

Neale's, auctioneers
192–194 Mansfield Road
0602 624141
Weekly mixed sales.

Nottingham Antique Centre
British Rail Goods Yard,
London Road
0602 504504
Comprehensive selection of
mid-range to shipping furniture,
bric-a-brac and general
antiques. Regular attenders
report some good buying
opportunities for bargain
hunters.

Pollock Antiques
110 Derby Road
0602 504027
Toys, scale models, steam
engines, automatica and general
antiques.

Second Chance
25 Radford Road
0602 421615
House clearance furniture and
effects. Closed on Thursday.

Val Smith
170 Derby Road
0602 781194
Numismatics, medals and
decorations, postcards,

ephemera, jewellery, toys and collectors' items.

Top Hat Antiques Centre
66–72 Derby Road
0602 419143
Mid-range to budget furniture, bric-a-brac, metalware, pictures and general antiques. An extensive selection covering a range of interests and prices.

The Treasure Chest
494 Mansfield Road
0602 606363
Furniture, including shipping and secondhand and general antiques.

OADBY
(LEICESTERSHIRE)

John Hardy Antiques
91 London Road
0533 712862
Furniture, metalware, bric-a-brac and a broad range of general antiques.

OAKHAM
(LEICESTERSHIRE)

Notons, auctioneers
96 South Street
0572 722681
Fortnightly general sales and monthly antique sales.

Oakham Antiques
16 Melton Road
066 479 571
Metalware, bric-a-brac, small furniture, pictures, lighting and collectors' items. Closed Tuesday and Thursday.

Swans Antique Centre
27 Mill Street
0572 724364
Around 15 dealers with a comprehensive stock of period and mid-range furniture, including pine, textiles, jewellery, porcelain, pictures and general antiques. Closed from Tuesday to Thursday.

PELSALL
(WEST MIDLANDS)

LP Furniture
152 Lime Lane
0543 370256
Mid-range, shipping and pine furniture.

PENKRIDGE
(STAFFORDSHIRE)

Golden Oldies
Clay Street
0785 714722
A mix of antique, shipping and secondhand furniture, plus bric-a-brac, pictures and house clearance goods.

South & Stubbs, auctioneers
Penkridge Market
0785 714905
General sales each Wednesday.

PRESTBURY
(CHESHIRE)

Prestbury Antiques
The Village
0625 827966
Mid-range furniture, bric-a-brac, silver, clocks, pictures, collectors' items and general antiques. Closed on Monday.

QUORN
(LEICESTERSHIRE)

Quorn Pine & Decoratives
Quorn
0509 416031
Stripped pine restoration.

RAVENSMOOR
(CHESHIRE)

Antiques & Curios
Swanley Lane
0270 624774
Furniture, including stripped
pine and vernacular, metalware,
bric-a-brac and general
antiques. Essentially mid-range
but with prices across the
board. Opening times vary so
phone first to check.

RUSHALL
(WEST MIDLANDS)

Turner Antiques
Meeks Farm, Pelsall Lane
0922 720871
Furniture, metalware, bric-a-
brac, collectables and general
antiques. Appointment
required.

RUSHDEN
(NORTHAMPTONSHIRE)

Sherwood Antiques
59 Little Street
0933 53265
Furniture, including shipping
and general antiques. Closed on
Monday and Thursday.

Shire Antiques
111 High Street South
0933 315567
Furniture, including shipping
and general antiques. Closed on
Wednesday.

SANDBACH
(CHESHIRE)

Andrew, Hilditch & Co
Hanover House,
1a The Square
0270 767246
Weekly general sales
(Wednesdays) and intermittent
antique and specialist sales.

SEAGRAVE
(LEICESTERSHIRE)

**Miller,
auctioneers**
Seagrave
0509 812037
General sales held in the village
hall on the last Sunday of the
month. Phone for information
about times.

SHENTON
(LEICESTERSHIRE)

**Whitemoor's
Antiques Centre**
Shenton
0455 212250
A large selection of mid-range
furniture, pictures, bric-a-brac
and general antiques. Worth
searching out (just off A444)
because the stock can be
interesting and varied and
prices reasonable. Closed on
Monday.

SILEBY
(LEICESTERSHIRE)

James Antiques
Ammonite Gallery,
25a High Street
050 981 2169
Furniture, including pine and
general antiques, as well as
some collectables.

SMETHWICK
(WEST MIDLANDS)

Grannie's Attic
437 Bearwood Road
021 429 4180
Furniture, jewellery, costume,
toys, pictures, metalware, bric-
a-brac, books and general
antiques. Stock is commendably
eclectic and imaginative and
good for the odd unplanned
impulse buy.

SOLIHULL
(WEST MIDLANDS)

Tilley's Antiques
021 704 1813
Open by appointment.
Jewellery, silver, general
antiques, including some
shipping goods.

SOUTHWELL
(NOTTINGHAMSHIRE)

Stroud's Antiques
3–7 Church Street
0636 815001
Large and comprehensive range

of furniture, period to shipping,
pictures and general antiques.

STAFFORD
(STAFFORDSHIRE)

Browse
127 Lichfield Road
0785 41097
Victorian, pre-war and repro
furniture, in extensive premises.

Hall & Lloyd, auctioneers
South Street
0785 58176
Fortnightly general sales, on
Thursday.

MINIATURE COLLECTABLES

Over the past 10 to 15 years, interest in collecting
miniatures has expanded enormously and the annual fair
which once fitted into Warwick cricket pavilion has
mushroomed into several high-powered trade and
collectors' fairs at the exhibition centres in Birmingham
and Glasgow. Prices are, of course, enormously variable.
For instance, you might pay 50p for small accessories or
around £3 for a miniature milking stool, but in contrast a
sum closer to £6,000 would be asked for a perfectly
calibrated facsimile of a William and Mary marquetry
bureau with accurate dovetails and functioning locks.
Miniature furniture making is a long-established craft. For
the Ancient Egyptian dead, small-scale reproductions of
everyday items were a reminder of the world they'd left
behind. For the daughters of a middle-class Dutch
household in the 17th century, the 'puppenhuis' with its
furniture, crockery and Lilliputian occupants, was an
educational tool, as much as a toy, devised for the purpose
of instilling the skills of homecrafting. Queen Mary's
house, designed by Lutyens and containing such marvels
as paintings by Nicholson and Lavery, and a lawn-mower
made by apprentices at the Atco lawn-mower company,
was a miniaturised expression of national achievement.
Today, collectors usually have a different motivation. For
David Kilpatrick, who displays his famous collection at the
North Pier in Oban, Argyllshire, during the summer
months, it started off as an inexpensive way of acquiring
top examples of furniture. His advice for would-be
collectors is to avoid buying some of the cheaper imported
pieces, and to concentrate on a lesser number of quality
items, like well-finished hand-made chairs at around £45.

Stafford Market
Guildhall Centre
Operating on Tuesdays, Thursdays, Fridays and Saturdays. Some antiques and bric-a-brac can be found amidst a typical market array of general goods and household items.

STAUNTON HAROLD
(LEICESTERSHIRE)

Ropers Hill Antiques
Ropers Hill Farm
0530 413919
Small furniture, shipping goods and variety of smaller collectors' items.

STOCKPORT
(CHESHIRE)

Traditionally a cotton-spinning and hat-making town, with the largest brick-built railway viaduct in Britain – 27 arches, and 11 million bricks. Local notables include the political theorist Richard Cobden, and Christopher Isherwood, who was born at nearby Wyversley Hall.

Antique Furnishing Warehouse
Units 3–4, Royal Oak Buildings, Cooper Street
061 429 8590
The range is comprehensive, with architectural pieces, vintage radios and TVs, bric-a-brac of every description, select objets d'art and more or less anything dealable jostling for space.

Barry's Antiques
Unit 2, Royal Oak Buildings, Cooper Street
061 429 0880

1930s furniture and general antiques.

Halcyon Antiques
435 Buxton Road,
Great Moor
061 483 5038
Silver, glass and porcelain. Also furniture and general antiques. A well-diversified stock with prices across the range.

Hole in the Wall Antiques
370 Buxton Road
061 483 6603
A shop plus warehouse with a comprehensive range of furniture, including shipping and general antiques.

Nostalgia Antiques
61 Shaw Heath
061 477 7706
Antique fireplaces.

Page Antiques
424 Buxton Road,
Great Moor
061 483 9202
Mid-range and shipping furniture and general antiques.

Zippy Antiques
Units 2–3 Royal Oak Buildings
061 477 7953
A vast space, with a varied mix, covering all periods from the 18th century to post-war, but with some concentration on late Victorian and Edwardian furniture and decorative items.

STOCKTON HEATH
(CHESHIRE)

Victoriana Antiques
85a Walton Road
0925 263263
Mid-range small furniture, up to pre-war, metalware including lighting and fireplace accessories, decorative and

general antiques. The accent is on style, rather than bargain-budget, and the premises are small but are a worthwhile browse for home-makers. Closed Monday and Thursday.

STOKE ON TRENT
(STAFFORDSHIRE)

Although technically a 1910 creation resulting from the amalgamation of five towns, the area was long known as 'the potteries'. Manufacturing started with the Romans and attained perfection with Josiah Wedgwood, who also built a model village – Etruria – for his workforce. Arnold Bennett captured the Edwardian atmosphere of the place in his novels. Needless to say, the local antique trade is a good source of ceramics.

Ann's Attic
72 Waterloo Road
0782 575494
House clearance basics.

Ann's Antiques
24–26 Leek Road
0782 503991
No connection with the above; mid-range furniture, jewellery, metalware, pictures, decorative items and general antiques.

Antiques Workshop & Boulton's Antiques
43–45 Hope Street, Hanley
Furniture, including pine and shipping, bric-a-brac and general antiques.

Butter's, auctioneers
Warner Street
0782 267752
Occasional general sales. Phone for details.

Castle Resales
299 King Street, Fenton
0782 331942
House clearance goods and secondhand basics.

Five Towns Antiques
17 Broad Street, Hanley
0782 272930
Pottery and porcelain, much of it locally produced, to pre-war and general antiques.

Jim's
11 Uttoxeter Road
0782 317097
Secondhand basics. The proprietor also operates **Yesterdays** (*13 Uttoxeter Road, Yarnfield*) selling general antiques.

LTB Furniture
140 Waterloo Road, Burslem
0782 814614
Secondhand furniture and house clearance goods. Closed on Thursday.

The Potteries Antique Centre
Waterloo Road, Cobridge
0782 201455
Furniture, mid-range to shipping, jewellery, bric-a-brac and collectors' items being offered by several dealers. Particularly strong on ceramics, as might be expected in this area, with Moorcroft, Doulton, Minton and other arts and crafts items much in evidence. The range is strong on mid-quality but comprehensively priced.

Smith's
75 St John Street
0782 281229
House clearance goods and secondhand basics.

The Tinder Box
61 Lichfield Street, Hanley
0782 261368
Furniture, jewellery, metalware
and oil lamps.

STONE *(STAFFORDSHIRE)*

Tomkinson, auctioneers
Mill Street
0785 813870
Weekly general sales.

STOURBRIDGE
(WEST MIDLANDS)

Topaz Bridge Antiques
32a Market Street
0384 379495
Small furniture, jewellery, bric-
a-brac, collectables and general
antiques.

Curio Corner
32 Park Street
0384 379652
Militaria, medals and
decorations. Closed on Monday.

SUTTON COLDFIELD
(WEST MIDLANDS)

Stancie Cutler Antiques & Collectors' Fair
Town Hall
0270 624288
A regular monthly fixture, with
stallholders selling general
antiques, small furniture, bric-a-
brac and collectables. Similar
arrangement and size as the
monthly fair at Nantwich.
Phone for dates and times.

SWADLINGCOTE
(DERBYSHIRE)

Armstrongs, auctioneer
Midland Road
0283 550326

Monthly sales of general goods
and occasional antiques.

TARPORLEY
(CHESHIRE)

Wright Manley, auctioneers
Beeston Castle
0829 260318
Two general sales a month, six
antique sales a year.

TATTENHALL
(CHESHIRE)

Great Northern Architectural Antique Company
New Russia Hall, Chester Road
0829 70796
A comprehensive stock of
architectural salvage and
decorative items including
grates and chimneypieces,
etched and stained glass, doors,
shutters and other fixtures,
decorative stone and brick,
garden and farm-related items
and some furniture.

THRAPSTON
(NORTHAMPTONSHIRE)

John Roe Antiques
Unit 14, Cottingham Way
0832 732937
3,000 square feet of furniture,
including shipping, jewellery
and general antiques.

Southam & Sons
Corn Exchange Saleroom
0832 734486
Monthly general sales.

TOWCESTER
(NORTHAMPTONSHIRE)

John & Jennifer Jones
2 Watling Street
0327 51898

Furniture, bric-a-brac, pictures and general antiques.

Shelron Collectors' Shop
9½ Brackley Road
0327 50242
Large selection of ephemera, postcards, books, some coins and die-cast toys, bric-a-brac, medals and general collectors' items. A recommended browse for collecting enthusiasts. Closed on Monday.

TRENTHAM
(STAFFORDSHIRE)

Car Boot Sales
Regularly on Sundays.

TUTBURY
(STAFFORDSHIRE)

Copes Antiques
The Old Chapel, Main Street
0283 812094
Mid-range and shipping furniture, metalware, bric-a-brac and general antiques.

Town & Country Antiques
40 Monk Street
0283 520556
Pine furniture, original and reproduction, general antiques and textiles, including lace and linen.

UPPINGHAM
(LEICESTERSHIRE)

Clutter
14 Orange Street
0572 823745
A shop that manages to live up to its name, with a multitude of goods at a wide range of prices, including general antiques, small furniture, bric-a-brac, metalware, jewellery, silver, period lace and linen,

kitchenalia and decorative items. Next door is **Tattersalls** *(14b Orange Street, 0572 821171)*, selling antique and household furniture, including sofas and rugs.

Gilberts of Uppingham
8 Ayston Road
0572 823486
3,000 square feet of budget antique and secondhand furniture.

UTTOXETER
(STAFFORDSHIRE)

Bagshaws, auctioneers
17 High Street
0889 562811
Monthly general sales, plus occasional farmhouse displenishments.

Groves Antiques
52 Bridge Street
0889 565374
Furniture, including pine and satinwood, country items, bric-a-brac, linen and kitchenalia.

WALSALL
(WEST MIDLANDS)

The Doghouse
309 Bloxwich Road
0922 30829
Instantly recognisable – two large stone dogs guard the street entrance. A full range of furniture, from antique and shipping to secondhand basics and cheaper reproduction, plus general antiques.

Past & Present
66 George Street
0922 611151
Mid-range furniture, general antiques, bric-a-brac, linen and collectors' items.

Walsall Antiques Centre
7a Digbeth Arcade
0922 725163
Around 50 dealers occupying a central location in the town's Victorian arcade, with a selection of mid-range and some shipping furniture, porcelain, commemorative and decorative items and general antiques.

WARRINGTON
(CHESHIRE)

Greenwood's
21 Winwick Street
0925 231590
A former pub which now accommodates two floors of shipping and secondhand furniture and general house clearance items. The same firm has outlets in Runcorn and Northwich.

The Rocking Chair
Unit 3, St Peters Way
0925 524091
Furniture, including some budget, bric-a-brac and general antiques.

WEEDON
(NORTHAMPTONSHIRE)

Architectural Heritage of Northants
The Woodyard
0372 349249
Architectural salvage and decorative items. The premises are located on the A5, just north of town.

Rococo Antiques
5 New Street, Lower Weedon
0327 41288
Decorative and architectural items, plus metalware and brass/iron beds.

Thirty-Eight Antiques
Building 14,
Royal Ordnance Department
0327 40766
Mid-range furniture and decorative antiques, including architectural items. Appointment advised.

The Village Antique Market
62 High Street
0327 42015
Around 40 stallholders with a wide range of antiques and collectors' items. A diverse mix, including jewellery and smaller collectables, with good browsing potential.

WELLINGBOROUGH
(NORTHAMPTONSHIRE)

Antiques & Bric-a-Brac Market
Market Square
0905 611321
Every Tuesday. Upwards of 100 stalls with a range of general antiques and collectors' items – assorted goods at assorted prices, but with some low-cost opportunities.

Wilford's, auctioneers
76 Midland Road
0933 226263/222760
Weekly general sales.

WEST BRIDGFORD
(NOTTINGHAMSHIRE)

Bridgford Antiques
2a Rushforth Avenue
0602 821835
Furniture, including mid-range and budget, general antiques, pictures, books and postcards.

Moulton's Antiques
5 Portland Road
0602 814354

Furniture, including pine and general antiques. Also specialising in old fabrics. Closed on Monday.

WHISSENDINE
(LEICESTERSHIRE)

Old Bakehouse Pine
11 Main Street
066 479691
Stripped pine furniture. Hours vary so phone before visiting.

WOLSELEY BRIDGE
(STAFFORDSHIRE)

Jalna Antiques
The Old Barn
0889 881381
Mainly furniture, often period and quality, but with some less expensive items such as sets of Edwardian high-back dining chairs. Also upholstered items, pottery and porcelain, metalware and general antiques in showroom premises plus an extensive warehouse.

WOODFORD HALSE
(NORTHAMPTONSHIRE)

The Corner Cupboard
18 Station Road
0327 60725
Mid-range furniture, including pine, brass and iron beds, upholstered items and general antiques. Closed on Monday and Tuesday.

YOXALL
(STAFFORDSHIRE)

Armson's Antiques
The Hollies
0543 472352
A comprehensive range of furniture, from period to shipping and general antiques.

Heron's Antiques
1 King Street
0543 472266
An extensive stock of furniture, ceramics, bric-a-brac, pictures and general antiques. Prices include some low-cost items.

EAST OF ENGLAND

For the bargain-hunter, the East of England is like the proverbial curate's egg – good in parts. In some areas buying opportunities are few and far between; in general, however, time spent exploring can certainly pay off.

The climate of trade varies from place to place, as do price levels and the type of goods available. Clearly, what sells well in the more prosperous areas of Suffolk, where the influence of London tastes and purchasing power is often pervasive, may be less appreciated on the northern fringes of Norfolk. This variation can often work to the junk-hunter's advantage; usually, it's a matter of knowing how to play the field. A good

• Lincoln

LINCOLNSHIRE

NORFOLK

Norwich •

CAMBRIDGESHIRE

Cambridge •

SUFFOLK

• Ipswich

Colchester •

ESSEX

Southend on Sea •

antique shop in a smart town might be pleased to get rid of a few less desirable pieces for a knock-down price, while a country auction in a Norfolk cattle-ring might be just the place to pick up an item of obscure significance, and high value, for a few pounds. There are certainly places which offer a comprehensive selection of goods from a wide array of outlets; Cambridge, like most university towns, caters for a social spectrum that includes impecunious students as well as prosperous academics with an enthusiasm for, say, historic scientific instruments or old master drawings. Norwich, too, enjoys the virtue of diversity, as well as a competitive trading climate. There is also a good crop of the rare and unusual in many out-of-the-way towns and villages such as Bawdeswell, Holbeach and Weasenham-all-Saints.

ABRIDGE (ESSEX)

Abridge Antique Centre
Market Place
0992 813113
Approximately a dozen dealers with mostly mid-range and collectors' items, plus some budget furniture and bric-a-brac. The proprietors also hold monthly general auctions. Phone for details.

ACLE (NORFOLK)

Lion Antiques
The Old Sale Ring,
Cattle Market
0493 751836
Furniture, up to pre-war, bric-a-brac and general antiques. Budget buying is a real possibility and there is usually much of interest to rummage through.

ALFORD (LINCOLNSHIRE)

Dickinson,
Davy & Markham,
auctioneers
7 Cornmarket
0507 607781
Monthly general sales.

AYLSHAM (NORFOLK)

GA Key, auctioneers
Palmers Lane
0263 733195
A popular local buying source, with general sales weekly, antique sales every three weeks and book and pictures sales alternating monthly.

BATTLESBRIDGE (ESSEX)

Battlesbridge Antique Centre
Battlesbridge
0268 734005
A complex housing approximately 50 dealers with a comprehensive range of furniture, general antiques, jewellery, bric-a-brac and several specialisations. In effect, several centres on one site, with a good mix of stock.

BAWDESWELL (NORFOLK)

Norfolk Polyphon Centre
Wood Farm
036 288 230
Anything associated with mechanical music, from

miniature musical boxes to organs and orchestrians, plus working automatica. No junk here, but a lot worth looking at and listening to. Appointment preferred.

BECCLES (SUFFOLK)

Waveney Antiques Centre
Peddars Lane
0502 716147
Around 25 dealers with a range of furniture, general antiques, jewellery, bric-a-brac, books and collectors' items.

BIRDBROOK (ESSEX)

Westrope Antiques
The Elms
044 085 365
Furniture, decorative items, dolls, toys and bric-a-brac.

BOSTON (LINCOLNSHIRE)

James Eley & Son, auctioneers
The Green, Wide Bargate
0205 361687
Well-stocked weekly general sales.

Mary Holland Antiques
7a Red Lion Street
0205 363791
General antiques, bric-a-brac and collectors' items. Open on Tuesday and Thursday.

Carol Hiley
48–51 Wormgate
Secondhand furniture.

Pen Street Antiques
9a Pen Street
0205 364118

Specialising in jewellery, pottery and porcelain and collectors' items.

Portobello Row Antiques Centre
High Street
0205 369456
Around 10 dealers with a range of furniture, shipping goods, ephemera, textiles and costume, kitchenalia, gramophones, lamps and general antiques. Usually an interesting assortment and a worthwhile browse.

That Little Shop
7 Red Lion Street
Jewellery, general antiques, dolls' houses and associated items.

Trash & Treasure
23 Wormgate
General antiques and bric-a-brac.

Wormgate Antiques
18 Wormgate
0205 354515
Furniture, general antiques. Appointment required.

BOXFORD (SUFFOLK)

The Corner Cupboard
The Old Bakery
0787 210123
Collectors' items, general antiques and Victoriana. Appointment required.

BRAMPTON (CAMBRIDGESHIRE)

Brampton Mill Antiques
87 High Street
0480 411204
Furniture and general antiques, including shipping goods.

BRANCASTER STAITHE (NORFOLK)

Brancaster Staithe Antiques
Coast Road
0485 210600
Furniture, general antiques and some collectables, from Victorian to pre-war periods.

BRENTWOOD (ESSEX)

Wendy Wood, auctioneers
45 North Road
0277 224599
Weekly general sales. Phone for details.

BROOMFIELD (ESSEX)

Hutchison Antiques
163 Main Road
0245 441184
Budget furniture, bric-a-brac, some collectables and general antiques.

BUNGAY (SUFFOLK)

Black Dog Antiques
51 Earsham Street
0986 895554
Furniture, textiles, collectors' items and general antiques. Prices are across the board and often good value. The furniture is a mix that includes period to pre-war oak and pine.

BURNHAM ON CROUCH (ESSEX)

Quay Antiques
28 High Street
0621 782468
Furniture, jewellery, pictures, bric-a-brac and general antiques.

BURY ST EDMUNDS (SUFFOLK)

Corner Shop Antiques
1 Guildhall Street
0284 762366
Smaller mid-range furniture and general antiques, jewellery, bric-a-brac and collectors' items. **Guildhall Antiques** at number 27 can also be a worthwhile visit.

Lacy Scott, auctioneers
10 Risbygate Street
0284 763531
General sales every two to three weeks, plus specialist sales occasionally.

CAMBRIDGE (CAMBRIDGESHIRE)

Home to one of the oldest universities, Cambridnge is dominated by pale-gold limestone spires and finials, well-manicured riverside lawns, and an overwhelming sense of history. On a purely practical level, it is also an important manufacturing centre, and a market town for much of East Anglia, all of which guarantees a diverse range of junk and antiques with everything from secondhand mops to medieval manuscripts.

Cambridge Resale
190 Mill Road
0223 210703
Secondhand furniture and house clearance lines.

Cheffins, Grain & Comins, auctioneers
2 Clifton Road
0223 213343
Weekly general sales and intermittent specialist sales.

Collectors' Centre
The Old Stables,
Hope Street Yard
0223 211632
Stripped pine and old and interesting pre-1950s furniture, as well as magic lanterns, old telephones and wind-up gramophones. A popular local source of low-cost furniture and unusual decorative items.

Collectors' Market
Dales Brewery,
Gwydir Street
0223 300269
A comprehensive selection, including furniture, pictures, bric-a-brac, kitchenalia and general budget to mid-range antiques, collectors' items on offer from eight dealers. Some definitie cheap-and-cheerful potentials for home-makers. Yet another excellent local source for good mid-range to budget furniture and interesting collectables.

Those Were The Days
93 Mill Road
0223 300440
Five dealers offering a range of general and specialist antiques, mostly furniture and lighting accessories.

CAMPSEA ASHE (SUFFOLK)

Abbots, auctioneers
Campsea Ash
0728 746323
Weekly general sales and monthly antique sales.

CANVEY ISLAND (ESSEX)

Leaches Stores
2 Futherwick Road
0268 680985
Secondhand furniture and house clearance goods.

CHELMSFORD (ESSEX)

Cooper Hirst, auctioneers
Granary Saleroom,
Victoria Road
0245 260535
Weekly general sales, plus about six antique sales per year.

Thursday Market
Market Street
Secondhand goods and bric-a-brac, at a market by the multi-storey car park.

CLACTON ON SEA (ESSEX)

Cater Antiques
329–331 Holland Road
0255 814769
Secondhand furniture, bric-a-brac and house clearance goods.

EJ Gilders, auctioneers
The Mart, High Street
0255 423592
General sales every four to six weeks.

Roberts Antiques
55 Oxford Road
0255 436470
Budget, secondhand and house clearance lines make up about 50% of the stock, the rest being new and cheap reproduction. Another branch is in Frinton (*4 Old Pier Street, 0255 679461*).

CLARE (SUFFOLK)

Clare Antique Warehouse
The Mill, Malting Lane
0787 278449

Upwards of 40 dealers offering period and mid-range furniture, general antiques and specialisations.

CLEY (NORFOLK)

Kerridge's Antiques
Rocket House, High Street
0263 741154
Mid-range furniture and general antiques as well as 18th- and 19th-century specialities.

COGGLESHALL (ESSEX)

Antique Metals
9a East Street
0376 562252
Metalware items, from steel fenders to brass beds.

Joan Jobson
5a Church Street
0376 561717
Furniture, including shipping, general antiques, bric-a-brac and collectors' items.

COLCHESTER (ESSEX)

Founded by the British warrior chief, Cymbeline, in AD10, it went on to become an important Roman garrison-settlement, sizeable fragments of which survive, as does the Norman castle, an early example of architectural salvage in that it includes several tons of recycled Roman bricks. A thriving junk and antiques trade continues the recycling tradition.

Aladdin's Cave
7 Clacton Road,
Elmstead Market
(2 miles from town)
0206 826744
Vast and comprehensive house clearance stock, from shoelaces and teaspoons, via records, fishing gear and bric-a-brac, to bookcases and wardrobes. Ideal for the first-time buyer on a budget.

Auctions
Auctioneers operating in the town include **William H Brown**, *(Paskell's Rooms, 11–14 East Hill, 0206 868070)*, **Reeman, Dansie, Howe & Son**, *(12 Headgate, 0206 574271)* both with weekly general sales and **Essex & Suffolk Market Auctions**, *(The Cattle Market, Wyncolls Road, 0206 842156)*, who hold a rumbustious and comprehensive auction about two miles outside town, where goods of all categories are offered each Saturday.

Badger Antiques
The Old House,
The Street,
Elmstead Market
0206 822044
An exponent of the portmanteau approach to dealing, with the occasional archaic lifestyle accessory such as high-class Victorian underwear. Otherwise, furniture, clocks, textiles, bric-a-brac and general antiques.

Barntiques
Lampitt's Farm, Turkeycock Lane, Stanway
0206 210486
Furniture, including pine and general antiques.

Barrack Street Discount Centre
6–12 Barrack Street
0206 793624
A large selection of budget furniture and house clearance goods.

Essex Antiques Centre
Priory Street
0206 871150
Upwards of 50 dealers with a comprehensive stock. Furniture and larger items upstairs; smaller antiques, bric-a-brac, fireplace accessories, lighting and general antiques on ground floor.

Sue Ryder Shop
16 St Botolph's Street
0206 43377
Typical charity shop stock of clothes, bric-a-brac and small items, plus a good range of secondhand furniture.

Trinity Antiques Centre
7 Trinity Street
0206 577775
Collectors' items and specialist lines, including clocks, textiles and jewellery, plus some furniture. A mini-market of about eight dealers.

COLTISHALL
(NORFOLK)

Eric Bates
High Street
0603 738716
A comprehensive stock of mid-range and shipping furniture.

Coltishall Antiques Centre
High Street
0603 738306
Nine dealers offering a comprehensive range of furniture and general antiques, including militaria, glass, orientalia and general collectors' items. A certain mid-market flavour, but a concentrated browse can certainly uncover some good purchases.

Gwendoline Golder
Point House,
High Street
0603 738099
Collectables and general antiques.

COMBERTON
(CAMBRIDGESHIRE)

Comberton Antiques
5a West Street
0223 262674
Mid-range and shipping furniture, bric-a-brac and general antiques.

CROMER (NORFOLK)

Brammall's Bargain Centre
The Gangway
0263 515153
Some budget new, some house clearance secondhand.

DEBENHAM
(SUFFOLK)

Gil Adams Antique Centre
Foresters Hall,
High Street
0728 860777
Across-the-range furniture from four dealers, plus some smaller goods, in extensive upper-floor premises (formerly the Debenham Antique Centre). Not particularly a budget call, but certainly worth inspection.

John Hart of Suffolk
48 High Street
0728 861174
Antiques, collectables, secondhand basics and house clearances.

Lanchester's
21 High Street
0728 860756

Secondhand furniture and some collector's items.

DISS (NORFOLK)

Gaze's Auction Rooms
Roydon Road
0379 650306
Weekly general sales.

Gostling's
13 Market Hill
0379 650360
About five dealers with a mid-market variety of furniture, general antiques and some specialisations.

DODDINGTON (CAMBRIDGESHIRE)

Doddington House Antiques
2 Benwick Road
0354 740755
Mid-range furniture, clocks and general antiques.

DOWNHAM MARKET (NORFOLK)

Barry Hawkins, auctioneer
The Repository, Lynn Road
0553 776600
Monthly general sales.

DUXFORD (CAMBRIDGESHIRE)

Mooney Antiques
4 Moorfield Road
0223 832252
A broad mix of antique and secondhand furniture as well as general antiques.

EARSHAM (SUFFOLK)

Earsham Hall Pine
Earsham Hall
0986 893423

An extensive selection of mid-range pine furniture.

EAST DEREHAM (NORFOLK)

Birds Secondhand
37 St Nicholas Street
0362 693541
House clearance goods and basics.

Dereham Antiques
9 Norwich Street
0362 693200
Furniture, jewellery, bric-a-brac, collectors' items and general antiques.

ELY (CAMBRIDGESHIRE)

Cheffins, Grain & Comins, auctioneers
Portley Hill Auction Premises, Littleport
0353 662266
Weekly general sales. Phone for details.

Waterside Antiques
The Wharf
0353 667066
Three floors with 65 dealers trading in a comprehensive range of furniture, collectors' items and general antiques 'from 50p upwards'. A fairly eclectic mix with some sensible prices.

EPPING (ESSEX)

Epping Galleries
64–66 High Street
0992 573023
Furniture, including reproduction and general antiques. A Saturday antiques and bric-a-brac market is held at the rear of the premises, usually with around 60 stallholders.

EXNING (SUFFOLK)

Derby Cottage Collectables
Fordham Road
0638 578422
Furniture, general antiques and collectors' items.

EYE (SUFFOLK)

The Corner Shop
Castle Street
0379 870614
A long-established source of bric-a-brac, collectors' items and general antiques.

FAKENHAM (NORFOLK)

Hugh Beck, auctioneers
The Corn Hall
0328 851557
Weekly general sales.

Courtyard Antiques
8 Norwich Road
Pine furniture, jewellery and general antiques.

Fakenham Antique Centre
Old Congregational Chapel,
14 Norwich Road
0328 862941
Furniture, mostly mid-range and some pine, collectors' items, books, porcelain, pictures and general antiques.

Market Place Antiques
28 Upper Market Place
Jewellery, collectors' items and general antiques.

FELIXSTOWE (SUFFOLK)

Diamond Mills, auctioneers
Orwell Hall, Orwell Road
0394 282281
Monthly sales of general secondhand goods.

McCulloch Antiques
1a Hamilton Road
0394 283126
Some furniture, but mostly smaller goods – clocks, metalware, pictures, bric-a-brac and general antiques. Generally a good rummage.

Norsk Antiques
91–93 St Andrews Road
0394 285886
A comprehensive stock of furniture, general antiques, collectables and house clearance goods.

Sunday Market
The Seafront
Some antiques and bric-a-brac stalls can be found at this seafront market.

FELSTED (ESSEX)

Argyll House Antiques
Station Road
0371 820682
Furniture, mostly mid-range, bric-a-brac, ephemera and collectors' items.

FORDHAM (CAMBRIDGESHIRE)

Clover Antiques
5–6 Soham Road
0638 720250
An extensive stock of across-the-board furniture, from mid-range to shipping.

FRAMLINGHAM (SUFFOLK)

Goodbreys
29 Double Street
0728 723756
Decorative furniture

predominates, plus a selection of smaller goods, including textiles, bric-a-brac, garden ornaments, lighting accessories, collectables and general antiques.

FRINTON ON SEA
(ESSEX)

Dickens Curios
151 Connaught Avenue
0255 674134
A sedate seaside town once more famous for what it didn't have – a fish and chip shop – than what it had, although this particular shop has been adding character for upwards of 20 years. Stock includes a comprehensive range of mid-range and cheaper furniture, jewellery, ephemera, numismatic items, collectables and general antiques.

FRITHVILLE
(LINCOLNSHIRE)

J & R Antiques
Barn House, Hale Lane
0205 750069
Victorian and shipping furniture, collectors' items and bric-a-brac. Appointment required.

GAINSBOROUGH
(LINCOLNSHIRE)

Hemswell Antiques Centre
Caenby Corner Estate,
Helmswell Cliff
0427 668389
Seven-day-a-week mega-market of approximately 250 dealers with a vast variety of specialist lines, furniture and general antiques. There are also frequent car boot sales *(0652 61616 for enquiries)*.

GARBOLDISHAM
(ESSEX)

Swan House
Hopton Road
095381 8221
A former 17th-century coaching inn (still with B & B on the premises) now selling a mix of new and craft items and mid-range to budget furniture, general antiques, books, records and bric-a-brac.

GORLESTON ON SEA
(NORFOLK)

More than half a dozen shops in town stock a range of secondhand furniture and house clearance lines, including: The Attic (*20 St Peters Road, 0493 850133***); Buy, Sell, Exchange (***3 St Peters Road, 0493 853303***); and Gorleston Trading Depot (***34 Baker Street, 0493 661926***).**

Second Choice
1 Pier Plain
0493 656225
The Proprietor, an ex-roadie, also sells secondhand instruments from **The Boogie Shop** next door.

GRANTHAM
(LINCOLNSHIRE)

Grantham Furniture Emporium
4–6 Wharf Road
0476 62967
Large selection of across-the-board Victorian and later furniture. Closed on Monday.

GRAYS (ESSEX)

Grays Galleries Antiques & Collectors Centre
6 London Road
0375 374883

Upwards of 40 dealers trading in some mid-range furniture, with mostly smaller antiques, collectors' items, jewellery, silver and pictures.

Kendons
10 London Road
0375 371200
Small collectables: stamps, coins, jewellery, books, postcards, cigarette cards. Open from Thursday to Saturday.

GREAT BADDOW
(ESSEX)

Baddow Antique Centre
The Bringy,
Church Street
0245 76159
Around 20 dealers trading in a variety of antiques and collectors' items, including mid-range to pre-war furniture, metalware and some specialisations.

GREAT BARTON
(SUFFOLK)

Heritage Auctions
The Village Hall
0953 884369
Monthly general sales.

GREAT WALTHAM
(ESSEX)

The Stores
The Main Road
0245 360277
The former village store, now retailing stripped pine furniture.

GREAT YARMOUTH
(NORFOLK)

Aldred's, auctioneers
Kitchener Road Salerooms
0493 844891

Occasional sales of general goods or antiques.

Howkins Antiques
39–40 & 135 King Street
0493 844639
An extensive range of furniture and general antiques, from period to 20th-century, including jewellery, silver, furniture and collectors' items. A wide choice displayed in several showrooms makes this a popular call for both locals and summer visitors.

Wheatleys
16 Northgate Street,
White Horse Plain
0493 857219
Jewellery, collectors' items and general antiques.

HADLEIGH (SUFFOLK)

Playthings of the Past
102a High Street
0473 824435
Antique and vintage toys, including teddy bears, dolls, cars, trains and associated items. Unbridled nostalgia for the young at heart.

Tara's Hall
Victoria House, Market Place
0473 824031
Jewellery, bric-a-brac, art nouveau and art deco, textiles and general antiques. Much with a *fin-de-siècle* flavour and some good rummaging.

HALESWORTH
(SUFFOLK)

Ash Tree Antiques
Ash Tree Farm, Wissett
0986 872867
Vernacular and country furniture, pottery and general rural antiques.

Number Six Antiques
6 Chediston Street
0986 875492
Furniture, including pine and shipping, decorative items, bric-a-brac and general antiques.

Halstead Antiques
71 Head Street
0787 473265
Smaller furniture, collectors' items, bric-a-brac and general antiques.

Napier House Antiques
Head Street
0787 477346
Beds, mostly Victorian and Edwardian and all in wood. Another branch in Sudbury stocks across-the-range general furniture.

Townsford Mill Antiques Centre
The Causeway
0787 474451
60 dealers selling furniture, general antiques and collectors' items – always good for a rake, seven days a week.

Mayflower Antiques
105 High Street,
Dovercourt
0255 504079
Automata, musical boxes, medical, scientific and nautical antiques and collectors' items, much of quality, most of it absorbing.

Stour Valley Auctions
23 Station Road,
Dovercourt
0255 241785
General auctions every three weeks.

The Guardroom Antiques Centre
Old RAF Hemswell,
near Caenby Corner
0427 668312
30 dealers selling general antiques, bric-a-brac and collectables.

Hemswell Antiques Centre
See under **GAINSBOROUGH**

All Our Yesterdays
North View, Penny Hill
0406 24636
Woodworking tools, treen and metalware.

Collectors Cabin
7 Cromer Road
0263 712241
Small but rummageable, bric-a-brac, bijouterie, old toys and a wide range of collectors' items.

Formerly famed for its horsemarket (the horses have gone but the horsedealers' pubs remain) the local antique trade is something like Topsy – it just grew; not so long ago, this was a two-traders town, but now there are around 50, including the stallholders at the Antiques Centre.

Clare Boam
22–38 North Street
0507 522381
Long-established and vast – 10,000 square feet – source of a

large selection of mid-range and shipping furniture, bric-a-brac and house clearance goods. Prices comprehensive and often competitive.

Frantique
23 North Street
0526 353495
A mix of small furniture, general antiques, bric-a-brac and collectors' items.

Robert Kitching
9–11 West Street
0507 522120
General antiques, including clocks.

The Lincolnshire Antique Centre
Bridge Street
0507 527794
Upwards of 30 dealers with a range of furniture, bric-a-brac, collectors' items and general antiques.

MC Trading Co & Seaview Antiques
Stanhope Road
0507 523287
An enterprising owner, in recently expanded premises, offering a large selection of furniture, Georgian and Victorian to low-cost to shipping, and general antiques.

Talisman Antiques
51–53 North Street
0507 526893
A large selection of furniture, including pine and satin walnut, collectors' items and scale-model trains. Closed Monday.

The Warehouse
Bank Street
0507 524569
Stripped pine furniture and general antiques.

HUNSTANTON
(NORFOLK)

Delawood Antiques
10 Westgate
0485 532903
Open Wednesday, Friday, Saturday, or by arrangement. Some furniture, mostly jewellery, collectors' items, books and general antiques.

Old Bakery Antiques
1 Church Street
0485 210396
Collectors' items, textiles, pottery and porcelain and general small antiques.

IPSWICH (SUFFOLK)

The administrative capital of Suffolk, and an historic port town which did well out of the wool trade. Cardinal Wolsey, son of a local butcher, who went on to become one of the most powerful – if ultimately ill-fated – men in England, gave the town a grammar school. There is also an interesting museum, Christchurch Mansion, and a tremendously varied range of rummageable antique shops.

Abbott Antiques
757 Woodbridge Road
0473 728900
Mid-range to shipping furniture, jewellery, clocks and general antiques – a notably comprehensive selection, with across-the-board prices.

Tony Adams
175 Spring Road
0473 714362
Valve radios, trains and toys, photographic items and a variety of similar collectables. Closed on Wednesday and Thursday.

Atfield & Daughter
17 St Stephens Lane
0473 251158
An antique shop since it closed
as a pub in 1901, now reduced
in size, but still offers a good
comprehensive, rummageable
range, including furniture, bric-
a-brac, metalware, militaria,
transport-related items and
books on collecting.

Bargain Corner
211 Spring Road
0473 713608
Secondhand furniture and
house clearance items.

Sonia Cordell Antiques
13 St Peters Street
0473 219508
Principally sewing collectables,
but also some jewellery, silver,
treen, toys, ephemera, pictures
and other collectors' items.

Country Bygones
13c St Peters Street
0473 253683
Vernacular antiques and
decorative rural items,
kitchenalia, pictures, bric-a-brac
and jewellery.

The Edwardian Shop
556 Spring Road
0473 716576
Edwardian and later furniture,
mostly 20s and 30s oak.

Hyland House Antiques
45 Felixstowe Road
0473 210055
A comprehensive stock of
furniture, to pre-war, general
antiques and bric-a-brac. Closed
on Wednesday and Thursday.

Orwell Galleries
1 Upper Orwell Street
0473 221190
Furniture, including antique

DELFTWARE

Delftware from the 17th
or 18th century can be a
rarefied field for
collectors but one
product from this period
can be acquired at a
moderate cost – the blue
and white fireplace tile.
The Spanish occupation
of the Netherlands and
early Dutch trade with the
orient were influential in
the early development of
Delftware but by the 17th
century it had evolved
into an unmistakably
Dutch product. It was also
exported in such
quantities that it became a
common ballast cargo for
the merchantmen that
crossed the North Sea to
Britain's east-coast ports.
Subjects depicted on each
tile, which was usually
about four inches square,
included flowers,
children at play,
landscapes, shipping
scenes, stylishly dressed
soldiers on rearing
horses and episodes from
the Bible such as Moses
receiving the Ten
Commandments from
God. The introduction of
the iron register grate at
the end of the 18th
century depressed
demand but tiles were
still being produced this
century. Nursery-rhyme
tiles, for example, might
surround an Edwardian
playroom fireplace,
featuring such favourites
as Pat-a-cake, Jack and
Jill, or The Cow that
Jumped over the Moon.'

pine, and some general antiques.

Phillips, auctioneers
Dover House, Wolsey Street
0473 255137
General sales every month, plus intermittent.

Thompsons
418 Norwich Road
0473 747793
Furniture, from mid-range Victorian to shipping and secondhand.

Websters, auctioneers
13 Great Colman Street
0473 257491
Monthly general sales.

IXWORTH (SUFFOLK)

Cousins Antiques
27 High Street
0359 30254
Period and mid-range to shipping furniture and general antiques. More of the same can be seen in the former school nearby, around 20,000 square feet in total.

KELVEDON (ESSEX)

Kelvedon Antiques Centre
139 High Street
0376 570896
Half a dozen dealers with a comprehensive range of furniture, jewellery, silver, bric-a-brac, metalware and collectors' items.

Ratcliffs Antiques
Menai House, 41 High Street
0376 570223
An extensive stock of furniture, mostly mid-range, decorative items and general antiques, with more available from trade

premises on the Coggeshall Road.

Times Past
110 High Street
0376 571858
Fin-de-siècle to pre-war decorative items, especially art deco. Closed on Monday and Wednesday.

KESGRAVE (SUFFOLK)

Mainline Furniture
83 Main Road
0473 623092
Furniture, mid-range to budget, clocks, bric-a-brac, collectors' items and general antiques. Closed on Wednesday.

KESSINGLAND (SUFFOLK)

Kessingland Antiques
36a High Street
0502 740562
A large selection of furniture, mostly 19th-century brownwood and shipping, plus jewellery, bric-a-brac, clocks and watches and general antiques.

KING'S LYNN (NORFOLK)

Once a thriving medieval port, the town's gradual economic decline was something of a blessing in disguise from the architectural historian's point of view. The best of its buildings are profoundly atmospheric and its antique shops eminently browsable, while there are good sources of secondhand goods for budgeting home makers.

Bob's Shops
2–4 Outsouth Gate
0553 762972

Everything and anything secondhand, particularly smaller goods such as crockery, cutlery, 78 records and house clearance bits and pieces.

Mostly Bygones
1 Kings Staithe Lane
0553 776933
A portmanteau assortment of everything collectable, including coins, stamps, postcards, bric-a-brac, pictures, medals, small furniture and 'general odds and ends'.

The Old Curiosity Shop
25 St James' Street
0553 766591
From the unusual to the ubiquitous; clothes, bric-a-brac, textiles, collectors' items, pre-war and earlier furniture, pictures, lighting accessories and general antiques. Closed on Wednesday.

The Old Granary Antiques & Collectors' Centre
Kings Staithe Lane
0553 775509
About 15 dealers with some mid-range to budget furniture and an excellent range of smaller inexpensive antiques, including jewellery, silver, metalware, bric-a-brac, books, textiles, ephemera and general antiques.

Sharpes Secondhand Furniture Warehouse
94 Hall Road, Clench Warton
0553 772572
A large stock of secondhand furniture and house clearance items.

Terrington Warehouse
20 Sutton Road,
Terrington St Clement
0553 829748

Secondhand furniture and effects.

KIRTON (LINCOLNSHIRE)

Kirton Antiques
3 High Street
0205 722595
A large selection of furniture, mid-range to shipping, bric-a-brac and general antiques in a combined space of 20,000 square feet.

LAVENHAM (SUFFOLK)

Suffolk's wool wealth was used to good effect in Lavenham, with its half-timbered houses which are, in the words of one visiting academic, 'eminently droolable'. Certainly, the 16th-century Guildhall is a masterpiece of late medieval carpentry.

The Antique Shop
14a High Street
0787 248524
At the heart of this quintessentially 'picture-postcard' English village and with a varied and interesting range of stock, including jewellery, textiles, porcelain, collectors' items and smaller general antiques. Closed Wednesday and Thursday.

Tom Smith Antiques
36 Market Place
0787 247463
A shop and warehouse containing across-the-range furniture, porcelain, pottery, eastern rugs and general antiques.

LEIGH ON SEA (ESSEX)

Like its neighbour, Southend-on-Sea, a traditional resort for work-weary Londoners and their

families, it supports a mix of good collectors' shops, regular auctions, and several sources of useable furniture.

Broadway Fayre
117 Broadway
0702 74156
An extensive range of secondhand basics and house clearance effects.

Buchans Antiques
135 The Broadway
0702 79440
Mid-range and cheaper furniture and general antiques.

Castle Antiques
72 The Broadway
0702 75732
A large selection of mostly good-quality pottery and porcelain, plus some more unusual items of ethnographica and taxidermy, both avine and piscine, as well as antiquities and weapons. An imaginative and eclectic mix, with distinct possibilities. Closed on Wednesday.

Chalkwell Auctions
New Arlington Rooms,
905 London Road
0702 710383 (enquiries)
Monthly sales of antiques, fine art, jewellery and collectors' items.

Collectors Paradise
993 London Road
0702 73077
A wide range of general collectors' items, including clocks, ephemera, bric-a-brac and cigarette cards. Closed on Friday.

The Curiosity Shop
113 Pall Mall
0702 715764
Furniture and general antiques, from mid-range to budget.

Pall Mall Antiques
104c Elm Road
0702 77235
Specialists in china and glass, but also some bric-a-brac, metalware and general antiques.

Past & Present
81–83 Broadway West
0702 79101
Small general antiques, bric-a-brac, metalware and collectors' items. Closed on Wednesday.

John Stacey & Sons, auctioneers & retailers
86–90 Pall Mall
0702 77051
Shop stock is mostly mid- to upper-market; mixed sales are held monthly.

Streamer Antiques
86 Broadway
0702 72895
Small furniture, jewellery, bric-a-brac and general antiques. Premises also at 212 Leigh Road. Closed on Wednesday.

Tilly's Antiques
1801 London Road
0702 557170
Mid-range furniture, collectable dolls and associated items and general antiques.

LEISTON *(SUFFOLK)*

Leiston Trading Post
13a High Street
0728 830081
Mid-range furniture, bric-a-brac, collectables and general antiques. Limited in size, if not in scope, and usually good for a rummage.

LINCOLN
(LINCOLNSHIRE)

Angela's
48 Ripon Street
0522 535861
Secondhand furniture and house clearance items. Closed on Wednesday.

Drings Antiques
111 High Street
0522 540733
Mid-range and shipping furniture, collectors' items, toys and bric-a-brac. Closed on Wednesday.

Eastgate Antique Centre
6 Eastgate
0522 544404
Around 12 dealers with a selection of mostly mid-market furniture, jewellery, silver, metalware, porcelain and general antiques.

Mansions
5a Eastgate
0522 513631
General antiques, linen, textiles and papier mâché.

Mawer, auctioneers
63 Monks Road
0522 524984
Fortnightly general sales.

LONG MELFORD
(SUFFOLK)

The Enchanted Aviary
63 Hall Street
0787 378814
Victorian taxidermy; sizes from trout and wrens, prices from around £20.

The Long Melford Antiques Centre
The Chapel Maltings
0787 379287
Upwards of 50 dealers with a range of furniture, general antiques and collectors' items, including porcelain, metalware, dolls, toys, decorative items and textiles. Mostly middle-market, but some cheaper goods can also be bought.

Tudor Antiques
Little St Mary's
0787 375950
Popularly referred to as 'the shop with the yellow blind', it is also known for a more rummageable line in stock, though it has recently curtailed its floor space. As with most of the shops in Suffolk's leading antiques village, the emphasis is on quality and style, though here it is less unremitting, with some less expensive general antiques also available.

The Old Maltings Antique Company
Hall Street
0787 379638
Strong on the stylish and decorative and a lot of it – more than 20,000 square feet.

LONG STRATTON
(NORFOLK)

The Old Coach House
Ipswich Road
0508 30942
Mid-range to shipping furniture, including pine, pictures, prints, metalware, bric-a-brac and general antiques. Closed on Monday.

LONG SUTTON
(LINCOLNSHIRE)

Talton's Antiques
15–19 Market Street
0406 362147
Mid-range furniture. Two doors

along from Poole's trade and shipping antique shop.

LOUTH (LINCOLNSHIRE)

Aswell Bargains
34–36 Aswell Street
0507 605811
House clearance goods.

Broadgate & Thompson, auctioneers
1 Cornmarket
0507 603101
Miscellaneous sales every Wednesday.

LOWESTOFT (SUFFOLK)

Curiosity Capers
289 London Road South
0502 500375
A stylish array of furniture and general decorative items, including furniture from the aesthetic movement through to utility and later, with some outlandish memorabilia such as a 1960s sofa designed for the *Doctor Who* set, and some chairs copied from Mackintosh's Argyle tearooms series, as subsequently used by the Adams Family. Also decorative china and art glass, architectural items and general odds and ends from the 1860s to the present.

Kessingland Antiques
36a High Street
0502 740562
Furniture, mid-range to good secondhand, clocks and watches, jewellery, bric-a-brac and general antiques packed in over two floors.

Northend Antiques
56–57 High Street
0502 568535

General antiques, bric-a-brac and collectors' items.

Osborne's
36 High Street
0502 562020
Furniture, mid-range to budget, bric-a-brac, postcards, collectors' items and general antiques.

MALDON (ESSEX)

The Antique Rooms
63d High Street
0621 856985
Situated in a small courtyard to the rear of the bookshop, a comprehensive stock of furniture, bric-a-brac, jewellery, textiles and associated items, costume, collectors' items and general antiques. Closed on Wednesday.

Maldon Antique Market
United Reform Church Hall, Market Hill
Enquiries: 07872 22826
Operates on the first Saturday of each month with around 20 dealers offering a range of general antiques, bric-a-brac, ephmera and collectors' items.

Walter's Workshop
11 Fambridge Road
0621 853898
House clearance furniture bought, sold and restored. Closed on Monday.

MARCH (CAMBRIDGESHIRE)

Collingwoods, auctioneers
Palace Hall Auction Rooms, Broad Street
0354 52488
Weekly general auctions.

Grounds, auctioneers
The Cattle Market, Elwyn Road
0354 52502
Monthly general sales.

MARLESFORD
(SUFFOLK)

The Antique Warehouse
Main Road
0728 747438
Furniture, decorative items,
lighting accessories and general
antiques; usually a good stock
of overmantel mirrors.

MARSHAM (NORFOLK)

Peads Antiques
Grove Farm
0263 732841
Storage premises adjacent to a
private house with mid-range
Victorian brownwood to
shipping and secondhand
furniture, including bedroom
suites, dining tables and chairs.

METHWOLD
(NORFOLK)

Methwold Auction Mart
High Street
0842 827398
Weekly general sales.

MILDENHALL
(SUFFOLK)

Hunt & Clement
10 North Terrace
0638 718025
Furniture, from mid-range
brownwood to pine and
shipping and general antiques.

MULBARTON
(NORFOLK)

Junk & Disorderly
Birchfield Lane
0603 748801

Secondhand furniture, bric-a-
brac and house clearance goods
on offer in a showroom above
the village post office and store.
Open only on Saturdays from
9am to 4pm.

NEEDHAM MARKET
(SUFFOLK)

Roy Arnold
77 High Street
0449 720110
Appointment advised. Tools,
gauges, scientific instruments
and books.

**Needham Market Antique
Centre**
The Old Town Hall, High Street
0449 720773
Several dealers with a range of
furniture, collectors' items and
general antiques.

NEWMARKET
(SUFFOLK)

Jemima Godfrey
5 Rous Road
0638 663584
Jewellery, collectors' items and
linen.

NORTH KELSEY
MOOR (LINCOLNSHIRE)

Sykes Antiques
The New Warehouse,
Station Yard
0652 678036
Stripped pine furniture.

NORTH WALSHAM
(NORFOLK)

Eric Bates
Melbourne House, Bacton Road
0692 403221
Mid-range to shipping furniture
and general antiques. Also at
COLTISHALL.

NORWICH *(NORFOLK)*

Norfolk's capital, with a fine Norman cathedral and a clutch of medieval churches, by the end of the 16th century it had become extensively settled by Dutch weavers. It went on to produce excellent shoes, and an acclaimed school of landscape painters. The local antique scene includes some interesting specialisations.

LG Abel
The Street, Costessey
0603 745223
Secondhand house clearance goods. Closed on Wednesday.

Allchin Antiques
22–24 St Benedict Street
0603 660046
Specialising in Victorian and early 20th century lighting, cast iron and marble fireplaces and accessories and some brass and iron bed frames.

Another One
140 Magdalen Street
0603 615302
Also answering to the name **Fagin's Alley**, the shop sells furniture, general antiques, bric-a-brac and collectors' items.

Cloisters Antique Fair
St Andrews and Blackfriars Hall, St Andrews Plain
0603 628477 (enquiries)
Council operated weekly Wednesday fair of about 20–25 traders, mostly with bric-a-brac, collectors' items and smaller antiques.

Clowes, Nash & Thurgar, auctioneers
The Corn Exchange, Norwich Livestock Market, Hall Road
0603 627261
Weekly sales of general secondhand goods.

Clive Dennett Coins
66 St Benedict Street
0603 624315
Jewellery, medal and decorations, coins, banknotes and numismatic items of all descriptions. Closed Thursday.

Ewings, auctioneers
Market Place, Reepham
0603 870473
Intermittent mixed sales.

Jarrett's
12–14 Old Palace Road
0603 625847
Mid-range and budget furniture and house clearance goods.

The Movie Shop
11 St Gregory's Alley
0603 615239
Movie literature, ephemera and related items, plus furniture, bric-a-brac, clothes and general antiques, to pre-war.

Norwich Record Exchange
42 St Benedict's Street
0603 620801
Phonographs, gramophones, valve radios and accessories, plus music on everything from cylinders to CDs.

St Mary's Antique & Collectors' Centre
St Mary's Plain
0603 612582
A wide selection of furniture, collectors' items, bric-a-brac, ephemera and general antiques on offer from 25 dealers.

St Michael at Plea Antiques Centre
Bank Plain
0603 619129

Around 30 dealers with a broad range of furniture, collectors' items, bric-a-brac and general antiques.

Second to Best
16 Onley Street, Unthank Road
0603 621653
Secondhand furniture, lighting, china, objets d'art, general antiques and house clearance goods.

This & That
56 Bethel Street
0603 632201
Furniture, including pine and general antiques.

Tooltique
54 Waterloo Road
0603 414289
Secondhand and collectors' woodworking tools.

Yesteryear
24d Magdalen Street
0603 622908
Mainly ceramics (1880–1940) but some decorative antiques, prints and pictures, and a particular penchant for character mugs.

PETERBOROUGH
(CAMBRIDGESHIRE)

Fitzwilliam Antiques Centre
Fitzwilliam Street
0733 65415
Around 50 dealers selling a comprehensive range of furniture, bric-a-brac, collectors' items and general antiques.

Fulbridge Furnishers
34 Eastfield Road
0733 311724
Secondhand furniture and house clearance goods.

Millwood Furnishers
132 Cromwell Road
0733 53565
Basics and flatfillers

20th Century Secondhand Furniture
21 Leofric Square
0733 313299
More basics and flatfillers.

RAMSEY
(CAMBRIDGESHIRE)

Abbey Antiques
63 Great Whyte
0487 814753
Particularly strong on ceramics from the aesthetic movement to art deco but also sells less specialised general antiques and furniture, metalware, pottery, porcelain and commemorative ware. Closed on Monday.

Yesteryear Antiques
79–81 High Street
0487 815006
Mid-range and shipping furniture, pictures, collectors' items and general antiques. Prices variable, and generally low, with good potential.

RAYLEIGH (ESSEX)

FG Bruschweiler
41–67 Lower Lambricks
0268 773761
Forty-years-established trade and shipping outlet occupying vast tracts of warehousing, also supplies the home market. Stock almost entirely furniture, varying from early Georgian to standard shipping pre-war oak. Closed on Monday. The same dealer also trades from Rettendon **Antiques Trade Warehouse** (*Rawlings Home Farm, Main Road, Rettendon, 0245 400046*).

RIDGEWELL (ESSEX)

Ridgewell Crafts & Antiques
Ridgewell
044 085 272
Furniture, collectors' items, bric-a-brac, metalware, clocks and watches and general antiques. Closed on Wednesday.

RISBY (SUFFOLK)

Risby Barn Antique Centre
Risby
0284 811126
Upwards of 20 dealers with a good range of antiques and collectors' items, including furniture, period to pre-war, bric-a-brac, woodworking tools, jewellery and general antiques.

ST IVES (CAMBRIDGESHIRE)

Broadway Antiques
31 The Broadway
0480 61061
Mid-range furniture, plus an array of smaller antiques and collectables, from corkscrews to snuff boxes.

SAFFRON WALDEN (ESSEX)

Lankester Antiques
The Old Sun Inn,
Church Street
0799 522685
An extensive mixed stock including across the range furniture, porcelain and pottery, metalware, pictures and books. A long-established local rummage, with much to offer.

Saffron Walden Auctions
1 Market Street
0799 513281
Weekly sales of miscellanea, with anything from chickens to chiffoniers, plus about eight antique and fine art sales per annum.

SAXMUNDHAM (SUFFOLK)

Antiques & Country Things
The Old Shop,
49 North Entrance,
High Street
0728 604171
A comprehensive stock covering all price ranges and including smaller furniture, jewellery, collectors' items, bric-a-brac and general antiques. Closed on Thursday.

William H Brown, auctioneers
Flick's Auction Rooms,
Church Street
0728 603232
Fortnightly general sales.

SCRATBY (NORFOLK)

Keith Lawson Antiques
Scratby Garden Centre,
Beach Road
0493 730950
A large barn open seven days a week for the sale of furniture, clocks and general antiques.

SHERINGHAM (NORFOLK)

Crowes
32 Station Road
0263 822891
In the house clearance business since the 1940s, Crowe's stock a mix of new and secondhand furniture, including some antiques and bric-a-brac in premises of around 5,000

square feet. Prices range from 5p for a saucer to about £1,000 for occasional choice items of furniture.

SIBLE HEDINGHAM
(ESSEX)

Hedingham Antiques
100 Swan Street
0787 60360
A shop and warehouse of mid-range furniture, general antiques and Victorian, bric-a-brac and collectors' items.

SKEGNESS
(LINCOLNSHIRE)

Romantiques
87 Roman Bank
0754 767879
A bracing selection of general antiques, including clocks, jewellery, porcelain, classic motor cycles and sundry eclectiana.

SLEAFORD
(LINCOLNSHIRE)

Daykin, auctioneers
69 Northgate
0529 413954
General sales every Monday, plus additional monthly antiques sales.

SNAPE (SUFFOLK)

Snape Antiques & Collectors' Centre
Snape Maltings Riverside Complex
0728 688038
Mostly high-class collectables, including silver, fine textiles, porcelain and pottery, glass, treen and vernacular items, though with around 50 dealers present at any one time the

occasional bargain buy does surface.

SNETTISHAM
(NORFOLK)

Cruso & Wilkins, auctioneers
Common Road
0485 542656
Weekly Friday sales, plus about six antique sales per year.

SOUTH BENFLEET
(ESSEX)

Fairdeal
592 High Road
0268 793040
Secondhand furniture and house clearance items.

SOUTHEND ON SEA
(ESSEX)

Kickshaws
20 Alexandra Street
0702 353630
General antiques, bric-a-brac and collectors' items with some budget-friendly prices. Closed on Wednesday.

The Secondhand Shop
The Victorian Market, York Road
0702 615092
Secondhand furniture and house clearance items. Closed on Wednesday.

SOUTH WALSHAM
(NORFOLK)

The Old Curiosity Shop
Broad Lane, Pilson Green
060 549 204
Established over a century ago and still in the Pratt family, stock is mainly upper- and mid-range furniture and general antiques, but some shipping

goods are also available.

SPALDING
(LINCOLNSHIRE)

Deans Antiques
The Walnuts, Weston St Mary's
0406 370429
Vernacular or country antiques.

STALHAM (NORFOLK)

Stalham Antique Gallery
High Street
0692 580636
Furniture, period to mid-range, silver, metalware, bric-a-brac.

Grandad George's Shed
63 High Street
A mecca for the rummager; bric-a-brac, collectables, crockery and cutlery, pictures, collectors' items and general household junk. Anything that could possibly have a use is probably here. A gloriously satisfying clutter.

Jonathan Howlett, auctioneer
Upperstaithe Road
0692 580203
Large weekly general auctions.

STAMFORD
(LINCOLNSHIRE)

Stamford Antiques Centre
Exchange Hall, Broad Street
0780 62605
Upward of 30 dealers with a range of general antiques and collectors' items.

Andrew Thomas
The Old Granary,
10 North Street
0780 62236
Specialising in Eastern European painted furniture, the shop also sells antique pine and

vernacular furniture, country antiques and other decorative and architectural items.

STAPLEFORD
(LINCOLNSHIRE)

Allens Antiques
Moor Farm
0522 788392
Stripped pine furniture.

STIFFKEY (NORFOLK)

Stiffkey Antiques
The Old Methodist Chapel
0328 830460
Also at **The Lamp Shop** *(Townshend Arms)*, the main location is shared with about five other dealers and carries a range of general antiques and collectables, including tinplate toys, books, architectural items, fireplaces and accessories and kitchenalia. The shop is particularly renowned for door and window furniture, with stock that ranges from simple handles, escutcheons and latches to 'completely vulgar and over the top' examples from mercantile chambers and churches. The Lamp Shop occupies the former village pub and sells electric, gas and oil lamps and light fittings, plus accessories and spare parts.

STOCK (ESSEX)

Sabine Antiques
38 High Street
0277 840553
Mid-range furniture and general antiques. Closed on Monday.

SUDBURY (SUFFOLK)

Bric-a-Brac & Antiques
54 Ballingdon Street
0787 373800

Mid-range to secondhand furniture, house clearance effects, bric-a-brac and collectables.

WH Brown, auctioneers
Olivers Rooms, Burkitts Lane
0787 880305
Weekly general sales and intermittent antique and fine art sales.

SUTTON BRIDGE
(LINCOLNSHIRE)

Old Barn Antiques Warehouse
New Road
0406 350435
An extensive selection of shipping goods, including decorative cast iron, lighting and accessories, beds, tools and anything irresistibly interesting. The owners have a further obsession: their museum, consisting of ten reconstructed shops and five rooms of a house, all dating from about 1900 and entirely built and furnished by the Nicholson's themselves. Truly amazing.

SUTTON ON SEA
(LINCOLNSHIRE)

Knick-Knacks
41 High Street
0507 441657
A shop and warehouse with general antiques and metalware.

SWAFFHAM (NORFOLK)

Swaffham Antiques Supplies
66–68 London Street
0760 721697
An extensive range of furniture, period to shipping and general antiques.

Tyrone Roberts, auctioneers
The Saleyard
0362 691267
General sales every Saturday, plus Sunday sales held weekly at *Lynford Hall, Mundford.*

TATTERSHALL
(LINCOLNSHIRE)

Wayside Antiques
10 Market Place
0526 342436
Furniture, porcelain and general antiques.

THUNDERSLEY
(ESSEX)

Bramley Antiques
180 Kiln Road
0702 551800
Mid-range to period furniture, jewellery, porcelain, metalware linen and some general antiques. Closed on Monday.

WALTON ON THE NAZE (ESSEX)

The Attic
90 High Street
0255 677515.
Secondhand furniture basics.

Terry's Antiques & Secondhand
38 Station Street
0255 671577.
Secondhand furniture and house clearance basics. Closed on Wednesday.

WANSFORD
(CAMBRIDGESHIRE)

Old House Antiques
The Old House, 16 London Road
0780 783999
Specialising in antique lighting and accessories.

WARBOYS
(CAMBRIDGESHIRE)

Warboys Antiques
Old Church School, High Street
0487 823686
General antiques, advertising
items and sports memorabilia.
Closed on Monday.

WEASENHAM ALL SAINTS (NORFOLK)

Sinclair's, auctioneers
The Old Reading Room
032 874 655
An Edwardian building where
locals used to gather to read the
latest news and now where the
Sinclairs hold general sales
twice a month (on the first and
third Thursday), plus occasional
other sales. The husband
conducts the auction while the
wife runs the village shop and
post office from home.

WELLS NEXT THE SEA (NORFOLK)

Church Street Antiques
2 Church Street
0328 711698
General antiques, jewellery,
textiles and collectors' items.
Closed on Monday.

Wells Antique Centre
The Old Mill, Maryland
0328 711433
Around a dozen dealers with a
wide range of furniture, general
antiques and collectors' items.

WESTCLIFF ON SEA (ESSEX)

**David, Jean & John
Antiques**
587 London Road
0702 339106
An extensive range of furniture,

from period to shipping, plus
porcelain, clocks and watches,
weapons and general antiques.
Closed on Wednesday.

Orchard Secondhand
244 Fairfax Road
0702 331311
Flatfillers and basics.

Prust & Son
9 West Road
0702 345972
Secondhand furniture and
household effects.

Ridgeway Antiques
66 The Ridgeway
0702 710383
Furniture, mostly Victorian and
Edwardian, with some art deco,
jewellery, collectors' items and
general antiques. The owners
also run **Chalkwell Auctions**
(0702 710383), Leigh on Sea.

WHEPSTEAD (SUFFOLK)

Waltons, auctioneers
6 Whiting Street
0284 762099
Monthly general sales.

WHITE RODING (ESSEX)

White Roding Antiques
Ivydene, Chelmsford Road
0279 876376
Furniture, period to shipping
and general antiques.
Appointment required.

WISBECH (CAMBRIDGESHIRE)

**Maxey & Sons,
auctioneers**
The Cattle Market
0945 584609
Weekly general sales.

WITHAM
(ESSEX)

Mill Lane Stores
Mill Lane
0376 516466
A mix of secondhand and
reproduction pine furniture and
some antiques.

WOODBRIDGE
(SUFFOLK)

Deben Furniture
Melton Road, Melton
0394 387880
Budget furniture and house
clearance goods. Closed on
Wednesday.

Housewives Choice
26 The Street, Melton
0394 385158
Furniture, including pine and
beds, kitchenalia, bric-a-brac
and general antiques.

Lambert's Barn
24a Church Street
0394 382380
An extensive stock of furniture,
mid-range to pre-war and
general antiques.

Melton Antiques
Kingdom Hall, Melton
0394 386232
Furniture, mostly mid-range
Victorian and Edwardian,
decorative and collectors items
and general antiques. Not
particularly spacious premises
but usually with a varied

assortment and a fairly broad
price spectrum, including low-
cost.

Man With a Van
The White House,
The Street, Eyke
0394 460498
Prosperous Woodbridge has
little in the way of true budget
furniture, but this outlet, about
four miles outside town, offers
some secondhand possibilities.
The owner suggests ringing first
to check availability.

Neal Sons & Fletcher, auctioneers
The Saleroom,
Theatre Street
0394 382263
Monthly general sales plus
periodic specialist sales.

WOOLPIT
(SUFFOLK)

Car Boot Sales
Regular Sunday car boot sales
on the road between
Stowmarket and Bury St
Edmunds.

WYMONDHAM
(NORFOLK)

Wymondham Antique Centre
No 1 Town Green
0953 604817
Furniture, collectors items and
general antiques, from around
17 dealers.

NORTH EAST ENGLAND

The prevailing view of North East England is one of gritty industrialism and coal dust but this is only part of the picture.

Within a few minutes' drive of densely populated urban areas such as Newcastle lies some exceptionally fine rolling countryside, and enough in the way of smart houses and highly polished Range Rovers to suggest that the local prosperity was not just the product of Tyneside's engineering workshops, important though these were. The character of the vast area to the east of the Pennines is delightfully diverse; likewise, the opportunities for picking up reasonably priced antiques. For the purposes of our survey, the North East is deemed to start on Humberside, where the antique trade is eagerly patronised by European shippers.

Berwick on Tweed

NORTHUMBERLAND

TYNE & WEAR

Newcastle upon Tyne

Durham

COUNTY DURHAM

Middlesborough

CLEVELAND

NORTH YORKSHIRE

York

HUMBERSIDE

Leeds

WEST YORKSHIRE

Hull

SOUTH YORKSHIRE

Sheffield

In history-rich York a rather different set of rules apply, with a predominance of private buyers, resident and visiting. Harrogate maintains a certain discreet, upmarket decorum, but even here there are pickings to be had. Around Newcastle the demand from both trade and private buyers seems to be fairly equally balanced, at least in the city's two main auction rooms, where bidding is often spirited. Auctions in the smaller county towns can also be rewarding, not least because of the surroundings; and if you don't succeed with your bid for that standard lamp, you can always console yourself with a visit to Britain's first all-electric stately home, Cragside, enjoy the Vanburghian extravagance of Castle Howard, or polish up your knowledge at the spectacular Bowes Museum, near Barnard Castle.

ABERFORD
(WEST YORKSHIRE)

Aberford Antiques
Hicklam House
0532 813209
Victorian and stripped pine furniture, pictures and general antiques.

ALNWICK
(NORTHUMBERLAND)

Country Pine Antiques
22 Bailiffgate
0665 603616
An extensive range of antique country furniture.

Ian Robertson
38 Narrowgate
0665 602725
Mid-range furniture and general antiques. The proprietor also conducts auction sales; household fortnightly, antiques about twice a year.

Tamblyn
12 Bondgate Without
0665 603024
Country furniture, porcelain, glass, pictures and collectors' items.

BARNARD CASTLE
(COUNTY DURHAM)

A well-preserved market town with a flourishing antique trade, as well as the stunning Bowes Museum in its landscaped setting.

Addison, auctioneers
13 Galgate
0833 38094
Fortnightly mixed sales.

Stephanie Grant Antiques
38–40 The Bank
0833 37437
Across-the-range furniture, decorative antiques and pictures.

Town House Antiques
7 Newgate
0833 37021
Open Wednesday, Friday and Saturday. Decorative antiques, Georgian, Victorian and Edwardian furniture and shipping goods.

Underwood's
26 Newgate
0833 31233
General antiques.

BARNSLEY
(SOUTH YORKSHIRE)

Charisma Antiques Warehouse
St Paul's Former Methodist Church, Market Street, Hoyland
0226 747599
Converted preaching hall containing an extensive stock of furniture, shipping goods and pictures and incorporating **Christine Simmons Antiques**, with smaller goods, pictures and collectors' items.

BARTON ON HUMBER
(HUMBERSIDE)

Elegance Antiques
Corner of Market Place
0652 635012
Trade and shipping goods.

BAWTRY
(SOUTH YORKSHIRE)

Swan Antiques
2 Swan Street
0302 710301
An extensive range of furniture, bric-a-brac, textiles and unusual and decorative items, including taxidermy.

BERWICK ON TWEED
(NORTHUMBERLAND)

A much disputed border town, now in England, although it started life as the county town of Berwickshire, in Scotland. Sights worth seeing include the Elizabethan town walls, the KOSB regimental museum, and the Burrell Collection – a local version of the magnificent bequest that shipping magnate Sir William Burrell left to Glasgow, although not, sadly, in quite the same league.

Castlegate Antiques
83 Castlegate
0289 306009
Furniture, clocks, militaria and general antiques. A comprehensive price range, from a few pounds to the upper hundreds.

Belford Auction Market
Mount Road, Tweedmouth
0289 307569
Mixed general and antique sales about six times a year.

The Treasure Chest
43 Bridge Street
0289 307736
Smaller antiques, jewellery, porcelain and collectors' items.

BEVERLEY
(HUMBERSIDE)

Well Lane Antiques
10 Well Lane
0482 882868
Art deco, Edwardiana and Victoriana; small general antiques and collectors' items, including linen. One of several in a town of smart antique shops.

BINGLEY
(WEST YORKSHIRE)

Bingley Antiques Centre
Keighley Road
0274 567316
Established almost 30 years as a source of mid-range furniture, general antiques, porcelain and decorative garden items. A nearby warehouse contains some cheaper budget and shipping furniture.

Curio Cottage
3 Millgate
0274 612975
Collectors' items, Victoriana,

some pine country furniture.

J & H Antiques
84 Main Street
0274 563134
Furniture, general antiques and
bric-a-brac.

BISHOP AUCKLAND
(COUNTY DURHAM)

Edkins, auctioneers
Auckland Auction Rooms,
58 Kingsway
0388 603095
Weekly general sales.

BLAYDON
(TYNE AND WEAR)

Blaydon Antique Centre
Bridge House, 10 Bridge Street
091 414 3535
Furniture, pianos, pictures, bric-
a-brac, general antiques and
collectors' items.

Joanne Stanton Antiques
Hedgefield Farm
091 413 3562
Shipping goods and general
antiques in a barn and
outhouse complex.

BOROUGHBRIDGE
(NORTH YORKSHIRE)

J Bates Antiques
Bridge Street
0423 324258
Collectors' items, silver,
furniture, walking sticks,
pictures and antiquarian books.
Premises shared with Anthony
Graham Antiques.

Joan Eyles Antiques
The Stone Yard, Fishergate
0423 323357
Furniture, pottery, fireplace
accessories, treen, textiles and
collectors' items.

Galloway Antiques
High Street
0423 324602
Mid- to upper-range furniture,
pictures, ceramics, decorative
items.

St James House Antiques
St James Square
0423 322508
Mid- to upper-range furniture,
metalware, porcelain and
general antiques.

BRADFORD
(WEST YORKSHIRE)

**With woollen mills built like
palaces, and much spruced up
now for the benefit of that new
great industry, tourism, the
town's outlets are relatively few
in number but can be
surprisingly good in quality.**

Ancient & Modern
Idle Hall, Idle
0274 618894
Two storeys of general house
clearance goods.

Collectors' Corner
5–7 Frizinghall Road
0274 487098
A diverse selection of
ephemera, bric-a-brac,
Victoriana and collectors' items
with low-price potential.

The Corner Shop
89 Oak Lane
Long-established (30 years)
stockists of collectors' items,
porcelain, clocks and small
antiques. Open Tuesday,
Thursday and Saturday.

Low Moor Antiques
233–234 Huddersfield Road,
Low Moor
0274 671047
Pine furniture, shipping goods

and general antiques.

Secondhand Rose
28 Manningham Lane
0274 722927
A large selection of secondhand furniture and assorted house clearance items on three well-cluttered floors.

The Wool Exchange
Fleamarket every Tuesday.

BRANDSBY
(NORTH YORKSHIRE)

Ward & Son
Bar House
03475 651
Pine furniture.

BRIDLINGTON
(HUMBERSIDE)

Antique Militaria
2 Princess Terrace
0262 676846
Militaria and related items.

Broader & Spencer, auctioneers
18 Quay Road
0262 670355
General sales every Thursday

Priory Antiques
47–49 High Street
0262 601365
An extensive large selection of mid-range furniture and general antiques.

Sedman Antiques
Carnaby Court
0262 674039
A varied stock of general antiques, collectors' items and shipping goods.

Smithsons
Quay Road
Secondhand furniture and house clearance items.

BROMPTON
(NORTH YORKSHIRE)

Country Pine Antiques
Unit 45, The Old Mill
0609 774322
Country furniture and Victorian pine.

CAWOOD
(NORTH YORKSHIRE)

Cawood Antiques
Sherburn Street
0757 268533
Furniture, pictures, metalware, shipping goods, bric-a-brac and assorted collectors' items. Fair browsing venue, offering interesting variety.

CLEETHORPES
(HUMBERSIDE)

Yesterday's Antiques
86 Grimsby Road
0472 343020
Mid-range Victorian and Edwardian furniture and general antiques.

CONSETT
(COUNTY DURHAM)

Harry Raine Antiques
Kelvinside House,
Villa Real Road
0207 503935
Appointment advised. Large stock of furniture and general antiques.

CORBRIDGE
(NORTHUMBERLAND)

Dyvil's Antiques
Station Road
0434 633566
2,000 square feet of stripped pine.

Judith Michael Antiques
20a Watling Street
0434 633165
Small furniture and decorative accessories.

Heathcote Antiques
1 Aire Street
0535 635250
A warehouse containing general antiques and pine furniture.

Home to the world's first regular rail freight service (1825) there is still much pride in the achievement. The local antique and junk sources are well worth a browse, and the range on offer is surprisingly comprehensive.

Auctions
Auctioneers include **Hunt Brothers** *(King Street, 0325 352328)*, with sales every six weeks, **Tarn Bainbridge** *(Northern Rock House, High Row, 0325 462633)*, who hold about six sales a year and **Thomas Watson** *(11 Northumberland Street, 0325 462559)*, who have sales of furniture and household effects every Tuesday.

Brown's Popular Mart
26 Hollyhurst Road (Shop);
Geneva Lane (Warehouse)
0325 354769
Extensive range of general antiques and some furniture. A popular source of low-cost items and varied collectables.

Bygones
3–5 McMullen Road
0325 461399

Victoriana, country antiques, fireplaces and collectors' items – some budget, some better quality, at a range of prices.

Collectables
154 Gladstone Street
0325 351195
General antiques and collectors' items.

Dotherbys
Clarks Yard, off High Road
0325 380333
Furniture, general antiques, architectural items. Saturday only.

The Quest
417 North Road
0325 286156
General antiques and collectors' items. Only open in the afternoon.

Alan Ramsey Antiques
Unit 10, Dudley Road,
Yarm Road Industrial Estate
0325 464860
Open Tuesday, Thursday and Saturday. An extensive selection of mid- to upper-range and shipping furniture in a trade warehouse.

Second Handtique Shop
119 Gladstone Street
0325 489007
Household clearance items and furniture.

Tango Curios
3a Houndgate
0325 465768
Collectors' items and general antiques.

Victoriana
5 Bucktons Yard
0325 284182 (home)
General antiques, bric-a-brac, collectors' items and furniture,

including mid-range and less expensive pieces.

Wrotts & Swindlers
85 Victoria Road
0325 383484
Mid-range Victorian and Edwardian furniture and general effects.

DENHOLME
(WEST YORKSHIRE)

Ye Olde Curiosity Shop
23 New Road
0274 542756
Furniture, bric-a-brac, general antiques, shipping goods.

DONCASTER
(SOUTH YORKSHIRE)

Antiques & Bargain Stores
26 Market Place
0302 344857
General collectables, bric-a-brac, toys, dolls, weapons and curios.

WH Brown, auctioneers
28 Netherhall Road
0302 367766
Monthly general sales; occasional antique sales.

Dannys
169 Sepulchre Gate West
0302 321261
Smaller secondhand basics.

Doncaster Auction Rooms
Queens Road
0302 328664
Weekly mixed sales. Part of the premises operates as a general antique market.

Doncaster Sales & Exchange
20 Copley Road
0302 344857

Small antiques, curios and collectables.

DURHAM
(COUNTY DURHAM)

Capercailzie
Langley Moor
091 378 0175
Furniture and general antiques.

Langley Moor Auction Rooms
Rear of Front Street, Littleburn Lane
091 378 2009
Sales every Tuesday.

Old & Gold
88 Clearpath
091 386 0728
Small antiques, collectors' items and jewellery.

EASINGWOLD
(NORTH YORKSHIRE)

Mrs Reynolds
42 Long Street
0347 21078
Victoriana, collectables and general antiques.

White House Farm Antiques
Thirsk Road
0347 21479
About two miles north on A19. Vernacular and country antiques, stoneware and garden ornaments, architectural salvage. A long-established dealer with a varied and interesting selection of goods. Appointment advised.

EASTBURN
(WEST YORKSHIRE)

Kelly Antiques
41 Main Road
0535 653002

Pine furniture and general antiques.

FILEY
(NORTH YORKSHIRE)

Cairncross & Sons
31 Bellevue Street
0723 513287
Stockists of militaria, medals and associated items.

Filey Antiques
1 Bellevue Street
0723 513440
General antiques, pictures, bric-a-brac, jewellery, collectors' items – a small shop but usually with a well-varied mix.

FISHLAKE
(SOUTH YORKSHIRE)

Fishlake Antiques
Pinfold Lane
0302 841411
Country furniture, stripped pine, clocks, tools and lamps, plus assorted farm accessories, particularly related to the wheel, including some original wright's tools.

FLAMBOROUGH
(HUMBERSIDE)

Lesley Berry Antiques
The Manor House
0262 850943
Jewellery – especially jet and amber – furniture, pictures, metalware, textiles and collectors' items.

FLAXTON
(NORTH YORKSHIRE)

Elm Tree Antiques
Elm Tree Farm
090486 462
Mid- to upper-range furniture, antiques and collectors' items.

GARGRAVE
(NORTH YORKSHIRE)

Forge Cottage Antiques
22/24 High Street
Small antiques and collectors' items.

Gargrave Gallery
48 High Street
0756 749641
Appointment advisable. General antiques and collectors' items.

GATESHEAD
(TYNE AND WEAR)

Boaden's of Hexham
28 The Boulevarde,
Antique Village, Metrocentre
091 460 0358
One of a number in Europe's largest shopping mega-complex offering a mix of general antiques, collectors' items and reproduction.

Uncle Sam's Shop
3 Collingwood Street
091 438 2888
General secondhand goods.

GOSFORTH
(TYNE AND WEAR)

The Causey Antique Shop
Causey Street
Small collectors' items, silver and general antiques.

H & S Collectables
149 Salters Road
091 284 6626
Bric-a-brac, clocks and watches, collectors' items.

GREAT DRIFFIELD
(HUMBERSIDE)

The Crested China Co.
The Station House
0377 47042

Goss crested and souvenir china, 60 years old and upwards.

Dee & Atkinson, auctioneers
Exchange Street
0377 43151
General sales every Saturday fortnight, plus six antique sales a year.

GREAT HOUGHTON
(SOUTH YORKSHIRE)

Farmhouse Antiques
7 High Street
0226 753263
General antiques, art deco, collectors' items and furniture, including stripped pine. Stock is eclectic and includes interesting variants from the norm such as Susie Cooper ceramics.

GREEN HAMMERTON
(NORTH YORKSHIRE)

The Main Pine Company
Grangewood, The Green
0423 330451
An extensive range of pine furniture, architectural items, bric-a-brac, linen and collectors' items.

GRIMSBY
(HUMBERSIDE)

England's largest fishing port, instantly recognisable to homeward-bound mariners by its 300-foot-high dockside water tower – an 1851 replica of Siena's Torre del Mangia.

Abbeygate Antiques Centre
14 Abbeygate, Bethlehem Street
0472 361129

Several dealers trading in a range of antiques and collectors' items.

Goodman Gold
47 Pasture Street
0472 341301
Jewellery, collectors' items, small furniture and bric-a-brac in a limited space but with a good mix of stock, much of it at low cost.

The Price Is Right
88 Hental Avenue
0472 344993
General secondhand and house clearance lines.

Simon Antiques
7 Saunders Street
0472 360740
Open strictly by appointment. Bric-a-brac, furniture, collectors' items and jewellery.

GUISBOROUGH
(CLEVELAND)

Atrium Antiques
12 Chaloner Street
0287 632777
Long-established local dealer in furniture, clocks, porcelain, jewellery and general antiques.

HALIFAX
(WEST YORKSHIRE)

A prosperous textile town with a taste for the opulent, Halifax decided that the architect most suited to designing its majestic city hall should be the best available, and so it had to be Charles Barry, famous for his tour-de-force, the Houses of Parliament. For the burghers of Halifax, however, it was to be the restrained Italianate rather than the flamboyant Gothic style that was chosen. In the same

spirit, one dealer said, 'People around here know what they want, and it's got to be damned good.' A great deal of it is, whether it's functional junk or exotic architectural salvage.

Ken Balme Antiques

12 Keighley Road
0422 344193
General antiques and collectors' items, including porcelain, glass and commemorative ware.

Collectors' Old Toy Shop

89 Northgate
0422 360434
Toys, clocks, automatica and collectors' items.

Halifax Antiques Centre

Queens Road
0422 366657
An extensive range of collectors' and decorative items, furniture, automatica, art deco, porcelain, linen and general antiques in a large complex with additional warehousing.

Halifax Sell-it Centre

Miall Street,
off Pellon Lane
0422 356766
A large selection of secondhand furniture and house clearance goods.

Hillside Antiques

Denholme Gate Road,
Hipperholme
0422 202744
Collectors' items, porcelain, glass, metalware and small general antiques.

North Bridge Antiques

571 North Bridge
0422 358474
General antiques and shipping goods.

The Piece Hall

Halifax
Regular markets for general goods, but with some furniture, metalware and antiques, organised by the City Council in premises where merchant weavers used to sell their cloth.

Scott & Varey

10 Prescott Street
0422 366928
Furniture and metalware, including decorative cast iron, and general antiques.

Andy Thornton Architectural Antiques Ltd

Victoria Mills,
Stainland Road,
Greetland
0422 377314
One of the country's leading architectural salvagers, with everything from shutter knobs to entire mahogany-panelled rooms, plus some reproduction, all displayed in an enormous former mill. The range on offer includes ecclesiastical, commercial and domestic architectural salvage plus garden ironwork and ornaments. A high-powered and well-organised set up.

HARROGATE
(NORTH YORKSHIRE)

Bond Street with a northern accent, say some, and certainly the stock on offer from the majority of the forty-odd dealers is almost entirely for those with up-market tastes and the matching resources. Even so, there are a few outlets with some possibilities for the less well-heeled.

Antiques & Collectables
37–39 Cheltenham Crescent
0423 521897
Jewellery, silver, collectors'
items.

Bloomers
41 Cheltenham Crescent
0423 569389
Period costume, fans, samplers,
linen and textiles.

Dragon Antiques
10 Dragon Road
0423 562037
Established almost 40 years and
well-known as a source of old
postcards, it also sells glass,
porcelain, collectors' items and
ephemera.

The Ginnel
Harrogate Antique Centre,
off Parliament Street
0423 508857
A complex of around 30
dealers, mostly specialist and all
trading in high-quality antiques
and collectables.

Montpelier Mews Antique Market
12 Montpelier Street
0423 530484
A wide selection of antiques
and collectors' items including
jewellery, bric-a-brac, furnishing
items, paintings and prints. The
market is adjacent to one of the
town's well-known larger
antique shops, **Weatherell's**.

Morphets, auctioneers
4–6 Albert Street
0423 530030
General sales every Thursday at
noon.

Traditional Interiors
Library House, Regent Parade
0423 560452
Pine and country furniture,
metalware, kitchenalia, treen
and collector items.

Used Furniture Centre
Cambridge Terrace
0423 505757
Distinctly un-Harrogate in its
ethos, stocks an appealing if
unambitious range of practical
secondhand basics.

HARTLEPOOL
(CLEVELAND)

Hartlepool Auction Rooms
Andrew Street
0429 275406
Sales every second Thursday.
There is also a shop selling
secondhand furniture.

HAWORTH
(WEST YORKSHIRE)

Haworth Antiques
Lees Mill, Lees Lane
0535 643535
An wide range of furniture and
general antiques in a village
famed for its Brontë
connections. Very much geared
towards trade buyers so a
telephone call is advised before
visiting.

HAYDON BRIDGE
(NORTHUMBERLAND)

Haydon Bridge Antiques
3 Shaftoe Street
0434 684200
Mid-range Victorian furniture,
pictures and shipping goods.

Revival Beds
Oddfellows Workshop,
Shaftoe Street
0434 684755
Traditional four-poster and half
tester beds.

HEBDEN BRIDGE
(WEST YORKSHIRE)

Cornucopia Antiques
9 West End
0422 844497
Furniture, bric-a-brac,
kitchenalia and lighting
accessories. Open Thursday to
Saturday.

HELMSLEY
(NORTH YORKSHIRE)

**Westway Cottage
Restored Pine**
*Ashdale Road
and 28 Bondgate
0439 70172*
Victorian pine furniture and
some general antiques.

HESSLE (HUMBERSIDE)

The Antique Parlour
21 The Weir
0482 643329
Bric-a-brac, collectors' items,
general antiques, curios and
unusual objects from a
rummageworthy outlet of some
25 years' standing.

HEXHAM
(NORTHUMBERLAND)

Famous for its ancient abbey,
with a Saxon crypt which
incorporates earlier Roman
masonry, it is also home to the

PHRENOLOGY

Although the phrenological head – a porcelain or plaster
bust with areas of the cranium delineated and labelled –
strikes most people as a weird curiosity, phrenology once
purported to be a 'rational science' which aimed to analyse
the localised functions of the brain. The system was
invented by a German physician, Franz Gall, who won an
early convert in George Combe, an Edinburgh lawyer, who
soon set about making the new 'science' into a cult.
Phrenology was based on the belief that the brain had 37
faculties, each of which was registered on the surface of
the skull. The virtues and failings of everyone could be
assessed easily and defects rectified by education. Combe's
credibility was helped along by media interest. Horace
Greeley, of *New Yorker* fame, was a devotee, as was Robert
Chambers, whose *Journal* was one of the most widely read
periodicals of the time. Marriage to Celia, daughter of the
great Sarah Siddons (although only after a thorough
phrenological inspection) also advanced Combe's cause, as
did the fact that his brother Andrew was physician to the
young Queen Victoria. Combe's *Constitution of Man*
became a bestseller and he attained the status of a guru.
Famous heads, living and dead, were subjected to
phrenological examination – Haydn, Burns, Goethe,
Sheridan, even President Ulysses S Grant – ended up with a
phrenological report. When phrenology crossed the
Atlantic, however, its commercial potential was viewed
more cynically, at least by the notorious Fowler brothers,
who turned the 'science' into a fairground sideshow.

first purpose-built prison in Britain (*circa* 1330). The atmosphere today is rather more sedate than it was in the era of cross-border skirmishing, and the antique business plays a significant role in the local retail economy.

Arthur Boaden Antiques
29–30 Market Place
0434 603187
Mid- to upper-range furniture, porcelain, paintings and jewellery plus some bric-a-brac and less prestigious collectables.

Candle Lane Antiques
3 Back Market Street
0434 606420
Antique and secondhand furniture, jewellery and militaria, plus some collectables.

Chattels Aladdin's Cave
The Bus Station
0434 603158
Five showrooms of furniture, bric-a-brac, pictures, clocks and jewellery.

The Eastgate Saleroom
3 Eastgate
0434 605200
Secondhand furniture and bric-a-brac.

Hedley's
3 St Mary's Chare
0434 603851
Mid-range furniture and general antiques.

Hexham Antiques
6 Rear Battle Hill
0434 603851
A large showroom with a mix

of furniture, clocks, bric-a-brac, treen and collectors' items, to pre-war. Much of high quality (and corresponding price) but some good browsing opportunities too.

The Old Warehouse
45 Hallstile Bank
0434 600510
Primarily Georgian, Victorian, Edwardian and stripped pine furniture, but also large decorative items and some small general antiques and collectables.

Turn of the Century Antiques
8 Market Street
0434 607621
General antiques, collectors' items, furniture, books, bric-a-brac, rural and decorative items and some shipping goods. Prices are often on the modest side.

HOLMBRIDGE
(WEST YORKSHIRE)

Upperbridge Antiques
9 Huddersfield Road
0484 687200
Collectors' items, curios, metalware, pottery, linen, small antiques.

HUDDERSFIELD
(WEST YORKSHIRE)

A major textile and engineering centre which gave the world Prime Minister Harold Wilson, actress June Whitfield, the amateur rugby league and some excellent choral music.

Auctions
Auctioneers include **Eddison** (*4–6 High Street, 0484 666680*),

Newtons *(69 Bradshaw Street, Honley, 0484 666680)* and **Frank Whitworth** *(Wood Street, 0484 427267).*

Beau Monde Antiques
343a Bradford Road, Fartown
0484 427565
Furniture, bric-a-brac, collectors' items and general antiques. A traditional outlet, with prices often below the average. These sizeable premises offer much scope for rummaging.

Berry Brow Antiques
92 Dodds Road, Berry Brow
0484 663320
Mid-range furniture, porcelain and bric-a-brac.

Brook Street Bric-a-Brac Market
Brook Street
Held every Saturday.

Heritage Antiques
10 Byram Arcade, Westgate
0484 514667
General antiques and collectors' items.

Huddersfield Antiques
170 Wakefield Road, Moldgreen
0484 539747
General antiques, ephemera, collectors' items and bric-a-brac, plus a trade and shipping warehouse stocking larger antiques.

Second Childhood
26 Byram Arcade, Westgate
0484 603854
Toys, teddys, dolls, dolls' houses and associated items.

Bruised or broken teddies and dolls will be rejuvenated to order.

HULL (HUMBERSIDE)

A principal east coast port and ferry terminal, where the antiques business is largely governed by the continental shipping trade. Its most famous son was local MP and anti-slavery campaigner William Wilberforce, whose house is now a museum.

Gilbert Bateson, auctioneers
Edwardian Auction Galleries, Wiltshire Road
0482 500500
Household sales held on Wednesday.

Boothferry Antiques
388 Wincolmlee
0482 666033
A large and varied selection of furniture, some period and much of it authentic pine, as well as general antiques and assorted shipping goods at prices that range right across the board.

De Grey Antiques
96 De Grey Street, Beverley Road
0482 442184
Mid-range furniture, general antiques, porcelain. glass, metalware, oil lamps and a variety of other collectors' items.

H Evans & Sons, auctioneers
1 St James's Street, Hessle Road
0482 23033
Fortnightly general sales, and intermittent antique sales.

Grannie's Parlour & Grannie's Treasures

33 Anlaby Road
0482 228258
Collectors' items, kitchenalia, toys, dolls and ephemera. On the first floor is a mini-market of four dealers offering a range of collectors' items; period clothing, ephemera, advertising goods, bric-a-brac and small furniture. A worthwhile source of the interesting and usefully picturesque as well as an excellent opportunity for pottering around, with some good purchasing potential as a bonus.

Lesley's Antiques

329 Hessle Road
0482 23986
Antiques, collectors' items, bric-a-brac, budget priced furniture and shipping goods.

Geoffrey Mole Antiques

400 Wincolmlee
0482 27858
More than 12,500 square feet of general antiques and shipping furniture.

Pearson Antiques

The Warehouse,
4 Dalton Street
0482 29647
Trade and shipping warehouse with an extensive stock of furniture, general antiques and shipping items as well as some taxidermy and metalware. Strong on middle-market variety.

Paul Wilson Ltd

Perth Street West
0482 447923
Country furniture, mostly British, Irish and continental pine.

ILKLEY
(WEST YORKSHIRE)

Keith Richardson Antiques

26 Leeds Road
0943 600045
Jewellery, porcelain, dolls, bric-a-brac and collectors' items.

KEIGHLEY
(WEST YORKSHIRE)

Barleycote Hall Antiques

2 Janet Street,
Crossroads
0535 644776
A varied selection of mid-range furniture, pictures, clocks, period costume, jewellery and collectors' items, in a remarkable setting,. An interesting place to explore, and in itself something of a local institution.

Simon Byrne

Unit 6, East Burne Mills,
Main Road, East Burne
0535 663439
Large converted mill with across-the-range antique stripped pine furniture and general items.

Richardson Antiques

72 Howarth Road,
Crossroads
0535 644982
Furniture, general antiques and shipping goods.

KIRK DEIGHTON
(NORTH YORKSHIRE)

Elden Antiques

23 Ashdale View
0937 584770
General antiques, small furniture and a variety of collectables.

KNARESBOROUGH
(NORTH YORKSHIRE)

After browsing through this picturesque town's antique shops and visiting its 14th-century castle, visitors should seek out the dropping well, in which objects are petrified with lime, and Nancy Button's house, which is carved out of rock.

Bowkett
9 Abbey Road
0423 866112
Small furniture, general antiques, metalware, books and collectors' items, including crested china, transferware pot lids and other fine bric-a-brac.

Cheapside Antiques
4 Cheapside
0423 867779
General antiques, furniture, collectors' items.

The Emporium
Market Flat Lane,
Lingerfield
0423 868539
General antiques, pine furniture and shipping goods in showroom premises plus large warehouse.

Reflections
23 Waterside
0423 862005
Mid-range furniture, paintings, prints, books and general antiques, plus collectors' items and bric-a-brac.

Charles Shaw
The Old Vicarage,
2 Station Road
0423 867715
Sporting books, paintings and artefacts, plus some smaller antiques, taxidermy and general country-related items.

LEEDS
(WEST YORKSHIRE)

The post-industrial reputation of West Yorkshire's largest city has gained immensely from the international piano competition that takes place there every three years. The remains of an opulent past are still much in evidence, typified by the baroque revival town hall.

Acorn Antiques
599 Meanwood Road
0532 740434
General antiques, furniture, porcelain and various collectors' items.

Aladdin's Cave
19 Queens' Arcade
0532 842425
Jewellery, bric-a-brac and collectors' items. Small, well-stocked shop with generally good prices.

The Antique Exchange
400 Kirkstall Road
0532 743513
Mid-range furniture, particularly satinwoods.

Aquarius Antiques
Abbey Mills,
Abbey Road
0532 789216
Restoration and sale of mid-range furniture and general antiques.

P & JM Bishop
169 Town Street, Rodley
0532 563071
General antiques and bric-a-brac.

Broadway Antiques
356 Kirkstall Road
0532 780749
Furniture and general antiques.

Burley Antiques
170–172 Kirkstall Hill
0532 434230
Mostly furniture, generally in
the affordable category,
including some period and
brownwood, pine, pre-war oak
and shipping. Prices range from
a fiver to about £800.

Car Boot Sale
Sunday at Cross Green
Industrial Estate.

Coins International
1–2 Melbourne Street
0532 434230
Coins, medals, curios, jewellery
and collectors' items.

Geary Antiques
114 Richardshaw Lane,
Stanningley
0532 564122
An outlet of 60 years' standing
with mid-range furniture and
general antiques, including
metalware, in large premises.

Hayton Antiques
166 Town Street,
Stanningley
0532 394401/625696 (home)
Irregular hours. Furniture,
house clearance lines, general
small goods.

Howarth Antiques
169 Cardigan Road
0532 306204
General secondhand and pre-
war furniture.

Kirkstall Antiques
366 Kirkstall Road
0532 757367
Furniture, including stripped
pine, general antiques and
shipping goods, plus a range of
smaller collectables. Stock
includes some low-cost
possibilities.

C Leek
48 Monkbridge Road
0532 740065
Secondhand furniture.

Mark's
9 Sheepscar Street South
0532 433040
Secondhand furniture and
house clearance items.

The Oxfam Shop
North Lane, Headingley
0532 746349
Furniture, bric-a-brac and
general secondhand goods.

Bryan Smith Antiques
26–28 Chapeltown, Pudsey
0532 555815
A mixed stock of mid-range
furniture, general antiques and
collectors' items, including
pictures and bric-a-brac.

Thursday Market
Kirkgate (local authority)
0532 476948
Secondhand goods.

Waterloo Antiques Centre
Waterloo House, Crown Street,
behind Corn Exchange
0532 444187
About 40 to 50 dealers with a
varied selection of furniture,
bric-a-brac, specialist lines and
general antiques.

Woodstock Antiques
2 High Street
0532 381310
A comprehensive range of
furniture, mid-range to budget.
Owner has a second shop at
Headingley

Year Dot
15 Market Street Arcade
0532 460860
Porcelain, metalware, pictures,
clocks and collectors' items.

Across-the-range quality, with some low-cost items.

LEPTON
(WEST YORKSHIRE)

KLM & Co. Antiques
The Antique Shop,
Wakefield Road
0484 607548
A large selection of mid-range and shipping furniture.

LEYBURN
(NORTH YORKSHIRE)

Tennant's, auctioneers
Harmby Road
0969 23780
On a five-acre site, with 40,000 square feet of covered space, this has to be the largest UK saleroom complex outside London. Frequent mega-sales of 1,000 lots or more attract large crowds and even the occasional helicopter arrival to the swish new custom-built premises. The operation is a calculated gamble that paid off, showing a 65% increase in turnover during recessionary 1991-92. The range is all-embracing, from boxes of house clearance cheapos at a few pounds to a suite of brass-inlaid rosewood furniture at almost a quarter of a million.

MALTON
(NORTH YORKSHIRE)

Boulton & Cooper, auctioneers
St Michaels House, Market Place
0653 692151
Monthly antique and fortnightly general sales at various venues.

Malton Antique Market
2 Old Maltongate
0653 692732
Mid-range furniture, general

antiques and bric-a-brac.

Mathew Maw Antiques
18 Castlegate
0653 694638
Furniture and shipping goods.

MARKET WEIGHTON
(HUMBERSIDE)

Grannie's Attic
Kiplingcotes Station
0430 810284
In operation since Dr Beeching's axe fell in the early 1960s, this use is perhaps not what the Victorians intended, but if you have to lose a station you might as well gain a good junk and antiques shop, and this is the case here. Stock in the former stationmaster's office and waiting rooms is diverse and interesting, and includes furniture, much of it budget, curios, bric-a-brac, kitchenalia, metalware and collectors' items.

Hornsey & Sons, auctioneers
33 High Street
0430 872551
Sales at intermittent intervals.

MARKINGTON
(NORTH YORKSHIRE)

Daleside Antiques
Hinks Hall Lane
0765 677888
Mid- to upper-range furniture and decorative items, plus pine and architectural antiques.

MELMERBY
(NORTH YORKSHIRE)

Terry Kindon Antiques
Unit 23 Melmerby Industrial Estate
0765 640522

Furniture, stripped pine, shipping goods.

MENSTON
(WEST YORKSHIRE)

Antiques
101 Bradford Road
0943 877634
Samplers, linen, porcelain and general antiques.

MIDDLESBOROUGH
(CLEVELAND)

Bradley's Antiques
327 Linthorpe
0642 850518
General antiques, collectables, jewellery, bric-a-brac and shipping items.

Look In
178a Union Street
0642 217180
Secondhand furniture and house clearance goods.

Seconds Best
58 Eastbourne Road
0642 812461
Secondhand and pre-war furniture and house clearance goods.

MIRFIELD
(WEST YORKSHIRE)

David Brooke Antiques
9a Pratt Lane
0924 492483
General antiques and collectors' pieces, including commemorative ware.

MORPETH
(NORTHUMBERLAND)

**Louis Johnson,
auctioneers**
63 Bridge Street
0670 513025

Monthly Saturday sales.

Mother Goose
12 Goose Hill
0670 518815
A general range of furniture, Victorian to pre-war, mixed bric-a-brac, fireplace accessories and general antiques. A small shop but usually with some good findables.

Pottery Bank
43 Bullers Green
0670 516160
General antiques and collectables.

NEWCASTLE
UPON TYNE
(TYNE AND WEAR)

Once the coal capital of the world, and the victim of frenetic planning in the 60s, the city still has a great deal going for it, including much Geordie optimism, some excellent auctions and a varied selection of antique and junk shops. Stockton and Darlington may have the first railway, but this is where they made the locomotives for it.

All Sorts
1a–b Bolingbroke Street, Heaton
091 276 0855
Budget furniture and secondhand house clearance goods.

**Anderson & Garland,
auctioneers**
*Marlborough House,
Marlborough Crescent*
091 232 6278
Sales every two months, with fortnightly general sales at Crawcrook *(091 413 834)*. A popular fixture for local junk and antique enthusiasts, both

trade and public, and usually with better-than-average prospects.

The Antiques Centre
St Mary's Place East,
Vine Lane
091 232 9832
A number of dealers trading in a variety of general antiques, furniture and collectors' items.

The Bargain Cave
1a Kingsley Terrace,
Westgate Road
091 226 0349
Flatfillers and secondhand basics.

Bygones
Rear of 141 Jesmond Road
091 281 7511
Mid-range and budget furniture.

Heaton Antiques
111 Heaton Park Road
091 265 5144/091 224 2855
Pre-war furniture, house clearance items and shipping goods.

Owen Humble
11–12 Clayton Road
091 281 4602
An extensive selection of furniture, small collectables and general antiques.

Lyndhurst Antiques
231 Jesmond Road
091 281 7286
Victorian to pre-war furniture, bric-a-brac and general antiques.

Thomas Miller, auctioneers
18–22 Gallowgate
091 232 5617
Weekly two-day sales with much budget and some interesting collectables.

Out of the Ark
8 Holly Avenue, Jesmond
091 281 5412
Furniture, general antiques and some collectables.

Shiners
123 Jesmond Road
091 281 6474
Fireplaces and general architectural salvage displayed in extensive premises.

W & J Walker's Antiques
231 Jesmond Road
091 281 7286
Furniture and general antiques.

NORHAM
(NORTHUMBERLAND)

Stewarts Antiques
6 and 8 West Street
0289 382376
Porcelain, bric-a-brac, collectors' items.

NORTHALLERTON
(NORTH YORKSHIRE)

Collectors' Corner
145–146 High Street
0609 775199
One of three shops in town with a range of general antiques and collectors' items.

NORTH SHIELDS
(TYNE AND WEAR)

Peter Coulson Antiques
8–10 Queen Alexandra
091 257 9761
Furniture, clocks and general antiques.

Maggie May's
49 Kirton Park Terrace
091 257 0076
General antiques, collectors' items, bric-a-brac, furniture, decorative items and pictures.

OTLEY
(WEST YORKSHIRE)

Butterchurn Antiques
32–36 Bondgate
0943 462579
Furniture, including stripped pine and general antiques.

Yap, Yap & Yap
7 Kirkgate Arcade
0943 467495
Textiles and general antiques.

PATELEY BRIDGE
(NORTH YORKSHIRE)

Cat in the Window Antiques
22 High Street
0423 711343
Jewellery – including amber, coral and jet – linen, lace, bric-a-brac, small furniture and collectors' items. A charming little emporium with a great deal going for it.

PATRINGTON
(HUMBERSIDE)

Clyde Antiques
12 Market Place
0964 630650
Furniture and general antiques.

PICKERING
(NORTH YORKSHIRE)

Antiques & Things
South Gate
0751 76142
Collectors' items, toys, dolls, textiles, linen and general antiques.

RIPON
(NORTH YORKSHIRE)

Skellgate Curios
2 Low Skellgate
0765 601290

General antiques and collectors' items, plus some silver and jewellery.

Yesteryear
6–7 High Skellgate
0765 607801
General antiques and bric-a-brac, jewellery, metalware and linen, with some budget potential.

ROTHBURY
(NORTHUMBERLAND)

Merlin Antiques
Townfoot
0669 21156
Pine, general antiques, decorative items and painted furniture.

Rothbury Auction Mart
Station Road
0669 20392
Intermittent general sales in the livestock ring.

ROTHERHAM
(SOUTH YORKSHIRE)

Roger Appleyard Ltd
Fitzwilliam Road,
Eastwood Trading Estate
0709 367670
A large-scale operation with an extensive range of furniture, general antiques and shipping goods covering a wide spectrum, including some low-cost possibilities.

John Shaw Antiques
Broad Street
0709 522340
A comprehensive stock of furniture and antiques, budget to top-of-the-range.

South Yorkshire Antiques
88–94 Broad Street
0709 526514

Established for almost 40 years as a source of furniture, general antiques and shipping goods.

Phillip Turnor Antiques
94a Broad Street,
Parkgate
0709 524640
Mid-range and pre-war furniture and shipping goods.

SALTBURN
(CLEVELAND)

Saltburn Salerooms
3 Diamond Street
0287 622366
Weekly general sales.

SCARBOROUGH
(NORTH YORKSHIRE)

Chapman's Auction Mart
North Street
0723 372424
Fortnightly Monday sales of general secondhand goods and occasionally antiques.

Gordon's Attic
35 Castle Road
0723 375963
Furniture and basics.

Hanover Antiques
10 Hanover Road
0723 374175
Militaria and associated objects, as well as collectors' items and toy cars.

Over the Moon
54 Seamer Road
0723 500027
Furniture and house clearance items.

Shuttleworth's
7 Victoria Road
0723 366278
General antiques.

SCUNTHORPE
(HUMBERSIDE)

Canter & Francis, auctioneers
8 Doncaster Road
0724 858855
Weekly general sales.

Jenny's Bargains
146 Frodingham Road
0724 851447
Secondhand furniture and house clearance goods.

SEAHAM
(COUNTY DURHAM)

Lynden Antiques
East Farm, Dalton-le-Dale
091 581 6321
A warehouse of furniture and decorative antiques, pine, shipping goods and architectural items, many of them interesting and competitively priced.

SETTLE
(NORTH YORKSHIRE)

The Folly Antique Centre
The Folly, Chapel Street
Mid-range furniture, collectors' items and general antiques at a variety of prices. Stock from period to low-cost pre-war.

Nanbrooks
The Roundabout, Duke Street
0729 823324
A long-established source of general small antiques, bric-a-brac, porcelain and books. Some emphasis on quality but well worth browsing too.

Well Cottage Antiques
High Street
0729 823593
Pine, bric-a-brac and ephemera with some raking potential.

SHEFFIELD
(SOUTH YORKSHIRE)

Long associated with the cutlery business – Sheffield knives were used in Chaucer's time – it is also the place where, in 1742, the process of silver plating copper was invented, which is the technique used to make Sheffield plate. Wartime bombing and 1960s planning changed the face of the city but the medieval cathedral and long-established university still provide a sense of continuity.

A & C Antiques
239 Abbeydale Road
0742 589161
Jewellery and general antiques.

Anita's Holme Antiques
144 Holme Lane
0742 336698
Victoriana and general antiques.

Auctions
Auctioneers include **Dowse & Son** *(Cornwall Galleries, Scotland Street, 0742 725858)*, with fortnightly general sales and several specialist sales a year, **Eadon, Lockwood & Riddle** *(Western Saleroom, Crookes, 0742 686244)*, with monthly general sales and occasional antique sales and **Ellis, Willis & Beckett** *(54 Campo Lane, 0742 729667)*, with antique sales twice a year.

Bay Tree Antiques
408 Sharrowvale Road, Ecclesall
0742 666849
Mid-range furniture, bric-a-brac and collectables. Prices start at a few pounds and rise to the low thousands. There are often some unusual and decorative pieces in stock and it is nearly always worth a browse.

Canterbury Place Antiques & Sheffield Pine Centre
Unit E, Lowfield Cutlery Forge, Guernsey Road
0742 336103
An extensive range of stripped pine and general antiques.

Cobwebs
208 Witham Road, Broomhill
0742 681923
Jewellery, pictures, collectors' items and porcelain, many in the lower price range. A popular student haunt.

Dronfield Antiques
375–7 Abbeydale Road
0742 550172
Furniture, general antiques and shipping goods.

Findley Antiques
314 Langsett Road
0742 346088
General antiques, bric-a-brac and shipping items.

Fun Antiques
72 Abbeydale Road
0742 553424
General trade items and shipping goods, including toys, fairground antiques and advertising related objects. Much colour on show, plus a plentiful helping of decorative whimsy.

Greybeard Antiques
101 Station Road
0742 469465
A warehouse, a chapel, plus a shop in Chapeltown, all containing an assortment of furniture and general goods.

Paraphernalia
66–68 Abbeydale Road
0742 550203
Furniture, including stripped

pine, lighting accessories, beds and general antiques.

Salt Antiques
Unit 2, Barmouth Road
0742 582672
Trade and shipping furniture, bric-a-brac, toys and an assortment of general antiques.

Tilley's Vintage Magazine Shop
281 Shoreham Road
0742 752442
Tuesday, Friday and Saturday opening. Treasure-trove of old magazines, newspapers, books and general ephemera. Something of a Mecca for nostalgists brought up on Dan Dare and Roy of the Rovers, who might have played at the neighbouring football ground.

SHIPLEY
(WEST YORKSHIRE)

Price-less Antiques
2 Gaisby Lane
0274 581160
General antiques and bric-a-brac.

SKIPTON
(NORTH YORKSHIRE)

Corn Mill Antiques
High Corn Mill, Chapel Hill
0756 792440
Country furniture, metalware, porcelain, pictures and general antiques. Quality is variable, with some stock at the higher end, although favourably priced pre-war items are also available.

SOUTH CAVE
(HUMBERSIDE)

Penny Farthing Antiques
60 Market Place
0430 422958

Furniture, samplers, linen, lace and collectables. **The Old Copper Shop** in the same street is also worth a browse.

SOUTH SHIELDS
(TYNE AND WEAR)

The Curiosity Shop
16 Frederick Street
091 456 5560
Furniture, porcelain, pictures, jewellery, general antiques.

STAITHES (CLEVELAND)

The Mariners Antiques
High Street
0947 840565
General antiques, oil lamps, bric-a-brac and jewellery.

STATION TOWN
(COUNTY DURHAM)

South Hetton & Windgate Auctions
Station Lane
0429 837245
General sales weekly, antique sales monthly.

STILLINGTON
(NORTH YORKSHIRE)

Pond Cottage Antiques
Brandsby Road
0347 810796
Country furniture and vernacular antiques, metalware, treen and kitchenalia in a traditional village shop with a well-mixed stock.

STOCKTON ON TEES
(CLEVELAND)

The Auction Rooms
17 Bridge Road
0642 607473
General sales every second Tuesday.

STOKESLEY
(NORTH YORKSHIRE)

Three Tuns Antiques
2 Three Tuns Wynd
0642 711377
Jewellery, bric-a-brac,
collectors' items and general
antiques.

SUNDERLAND
(TYNE AND WEAR)

Car Boot Sales
Essentially basic, these
weekend sales begin on
Saturday at Hylton Redhouse
School. On Sunday the sale is at
Sunderland Motor Auctions.
And Monday's sale is at
Crowtree Leisure Centre.

Peter Smith Antiques
12–14 Borough Road
091 567 3537
At more than 20,000 square
feet, one of the largest antiques
warehouses in the North East.
Quality from shipping basics to
upper market. Prices are
remarkably diverse, ranging
from a few pounds to upwards
of ten thousand, but there is a
solid core of mid-range
possibilities.

THIRSK
(NORTH YORKSHIRE)

**Cottage Antiques
& Curios**
1 Market Place
0845 522536
Furniture, bric-a-brac,
metalware, general antiques.

THORNTON LE DALE
(NORTH YORKSHIRE)

Stable Antiques
4 Pickering Road
0751 74435

Small furniture, metalware, bric-
a-brac, silver and collectables.

TOCKWITH
(NORTH YORKSHIRE)

Tomlinson Antiques
Moorside
0423 358833
A large and comprehensive
stock of trade and shipping
furniture as well as some
general antiques.

TODMORDEN
(WEST YORKSHIRE)

Echoes
650a Halifax Road
0706 817505
Jewellery, costume, linen, lace,
samplers and textiles.

TYNEMOUTH
(TYNE AND WEAR)

Car Boot Sales
Held at weekends on the
seafront and in the local school
playing fields.

Renaissance Antiques
11 Front Street
091 259 5555
Victorian and pre-war furniture,
bric-a-brac, metalware and
shipping goods.

Saturday Market
Held beside the station with
some bric-a-brac and
secondhand goods.

WALSDEN
(WEST YORKSHIRE)

Cottage Antiques
788 Rochdale Road
070 681 3612
Furniture, including pine,
kitchenalia and general
antiques.

WETHERBY
(WEST YORKSHIRE)

Car Boot Sales
Wetherby Race Course
091 427 7630 (enquiries)
Held at the race course on
Sundays.

WHITBY
(NORTH YORKSHIRE)

St Hilda's Abbey of AD 657 has
gone, replaced by later remains
which were knocked about a bit
by Zeppelin raiders during the
First World War. It was the scene
of a spirited exchange of views
(over the dating of Easter,
among other things) between
clergymen in 663. The two best-
known local products were
black jet jewellery and Captain
James Cook, who served his
apprenticeship there before
sailing to explore the coast of
Australia. The town also staked a
(disputed) claim to fame as the
setting for Bram Stoker's
Dracula.

Aird Gordon Antiques
15 Baxtergate
0947 601515
Jewellery, including Whitby jet,
collectors' items and small
general antiques.

Auctions
**Nationwide Fine Art &
Furniture** (*West End
Salerooms, The Paddock, 0947
603433*) hold fortnightly
household and monthly antique
sales. **Richards & Smith** (*8
Victoria Square, 0947 602298*)
hold general sales on
intermittent Thursdays.

WHITBY JET

'Organised gloom' is the phrase often applied to that great
Victorian institution, the mourning industry. Prince
Albert's untimely death in 1861 was turned to advantage by
those with the wit to gain from it. Sepulchral black slate
mantel clocks began to appear in loyal homes, the silk
mills of Leek, in Staffordshire, suddenly found the demand
for black bombazine was insatiable, and there was an
overnight revival of sombre black Biedermeier furniture.
Few towns, however, were as well placed as the Yorkshire
port of Whitby, which sat at the centre of a seam of a rich
black variety of lignite, or bitumastic shale, now better
known as jet. Vast deposits were worked out of the ground
in the area between Ravenscar and Saltburn, to be made
into highly polished brooches, earrings and necklaces for
the stylishly grief-stricken ladies of Britain. By the 1880s,
however, memories of Prince Albert's death were fading
and rather more louche fin-de-siecle tastes were beginning
to assert themselves. Whitby jet carvers who, naturally,
were dependent upon death for their living, became
something of an endangered species themselves.
Fortunately for them, however, relief arrived just in time
when Queen Victoria, who had done so much for the town
by popularising the mourning cult, obligingly departed
this life herself, and demand picked up.

The Bazaar
7 Skinner Street
0947 602281
Furniture, general antiques, collectors' items, jewellery.

Bobbins Wool Craft Antiques
Wesley Hall, Church Street
0947 600585
General antiques and some interesting oil lamps.

Caedmon House
14 Station Road
0947 602120
Dolls, bric-a-brac, jewellery, general antiques.

Jowsey & Roe
7 Sandgate
0947 602252
Jewellery and small collectors' items, including Whitby jet.

The Mount Antiques
Khyber Pass
0947 604516
Country furniture, kitchenalia, architectural antiques, Victorian and Edwardian tables and dining chairs.

The Quarter Deck
8 Silver Street
Bric-a-brac and collectables.

WHITLEY BAY (TYNE AND WEAR)

Treasure Chest
2–4 Norham Road
091 251 2052
General antiques and collectors' items.

WOOLER (NORTHUMBERLAND)

Hamish Dunn Antiques
17 High Street
0668 81341

A welcoming guddle of furniture, general antiques, bric-a-brac, collectors' items and secondhand books in a double-fronted shop with a showroom at the back.

Hooty's Antiques
West Weetwood Farm
0668 81910
A diversified steading in a Northumbrian rural setting with a range of general antiques, bric-a-brac, loo-commodes, pictures and furniture.

James Miller Antiques
1–5 Church Street
0668 81500
Shop and warehouse with mid-range trade and shipping furniture and general antiques.

YARM (CLEVELAND)

Ruby Snowden Antiques
20 High Street
0642 785363
Mid- to upper-range furniture, jewellery, porcelain and metalware.

YORK (NORTH YORKSHIRE)

Known as Eboracum to the Romans, York was important enough to be the site of Emperor Constantine's coronation, and later became a major Viking settlement, called Jorvik. Young boys are among its most enthusiastic visitors, because of its highly popular railway museum and its long association with the chocolate industry. Others are equally impressed by its 12th-century minster and medieval city walls. The antique and junk business is remarkably diverse, with some good browsing possibilities.

Acomb Antiques
3 Westview Close,
Boroughbridge Road
0904 791999
Furniture, general antiques,
trade and shipping items.

Aladdin's Cave
7 Apollo Street
0904 621405
Furniture and secondhand
goods.

Auctions
Auctioneers include
Summersgill *(Village Hall,*
Main Street Huby, 0904
791131) who hold intermittent
sales in the village and
Wombwell & Sons *(Church*
Hall, Marygate, 0757 288764),
who hold occasional sales in St
Olive's Church Hall, Marygate.

Barker Court Antiques & Bygones
44 Gillygate
0904 622611
Bric-a-brac and collectables.

Bobbins
31–33 Goodramgate
0904 653597
Country furniture, chairs, tools,
clocks and oil lamps.

Bulmer's Selling Service
1–7 Lord Mayor's Walk,
Monkbar
0904 654461
Rummageable secondhand,
collectors' items, odds and ends
and fishing tackle in a
delightfully old-fashioned
clutter within sight of the
famous 'Bile Beans' gable end.

Central Furniture
49–51 Tanner Row
0904 646126
Secondhand furniture and
house clearance items.

Clocks & Gramophones
11 Walmgate
0904 611924
Wind-up gramophones, 78s,
clocks and associated items.

Danby Antiques
61 Heworth Road
0904 415280
Unusual collectors' items,
boxes, old pens, pencils and
anything to do with the art and
craft of writing.

Hunter
22–24 Acomb Road
0904 781161
Secondhand furniture and
house clearance items.

Lendal Antique Centre
2 Lendal
0904 641445
Several dealers trading in a
variety of antiques and
collectors' items.

Newgate Antique Centre
14 Newgate
0904 679844
About six dealers offering a
range of antiques and
collectables.

St John Antiques
26 Lord Mayor's Walk
0904 644263
Furniture, including stripped
pine, bric-a-brac and collectors'
items.

Summersgill, auctioneers
Village Hall, Main Street, Huby
0904 791131
Intermittent sales at the village
halls of Stillington and Huby.

Yates Antiques
5 The Shambles
0904 654821
General antiques and collectors'
items.

NORTH WEST
ENGLAND

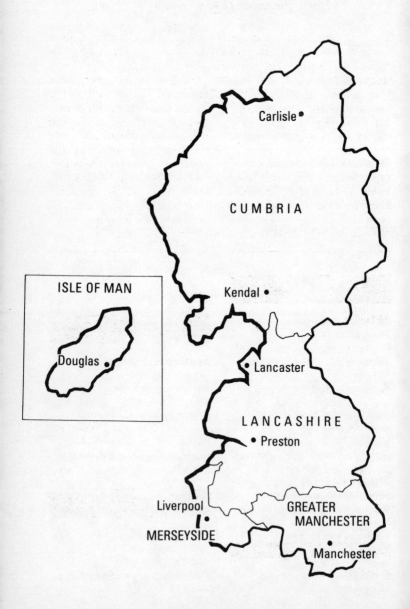

Carlisle

CUMBRIA

ISLE OF MAN

Kendal

Douglas

Lancaster

LANCASHIRE

Preston

Liverpool

GREATER
MANCHESTER

MERSEYSIDE

Manchester

While the 'muck and brass' reputation of industrial Lancashire has perhaps become something of a cliché, the antique and junk business provides evidence enough that the family of means in these parts – even slender means – had an eye for value when it came to furnishing a home.

The front-parlour culture may now be little more than a memory, but the goods and chattels have stayed around to remind us that a wage hard-earned was usually money well spent. In Liverpool and its surrounding area, too, mercantile profit created a market for well-made goods, as well as the usual seaboard tastes for overseas exotica. It takes some finding now, but for those who persist, it's still around, though one or two disconsolate dealers are convinced that the 'really good stuff' won't be around for much longer. Farther up the coast, the trade in Blackpool continues to benefit from a mix of browsing visitors and a low-cost B&B tradition, which provides a market for the robust secondhand. Holidaymakers also visit Cumbria and the Lakes, but here the ethos seems to be rather different. Picturesque Cartmel, for example, supports a dealer specialising in collectable corkscrews.

ACCRINGTON
(LANCASHIRE)

Abbey Auctions
Jacob Street
0254 396466
Strictly retail, despite the name, with secondhand furniture and house clearance items.

Accrington Auctions
St James' Street
0353 381739
General sales every Thursday.

This & That
378–380 Blackburn Road
0254 399202
Basics and flatfillers.

ALLONBY (CUMBRIA)

Cottage Curios
Main Street
General antiques. Open afternoons only.

ASHTON UNDER LYNE
(LANCASHIRE)

Tameside Antiques
Cavendish Mill,
85 Cavendish Street
061 344 5477
An extensive and mixed selection of furniture, period to Edwardian shipping, clocks, pictures and various decorative items.

ATHERTON
(LANCASHIRE)

Victoria's
144–146 Bolton Road
0942 882311
Pine furniture and general antiques.

BARROW IN FURNESS (CUMBRIA)

Vincent Antiques
237 Rawlinson Street
0229 823432
Dealer of more than 25 years' standing, selling bric-a-brac, metalware, jewellery, furniture, pictures and collectors' items.

BIRKENHEAD (MERSEYSIDE)

William Courteney & Sons
11–19 Cross Street
051 647 8693
Furniture, shipping goods, general antiques, collectors' items.

BLACKBURN (LANCASHIRE)

Griffin Furniture
85a Bank Top
0254 664353
Secondhand furniture and house clearance items.

Mitchell's Antiques
76 Bolton Road
0254 664663
Furniture, bric-a-brac, general antiques and jewellery.

Patel Secondhand Goods
5 Lower Audley Street
0254 676989
General house clearance items.

BLACKPOOL (LANCASHIRE)

Despite the effects of cheap Spanish package holidays, the city still manages to coast along on the strength of its famous pleasure beach, illuminations, and Eiffel Tower look-alike, with some help from the conference business. Seaside landladies help keep the local antique and secondhand shops going, although summer trade provides an essential uplift for most of the dealers.

Blackpool Antiques Centre
Back Reads Avenue, Hornby Road
0253 752514
General antiques, collectors' items and shipping furniture.

Peter & Ann Christian
400–402 Waterloo Road
0253 763268
General antiques and furniture, including stripped pine.

Peter Ireland
31 Clifton Street
0253 21588
General antiques, collectors' items, numismatics, militaria, commemorative ware, jewellery.

Nostalgia
95 Coronation Street
0253 293251
Commemorative collectors' items.

Past and Present
126 Harrowside
0253 42729
Bric-a-brac, collectors' items and general antiques. Closed on Wednesday.

Waterhouses Ltd
Exchange Auction Rooms, Caunce Street
0253 22919
Part retail, with a mix of secondhand and new, and part auction, every Wednesday and every second Thursday, with mostly smaller goods and bric-a-brac. Other Blackpool auctioneers include **Gordon**

Round (*4 Bloomfield Road, 0253 43588*), holding general sales each Thursday, and **Charles Ford** (*Royal Oak Buildings, Waterloo Road, 0253 45458*), holding two sales a month.

BOLTON (LANCASHIRE)

Bolton Antique Centre
Central Street
0204 362694
Around 40 dealers trading in a range of general antiques and collectors' items.

Corner Cupboard
2 Hawarden Street
0204 308948
Small general antiques, collectors' items and bric-a-brac. Closed Monday and Wednesday.

The Curiosity Shop
832 Bury Road, Brightmet
0204 21290
A mix of secondhand and house clearance items, budget antiques, bric-a-brac and shipping goods, mostly at the lower end of the price scale.

The Emporium
304 Blackburn Road
0204 397414
Secondhand furniture and house clearance lines.

Last Drop Antique & Collectors' Fair
Last Drop Hotel, Bromley Cross
On Sunday, 40 dealers in general antiques.

Memory Lane Antique Centre
Gilnow Lane, Deane Road
0204 380383
Eleven dealers trading in a variety of general antiques.

G Oakes & Son
160–162 Blackburn Road
0204 26587
Mid-range and budget furniture, bric-a-brac and shipping goods.

Val's
34 Chorley Old Road
0204 34017
Secondhand goods and house clearance items.

BOLTON BY BOWLAND (LANCASHIRE)

Farmhouse Antiques
23 Main Street
0200 446244
A small shop with an eclectic range of goods, including Victoriana, metalware, pottery and porcelain, jewellery and textiles, notably quilts and linen. Appointment advised although usually open at the weekend.

BOWNESS ON WINDERMERE (CUMBRIA)

The Birdcage
College Road
05394 45063
General antiques, oil and gas lamps, small country furniture and collectors' items.

Century Antiques and Victoria Gallery
Victoria Cottage,
13 Victoria Street
05394 44126
General antiques and collectors' items.

Thornton's Antiques Supermarket
North Terrace; also with shop at 4 Victoria Street, Windermere
05394 42930

Furniture, pictures, architectural antiques, shipping items, bric-a-brac and pine.

Utopia Antiques
Lake Road
05394 88464
Country furniture, stripped pine, decorative items. Also worth visiting is **K Thompson**, who has a shop in the same road.

BROUGHTON
(LANCASHIRE)

Cowell & Sons
Church Hill Barn
0772 864551
Strictly by appointment. Architectural antiques, decorative objects, stained glass.

Village Antiques
488 Garstang Road
0772 862648
Jewellery, dolls, toys, collectors' items and general antiques.

BURNLEY
(LANCASHIRE)

Alec's Antiques & Secondhand Goods
16 Plumbe Street
0282 37958
Shipping goods and secondhand furniture, some pre-war.

Burnley Antiques & Secondhand Shop
12 Briercliffe Road
0282 34262
Mid-range furniture to flatfillers and basics.

Brun Lea Antiques
Dane House Mill
3–5 Standish Street
0282 413513

A comprehensive stock of mid-range and shipping furniture and general antiques from an outlet with a generally good trade reputation. The range is mixed and prices can be modest.

Carl's
22a Plumbe Street
0282 39394
General secondhand goods.

Cunningham's
Holden Farm,
Todmorden Road, Briercliffe
0282 32239
Furniture and secondhand goods.

BURSCOUGH
(LANCASHIRE)

West Lancs Antiques
Victoria Mill,
Victoria Street
0704 894634
Over 20,000 square feet of furniture and shipping antiques.

BURY (LANCASHIRE)

Newtons
151 The Rock
061 764 1863
General antiques and collectors' items.

CALDBECK (CUMBRIA)

Victoria Park Antiques
Upton
06974 78413
Mid-range small furniture, porcelain, general antiques and textiles.

CARLISLE (CUMBRIA)

Long-fortified against unwelcome neighbours to the

north, its 12th-century cathedral and castle seems to have fared better than most in the borders. The local auctioneers can be a particularly good source of antique or secondhand furniture and household goods.

Carlisle Antique & Craft Centre
Cecil Hall,
Cecil Street
0228 21970
Six dealers trading in a variety of general antiques and collectors' items, including jewellery, art deco, stripped pine, architectural items, clocks, quilts and linens, textile printing blocks and pictures. Specialities include art pottery by Clarice Cliffe and Susie Cooper, architectural antiques and clocks. There is also a warehouse with an extensive range of trade goods.

The Carlisle Swop Shop
206 Greystone Road
0228 41553
Part-time opening; small secondhand items.

Castle Antiques
16 Fisher Street
0228 49001
Decorative antiques, furniture, including pine, pictures, quilts and textiles and ceramics.

Charm Antiques
5 Lonsdale Street
0228 23035
Mid-range furniture, including pine, bric-a-brac and collectors' items.

Cumbria Auction Rooms
12 Lowther Street
0228 25259
General sales every Monday.

Daisie's Antiques
16a Fisher Street
0228 47198
Jewellery, decorative items, small furniture, linen and textiles.

Dalton & Sons, auctioneers
Botchergate
0228 21102
General sales every Saturday.

Harrison & Hetherington
Borderway Mart,
Rosehill
0228 26292
General sales every Thursday.

Souvenir Antiques
Treasury Court
0228 401281
Collectors' items, coins, jewellery, bric-a-brac, ephemera and small furniture.

CARNFORTH (LANCASHIRE)

The Secondhand Shop
41 New Street
0524 732138
An extensive selection of furniture and house clearance items.

CARTMEL (CUMBRIA)

Bacchus Antiques
Longlands
053 95 36475
Specialists in corkscrews, from curio items costing only a few pounds, to museum-quality examples. Contact either by appointment or mail.

Weekend Rummage Shop
Near the Cavendish Hotel
A useful source of budget goods, although it is only open during the tourist season.

CASTLETOWN
(ISLE OF MAN)

J & H Bell Antiques
22 Arbory Street
0624 822414
Jewellery, porcelain, furniture
and general antiques.

CHARNOCK RICHARD (LANCASHIRE)

Antiques Fair & Market
0257 793773 (enquiries)
A colossal antiques event, held
every week and popularly
known as 'The Bermondsey of
the North', this outdoor market
and warehouse complex has
more than 300 dealers.

CHATBURN
(LANCASHIRE)

Brindle Antiques
6–8 Sawley Road
0200 440025
Furniture and decorative
antiques.

CHORLEY
(LANCASHIRE)

Old Road Antiques
205 Old Road
0257 263564
Furniture and general antiques.

**Smith, Hodgkinson,
McGinty, auctioneers**
St Thomas' Road
0257 263633
Antiques included in household
sale every Tuesday.

CLEVELEYS
(LANCASHIRE)

**Spencer's Quality Used
Furniture**
4 Rossall Road
0253 856462

Furniture and house clearance
goods.

**Smythe Son & Walker,
auctioneers**
174 Victoria Road
0254 852184
Intermittent general sales.

CLITHEROE
(LANCASHIRE)

Castle Antiques
15 Moor Lane
0200 26568
A comprehensive stock of
furniture, decorative items,
stained glass and shipping
goods.

Lee's Antiques
59 Whalley Road
0200 24921
Furniture and general antiques.

McKenna's, auctioneers
0200 4466052
Monthly general sales in
Pendleton Village Hall just
outside the town.

Rebecca Antiques
22 Moor Lane
0200 29461
Furniture, decorative antiques,
garden and architectural items,
metalware and pictures.

COCKERMOUTH
(CUMBRIA)

Cockermouth Antiques
5 Station Street
0900 826746
Furniture, textiles, pottery and
porcelain, books and general
antiques.

**Cockermouth Antiques
Market**
Courthouse, Main Street
0900 824346

Several dealers offering a range of general antiques and collectors' items, from furniture to toys, textiles, jewellery and ephemera. **Bridgehouse Antiques** are adjacent.

Holmes Antiques
1 Market Place
0900 826114
Furniture, pictures and general antiques.

Mitchell's, auctioneers
Station Street
0900 822016
Weekly general auctions on Thursday morning.

Enloc Antiques
Birchenlee Mill, Lenches Road
0282 867101
A former handkerchief mill, now with more than 5,000 square feet of authentic pine furniture, usually with 500 to 700 pieces available for sale at a range of prices. Stained glass and architectural antiques are also sold.

Ingleside Antiques
13 Keighley Road
0282 860046
Furniture, from mid-range Georgian to pre-war shipping, clocks, porcelain, including bisque, metalware, phonographs and general antiques.

The Old Rock
Keighley Road, Trawden,
0282 869478
General antiques, particularly stained glass, domestic and ecclesiastical, and flower arrangements.

The Old Man Antiques
Yewdale Road
053 94 41389
Mid-market general antiques, including clocks and barometers.

Cottage Antiques
135 Blackburn Road
0254 775891
General mid-range antiques and porcelain.

Darwen Antique Centre
Provident Hall,
The Green
0254 760565
Extensive premises, now established more than 20 years, with a browser-friendly range of furniture, pictures, collectors' items and general antiques.

Home Furnishers
81 Duckworth Street
0254 706880
Secondhand furniture.

Jabrex Antiques
61 Duckworth Street
0254 873474
Mid-range and shipping furniture and general antiques.

John Corrin Antiques
73 Circular Road
0624 629655
Mostly mid- to upper-range furniture, plus some smaller antiques, including clocks and barometers.

ECCLESTON
(LANCASHIRE)

Bygone Times
Grove Mill, The Green
0257 453780
Portobello Road meets
Disneyland in this seven-days-a-
week mega-market of around
120 dealers trading in a range
of antiques and decorative
items, from collecting
specialities and architectural
salvage to Americana and
colourful, whimsical, eccentric
and unclassifiable items.

EDENFIELD
(LANCASHIRE)

The Antique Shop
17 Market Street
070 682 3107
A large and comprehensive
range of furniture, general
antiques, clocks, decorative
items and shipping goods.

FARNWORTH
(LANCASHIRE)

Aladdin's Cave
68 Market Street
0204 861134
Collectors' items, enamel
badges, militaria, jewellery.

Ian's
130 Worsley Road North
0204 792622
General secondhand furniture
and occasional shipping pieces.

FENISCOWLES
(LANCASHIRE)

The Old Smithy
726 Preston Old Road
0254 209943
Architectural and decorative
items, furniture, lighting
accessories, costume and
textiles, metalware, musical
instruments, jewellery and
collectors' items. A highly
eclectic mix.

FLEETWOOD
(LANCASHIRE)

Ernie Used Furniture
15 Poulton Street
0253 771112
Secondhand furniture and
house clearance items.

The Passage Antiques
31 St Peter's Place
0253 770760
General antiques and collectors'
items.

GARSTANG
(LANCASHIRE)

The Auction Room
Catterall Gates Lane
0995 605982
Sales every Saturday fortnight.

**Claire's Antiques &
Auction Galleries**
Wheatsheaf Buildings, Park Hill
0995 605702
Mostly mid- to upper-market
porcelain, jewellery and smaller
antiques on retail side; also
intermittent auctions.

GRASMERE
(CUMBRIA)

Aladdin's Cave
Helm House, Langdale Road
05394 35774
Cheap to mid-range furniture,
country antiques, metalware
and pictures.

The Stables
College Street
05394 35453
Bric-a-brac, metalware, books,
pictures and lamps.

GREAT HARWOOD
(LANCASHIRE)

Benny Charlesworth's Snuff Box
51 Blackburn Road
0254 888550
A mini-emporium with a great clutter of stock, including furniture, collectors' items, textiles, jewellery, pictures, bric-a-brac and general antiques.

Duke's Stores
92–98 Queen Street
0254 876602
Secondhand furniture and house clearance goods.

GREYSTOKE
(CUMBRIA)

Roadside Antiques
Watson's Farm, Greystoke Gill
07684 83279
Mid-range furniture and bric-a-brac, jewellery, porcelain, collectors' items and general antiques.

HASLINGDEN
(LANCASHIRE)

Brown's Antiques
8 Church Street
0706 224888
A large choice of furniture, antiques and shipping goods.

Fieldings
176–180 Blackburn Road
0254 263358
An extensive stock of furniture, including pine, decorative items, clocks and automatica, toys, vintage motorbikes and car accessories, steam engines and shipping goods.

Norgrove's Clock Shop
38 Bury Road
0706 211995
Appointment required. Across-the-range antique clocks.

Taylors, auctioneers
15 Greenfield Street
0706 214870
General sales every Saturday.

HESWALL
(MERSEYSIDE)

The Antique Shop
120–122 Telegraph Road
051 342 1053
Jewellery, bric-a-brac and collectors' items.

HIGH NEWTON
(CUMBRIA)

WRS Architectural Antiques
Yew Tree Barn,
Low Newton,
Grange-over-Sands
05395 31498
A range of general antiques, furniture and architectural and garden items in a vast and rambling warehouse complex plus outdoor yard. Some good browsing with much variation in price and stock.

HOLLINWOOD
(LANCASHIRE)

Fernlea Antiques
305 Manchester Road
061 682 0589
One of two dealers in the street selling furniture, general antiques and shipping goods.

HOLME (CUMBRIA)

JBW Antiques
Green Farm, Duke Street
0524 781377
Jewellery, collectors' items, silver, porcelain, small furniture and brass beds.

HORWICH
(LANCASHIRE)

Alan Butterworth
7 Ardley Road
0204 68094
Mid-range and shipping
furniture, general antiques,
metalware and porcelain.

Stag's Head Antiques
165 Chorley New Road
0204 690962
Furniture and general antiques.

Von's Buy & Sell
46 Lee Lane
0204 697207
General secondhand goods.

HOYLAKE
(MERSEYSIDE)

Hoylake Antique Centre
128–130 Market Street
051 632 4231
Three dealers offering a range
of furniture, general antiques,
bric-a-brac, silver, collectors'
items and decorative antiques,
through to art deco. Usually a
good, all-round mix, with some
buying potential.

Market Antiques
80 Market Street
051 632 4740
Furniture, pictures, general
antiques and shipping goods.

Olde England
1 Cable Road South
051 632 4740
General antiques and furniture,
including upholstered.

KENDAL (CUMBRIA)

Below Stairs
78 Highgate
0539 741278
General antiques, metalware

and collectors' items, including
coloured glass.

Cottage Antiques
80 Highgate
0539 722683
Small furniture, including pine,
country antiques, metalware,
treen, pottery, tools and
kitchenalia.

Dower House Antiques
Kirkland
0539 722778
Furniture, pictures and general
antiques, including some
shipping goods.

Edmondson's
Dockray Hall Mill
Dockray Hall Road
0539 724439
Furniture basics and house
clearance items.

Edwards Antiques
Crosscrake Farm
0539 560313
Mid-range period and country
furniture and general antiques.

The Silver Thimble
39 All Hallows Lane
0539 731456
Jewellery, collectors' items,
textiles, metalware and
porcelain.

KESWICK (CUMBRIA)

And So To Bed
Lake Road
076 87 74881
Brass beds, lighting, mirrors,
linen and bedroom accessories.
Country Living Antiques
(Packhorse Court) is another
local source that stocks a more
general range.

John Young & Son
Antiques

12–14 Main Street
076 87 73434
A long-established (1890) dealer
offering mid-range furniture
and general antiques.

KIRKBY LONSDALE
(CUMBRIA)

Beckhead Gallery
Former council offices
05242 71314
Small furniture, general
antiques and collectors' items.

James Thomson,
auctioneers
64 Main Street
076 83 71302
Antique sales every month;
picture sales every two months.

KIRKBY STEPHEN
(CUMBRIA)

Haughey Antiques
28–30 Market Street
076 83 71302
Furniture and general antiques,
decorative items, pictures,
garden ornaments.

Mortlake Antiques
32–34 Market Street
076 83 71666
Furniture, including stripped
pine, vernacular collectables,
treen, bric-a-brac, metalware
and kitchenalia.

LANCASTER
(LANCASHIRE)

A royal city until the death of
Henry VI in 1471, it later had to
concede its administrative
power to Preston. Even so, the
red rose is still a potent symbol
(if no longer a call to arms
against Yorkshiremen) and the
medieval castle evokes a
dignified past.

Articles Antiques
134/136 Greaves Road
0524 39312
Mid-range furniture, clocks,
general antiques and shipping
items.

The Assembly Rooms
King Street
0524 66627
An antiques and collectors'
market is held every Thursday,
Friday and Saturday. Several
dealers with both general and
specialised stock.

GB Antiques Ltd
Lancaster Leisure Park,
Wyresdale Road
0524 844734
A large market offering a range
of smaller antiques, jewellery
and collectors' items.

SAMPLERS
Samplers offer an
interesting scope, and a
wide price range, for
collectors, with simple,
later examples still being
relatively cheap. Samplers
were, in essence, an
educational exercise for
young girls and, just
occasionally, young boys.
The aim was to inculcate
the skills necessary for
good needlework, with
the incidental benefits of
the odd improving
homily and a laboriously
worked alphabet. After a
generation or two,
samplers 25often became
venerated objects within
the family, and they are
appreciated today as a
touching and picturesque
aspect of childhood in
past centuries.

GW Antiques
47 North Road;
also at St George's Quay
0524 32050
A comprehensive range of
furniture, including pine.

Lancastrian Antiques
66 Penny Street
0524 843764
Furniture and general antiques.

Vicary Antiques
18a Brock Street
0524 843322
Art nouveau and art deco
antiques and collectors' items,
pictures, ceramics, textiles and
furniture. Tends towards the
less expensive end of the
decorative movement, rather
than junk as such, but with
much worth looking at.

The Warehouse
49 North Road
0524 39024
4,000 square feet with a
comprehensive range of
furniture from Georgian to pre-
war and including stripped
pine. Also general antiques and
shipping items.

LEIGH
(LANCASHIRE)

Grundy
90 Railway Road
0942 676000
Secondhand furniture and
budget pre-war antiques.

Leigh Jewellery
4 Queens Street
0942 607947
Collectors' items, jewellery and
general antiques.

Mooch Around Antiques
39 Leigh Road
0942 674360
General secondhand goods and
bric-a-brac.

LEYLAND (LANCASHIRE)

Warren & Wignall, auctioneers
The Mill, Earnshaw Bridge,
Leyland Lane
0772 451430
Sales every Wednesday, usually
household and general, with
antique every third week.

LIVERPOOL
(MERSEYSIDE)

**Fortunes were built on trade
with the Americas, as were some
stupendous architectural
landmarks, like Britain's largest
ecclesiastical structure, the
Anglican cathedral. St George's
Hall and the Royal Liver building
are equally impressive. The
merchant-city heyday may be a
thing of the past, yet there is still
an air of determined confidence
around, plus a continuing trade
in everything from top-quality
antique furniture to cheap and
cheerful junk, and some
worthwhile auctions.**

Anderson Antiques
348 Longmoor Lane
051 525 6996
Small general antiques and bric-
a-brac. Open only on Friday
evenings and Saturday.

Antiquity
51 St John's Road, Waterloo
051 920 4808
Secondhand and shipping
furniture.

Architectural Antiques
60 St John's Road, Waterloo
051 949 0819
Fireplaces, grates and some
general architectural salvage.

Auctions

Auctioneers holding sales of antiques and secondhand collectables include: **Abram & Mitchell** *(32 Bedford Road, 051 525 1718)*, holding sales every Wednesday fortnight; **Cato, Crane & Co**, *(6 Stanhope Street, 051 709 5559)* with fortnightly general sales and approximately ten antique sales a year; **Worrals** *(15 Seel Street, 051 709 2950)*, with mixed sales about once a month; **Hartley & Co** *(12–14 Moss Street, 051 263 6472)*, with weekly general sales; **Outhwaite & Litherland** *(Kingsway Galleries, Fontenoy Street, 0512366561)*, who hold a general sale every Tuesday and four or five antique and fine art sales a year; and **Turner & Sons** *(28–36 Roscoe Street, 051 709 4005)*, with general sales every Thursday and six antique sales a year.

The Buttonhook

24 Matthew Street
051 236 0036
Jewellery, small collectors' items, pictures, and some furniture.

Car Boot Sale

Dock Road
Every Sunday.

Kensington Tower Antiques

Christ Church
051 260 9466
Furniture, general antiques, trade and shipping goods.
Swainbanks Ltd *(Christchurch, Kensington, 051 260 9466)* nearby sells similar stock.

Liverpool Militaria

48 Manchester Street
051 236 4404
Militaria, and specialising in samurai swords.

Maggs Antiques

26–28 Fleet Street
051 708 0221
Furniture, general antiques and shipping items.

Nothing Fancy

184 Derby Lane
051 259 1661
Secondhand goods, bric-a-brac, some budget antiques.

Oddfellows Antiques

59 Allerton Road,
Woolton Village
051 428 9327
Furniture, budget antiques and house clearance lines.

Pilgrim's Progress

1a and 3a Bridgewater Street
051 708 7515
Around 40,000 square feet of mid-range furniture, Georgian to Edwardian, and some general antiques.

Pryor & Son

110 London Road
051 709 1361
Long-established (1876) stockists of general antiques, collectors' items, pictures and decorative objects.

Richards of Liverpool

20 Newington
051 708 6845
Two floors of smaller secondhand goods, bric-a-brac and collectors' items.

Ryan-Wood Antiques

102 Seel Street
051 709 7776
Furniture, from Victorian to pre-war, bric-a-brac, pictures, collectors' items and general antiques.

Secondhand Goods
59c Breck Road
051 263 2300
Furniture and house clearance
goods.

Smithdown Road House Clearance
54 Smithdown Road
051 733 1235
Furniture and general
secondhand goods on three
floors.

Theta Gallery
29–31 Parliament Street
051 708 6375
A trade and shipping
warehouse of furniture, clocks
and general antiques; open to
the public by appointment.

LONGRIDGE
(LANCASHIRE)

Henry Holden, auctioneers
Towneley Road
0772 783274
General sales on alternate
Saturdays.

Joy's Shop
83 Berry Lane
0772 782083
Furniture, including pine, linen,
jewellery, lamps and bric-a-
brac.

Kitchenalia
The Old Bakery,
Inglewhite Road
0772 785411
Country furniture, decorative
items, church pews, kitchen
items, pottery and metalware.

Newberry Hill Antiques
1 Berry Lane
0772 784880
Collectors' items, pictures and
jewellery.

LYTHAM (LANCASHIRE)

Clifton Antiques
8 Market Square
0253 736356
Jewellery, metalware, textiles,
collectors' items, furniture
(including pine) and general
antiques.

LYTHAM ST ANNE'S
(LANCASHIRE)

All Our Yesterdays of Lytham
3 Station Road
0253 734748
General antiques, collectors'
items and small antiques.

Pine Mine Antiques
14 Park Road
0253 720492
Pine furniture, architectural
items, including grates and
fireplaces, bric-a-brac and
general antiques. Much
medium-priced middle-of-the-
road stock, plus some cheaper
items.

The Snuff Box
5 Market Buildings
0253 738656
Jewellery, watches, silver and
some small collectors' items,
plus white linen.

MANCHESTER
(LANCASHIRE)

**The city where cotton was king,
and palaces were raised to house
bank staff, insurance clerks and
bales of textiles, rather than
princes. The arts were given a
splendid Greek temple, while
books have the quintessentially
gothic John Rylands library. The
equally gothic town hall has
some superb murals by Ford
Maddox Brown. Liberal causes**

were a 19th-century pre-occupation, with Chartism and the *Manchester Guardian* leading the way. The Stockport Road is now a sort of pilgrim's way for those with an interest in antiques and junk.

Acorn Antiques
Coach House, Blackburn Street, Prestwich
061 798 7117
Clocks, general antiques and scientific instruments.

The Antique Hypermarket
965 Stockport Road
061 224 2410
Around 10 dealers offering a range of furniture, general antiques and collectors' items.

AS Antiques
26 Broad Street, Salford
061 737 5938
Furniture, lighting accessories, decorative items, art nouveau and art deco and general antiques.

Authentiques
373 Bury New Road
061 773 9601
Small furniture, collectors' items, porcelain, pictures and general antiques.

Baron Antiques
1–11 Church Lane, Prestwich
061 773 9929
An extensive range of mid- to upper-market furniture, plus some shipping goods and general antiques.

Bulldog Antiques
393 Bury New Road
061 798 9277
Mid-range and shipping furniture, clocks, militaria, porcelain, pictures and general antiques.

TEXTILES

Costume-related textiles have become a popular collecting area in recent years. The appliqué shawls of Norwich are particularly sought after, as are the woven shawls of Indo-Persian design which spread the name of Paisley far and wide in the late 18th- and early 19th-centuries. The textile business was particularly open to ideas from overseas. Sometimes the influence was direct, brought in, say, by Huguenot and Flemish weavers settling in country towns or urban enclaves such as Spitalfields in London. In other cases it was a matter of imitation, as with the damask (i.e. Damascus-style) linen table cloths of Dunfermline or the Shetland knitwear patterns which, according to legend, owe something to the Iberian designs of shipwrecked sailors from the Armada. Collecting textiles is not without its problems. One of these is display, another the matter of whether or not an item should be used, particularly where age and dye-types could mean that conventional cleaning methods are risky. One solution is to collect textile objects that were made to be decorative, although this can mean moving into rarefied fields such as Elizabethan stumpwork.

Capes Dunn, auctioneers

38 Charles Street
061 273 1911
General sales every Monday, specialist sales every Tuesday.

Chorlton Quality Used Furniture

388 Barlow Moor Road, Chorlton
061 860 7667
Secondhand basics.

Christabelle's Antiques

973 Stockport Road, Levenshulme
061 225 4666
Mid-range and shipping furniture and general antiques on three floors.

Didsbury Antiques

21 Range Road, Whalley Range
061 227 9979
A warehouse with furniture, pictures, general antiques and some shipping goods.

The Ginnell

16 Lloyd Street
061 833 9037
Around five dealers with a range of antiques and collectors' items, particularly pre-war, 1950s and 1960s, but also some Victorian and art nouveau furniture. A varied range of stock, and often good on smaller decorative items.

Malik Antiques

10–12 Slade Lane
061 225 4431
General antiques and furniture, including shipping.

Royal Exchange Shopping Centre

Antiques Gallery, St Annes Square, Exchange Street
061 834 3731
Around 20 dealers offering a comprehensive range of antique furniture, jewellery, textiles and collectors' items.

Second Hand Bargain Centre

913 Ashton New Road, Clayton
061 370 3485
Basics and flatfillers.

Stephen Shawcross, auctioneers

103–105 Church Street, Eccles
061 789 3537
General auctions every Monday, plus occasional antique sales.

MILBURN (CUMBRIA)

Netherley Cottage Antiques

Milburn
076 83 61403
Country-related items, treen, porcelain and pottery, metalware and kitchenalia.

MILLOM (CUMBRIA)

Gordon's Bazaar

35–37 Queen Street
0229 770092
Furniture and secondhand goods.

Harrison Coward, auctioneers

St George's Hall
0229 772314
Occasional furniture and bric-a-brac sales.

MILNTHORPE (CUMBRIA)

The Antique Shop

Park Road
05395 62253
Furniture, collectables, general antiques and books.

MORECAMBE
(LANCASHIRE)

Cobwebs
12 Poulton Square
0524 413332
General secondhand goods.
Similar stock is sold by
Chippendales *(23 Pedder
Street, 0524 425063).*

GG Exports
25 Middleton Road
0524 851565
An 18,000 square foot trade and
shipping warehouse with an
extensive range of general
antiques and furniture,
including pine. Also worth
contacting, by appointment, for
similar goods is **Luigino
Vescovi** *(1/3 Back Avondale
Road East, 0524 416732).*

Magpie's Nest
*Unit 4, Plaza Shopping Arcade,
Queen Street*
0524 423328
Collectors' items, militaria,
cutlery and bric-a-brac.

NELSON (LANCASHIRE)

Brooks Antiques
7 Russell Street
0282 866234
Mid-range furniture, collectors'
items and ephemera. A
comprehensive stock,
comprehensively priced. One of
about four visitable outlets in
the town.

NEWTOWN
(LANCASHIRE)

Silverwoods,
auctioneeers
The Village Hall
0200 446652
Monthly sales of general goods
and occasionally antiques.

Phone for more specific
information.

OLDHAM (LANCASHIRE)

**Cotton-spinning wealth
produced the revenue to build
Oldham's awe-inspiring and
typically northern town hall,
although why it should be based
on an Athenian original
dedicated to Ceres, goddess of
agriculture, remains a mystery.
Its most famous local MP, Sir
Winston Churchill, is
remembered with a mixture of
affection and the sort of cool
northern detachment generally
reserved for a southerner.**

Aladdin's Cave
9–11 Mumps Street
061 633 0164
Secondhand furniture, bric-a-
brac and house clearance lines.

Failsworth Mill Antiques
Trade Warehouse
Ashton Road, Failsworth
Ten dealers with around 20,000
square feet offering a
comprehensive range of
antiques and shipping goods.

Fernlea Antiques
*305 Manchester Road,
Hollinwood*
061 682 0589
Furniture, general antiques and
shipping items. A similar range
of stock is carried by
Hollinwood Antiques
*(319–321 Manchester Road,
061 6835581)* and **R & J
O'Brien** *(293 Manchester Road,
061 6834717).*

Heritage Antiques
123 Milnrow Road, Shaw
0706 842385
Furniture, including shipping
and general antiques.

Second Chance
292 Middleton Road
061 626 3559
Musical instruments and
secondhand associated
equipment: keyboard, drums,
guitars, p.a. systems etc.

Valley Antiques
Soho Street
061 624 5030
Mid-range and shipping
furniture, pine and general
antiques.

David Vincent Antiques
384 Hollins Road
061 626 9045
Victorian furniture and
decorative items.

Waterloo Antiques
16 Waterloo Street
061 624 5975
Recently enlarged and now
with more furniture; also
general antiques, jewellery and
porcelain.

ORMSKIRK
(LANCASHIRE)

Edward Abbot, auctioneer
The Saleroom, Church Street
0695 579104
Mixed household and antiques
sales every second Tuesday.

Browzearound
16 Derby Street West
0695 576999
Secondhand and shipping
furniture, bric-a-brac and
household items.

Moorgate Antiques
10a Moorgate
0695 576901
General antiques, bric-a-brac,
collectors' items, house
clearance goods, mid-range and
budget furniture.

OSWALDTWISTLE
(LANCASHIRE)

Furnway Removals
235 Union Road
0254 386381
Secondhand furniture and
house clearance lines.

PADIHAM
(LANCASHIRE)

Crowther's Antiques
47 Higham Hall Road
0282 774418
Furniture, general antiques and
shipping goods.

PEEL (ISLE OF MAN)

The Golden Past
18a Michael Street
0624 843839/842170
Furniture, porcelain, collectors'
items, pictures, jewellery, books
and general antiques, from
Victorian to pre-war. A
comprehensive selection with
much at the low end of the
price spectrum.

PENRITH (CUMBRIA)

Antiques of Penrith
4 Corney Square
0768 62801
Mid-range furniture, metalware,
general antiques, porcelain,
clocks and collectors' items.

Arcade Antiques
11 Devonshire Arcade
0768 67754
Jewellery, porcelain, collectors'
items and small furniture.

Penrith Coin & Stamp Centre
37 King Street
0768 64185
Coins, stamps, jewellery and
small collectors' items.

Penrith Farmers, auctioneers

Devonshire Chambers, Devonshire Street
0768 62135
About three general sales and one antique sale, per month, held at Castlegate.

PORT ERIN
(ISLE OF MAN)

The Spinning Wheel

Church Road
0624 833137
Jewellery, collectors' items, bric-a-brac, metalware, clocks and watches, furniture and linen.

PRESTON
(LANCASHIRE)

The ancient core of the imaginatively named Central Lancashire New Town, the city provided the venue for a decisive battle in the Civil War. There is a well-varied antique trade, offering an interesting range of goods of all types.

The Antique Centre

56 Garstang Road
0772 882078
Around 20 dealers offering a range of furniture, pictures, collector items and general antiques.

Car Boot Sales

Preston Market Place
Tuesdays and Thursdays.

North Western Antique Centre

The Mill, Horrock's Yard, New Hall Lane
0772 794498
Around 20 dealers with general antiques, shipping items and furniture. Neighbouring shops selling furniture, collectables

and general antiques include **Duckworth's Antiques** (*45 New Hall Lane, 0772 794336*), **Peter Guy Antiques** (*26–30 New Hall Lane, 0772 703771*), **Just a Living** (*35 New Hall Lane, 0772 794336*), **Ray Wade Antiques** (*111–113 New Hall Lane, 0772 792950*) and **We Buy Anything** (*9 New Hall Lane, 0772 704073*).

Swag

24 Leyland Road, Penwortham
0772 744970
Collectors' items, antique dolls and associated objects, porcelain, furniture and general antiques.

PRESTON PATRICK
(CUMBRIA)

Hodgson's, auctioneers

10 Highgate, Kendal
0539 721375
Monthly general auctions.

RISHTON
(LANCASHIRE)

Speakman's

8 Church Street
0254 885848
Long-established (1856) stockist of decorative antiques, glass and porcelain, paintings and clocks. Appointment required before visiting.

ROCHDALE
(LANCASHIRE)

Antiques & Bygones

100 Drake Street
0706 48114
General antiques, collectors' items, medals, bric-a-brac and small decorative objects.

Ian Gartside
19 Milnrow Road
0706 59262
Secondhand furniture and
house clearance goods.

Magpie Antiques
285 Oldham Road
0706 43896
Restorers and stockists of a
wide selection of budget to
mid-range furniture, including
pine.

SABDEN (LANCASHIRE)

Pendle Antique Centre
Union Mill,
Watt Street
0282 776311
Around a dozen dealers trading
in furniture and general
antiques across the range.

SADDLEWORTH (LANCASHIRE)

Heyday Antiques
Huddersfield Road, Delph
061 628 2246
Furniture, decorative objects, art
nouveau and art deco,
architectural items and general
antiques.

ST ANNES ON SEA (LANCASHIRE)

The Victorian Shop
19 Alexandria Drive
0253 725700
General antiques, furniture and
shipping goods.

SAMLESBURY HALL (LANCASHIRE)

Samlesbury Hall
Preston New Road
0254 81 2010
A listed building dating from
1325, selling a wide range of
jewellery, furniture, porcelain,
silver and other collectables.

SCARISBRICK (LANCASHIRE)

Carrcross Gallery
325 Southport Road
0704 880638
Furniture, fireplaces and metal
items; brass and iron beds,
grates and fireplace accessories.

SEDBERGH (CUMBRIA)

**Sedbergh Antiques &
Collectables**
59 Main Street
05396 21276
Victorian and Edwardian
furniture, general antiques,
linen and bric-a-brac.

Stable Antiques
Wheelwright Cottage,
15–16 Back Lane
05396 20251
Collectors' items, metalware,
porcelain, pictures, decorative
items and small furniture.

SHAWFORTH (LANCASHIRE)

Shawforth Antiques
139 Market Street
070 685 3402
General antiques, collectors'
items, clocks and bric-a-brac.

SOUTHPORT (MERSEYSIDE)

**A major attraction is the annual
flower show, and there are some
rich pickings to be had in its
antique shops, with some
notable specialisation.**

Aladdin's Cave
57–59 Duke Street
0704 538355

Double shop plus restoration workshop with an extensive stock of secondhand and shipping furniture.

Back Street Emporium
18 Cable Street
0704 533788
Furniture, including shipping and secondhand and general antiques.

Cobern's, auctioneers
93b Eastbank Street
0704 500515
Fortnightly household and general sales, plus about six antique sales a year.

K & J Doyle
58 Shakespeare Street
0704 549775
House clearance furniture, including some pre-war shipping stock.

Little Thatch Antiques
54 Botanic Road,
Churchtown
0704 27096
General antiques and paintings.

Molloys
6 and 8 St James Street
0704 535204
A large selection of mid-range and shipping furniture.

Oldfield Cottage Antiques
97 East Bank Street
0704 501899
General antiques and furniture, including pine, country items, textiles, metalware and porcelain. Another branch based in Saddleworth.

Osiris Antiques
104 Shakespeare Street
0704 500991

Specialists in art nouveau and art deco and later; jewellery, costume and small decorative items. Price range extends from a few pounds to around a thousand, although much of the stock is at the low to middle end. Aesthetic movement and lesser decorative arts predominate.

The Spinning Wheel
1 Liverpool Road,
Birkdale
0704 67613
General antiques and collectors' items.

Sutcliffe's Antiques
130 Cemetery Road
0704 537068
Established almost 25 years, a shop and warehouse *(37a Linaker Street)* with an extensive selection of mid-range and shipping furniture and general antiques. In total there are approximately 40,000 square feet of space, usually with a comprehensive range of stock.

The White Elephant
22 Kew Road
0704 60525
Collectors' items, ephemera, books, ethnographica and general antiques.

ULVERSTON
(CUMBRIA)

A1A Antiques
59b Market Street
0229 869745
An extensive range of mid-range furniture, including shipping items, pictures, clocks, bric-a-brac, collectables, decorative pieces and general antiques. Appointment required.

Elizabeth & Son
Market Hall
0229 52763
Jewellery, silver, metalware and secondhand books plus an interesting selection of antique glass.

UPHOLLAND
(LANCASHIRE)

Lancashire Bygones
12 Parliament Street
0695 625624
A varied selection of furniture, general antiques and collectors' items.

WALLASEY
(MERSEYSIDE)

Decade Antiques
62 Grove Road
051 639 6905
Furniture, textiles, decorative items and general antiques displayed in extensive premises.

WEST KIRBY
(MERSEYSIDE)

Oliver Antiques
62 Grange Road
051 625 2803
General antiques and collectors' items from Victorian to pre-war periods.

WHALLEY
(LANCASHIRE)

Abbey Antiques
43–45 King Street
0254 823139
Furniture, porcelain, metalware and general antiques.

N Jogee
34 Whalley Banks
0254 675535
Secondhand furniture and bric-a-brac.

WHITEHAVEN
(CUMBRIA)

Michael Moon
41–43 Roper Street
0946 62936
Essentially a bookshop in a converted theatre and newspaper print works, but also with a rummageable selection of old prints, particularly relating to the landscape and history of Cumbria. A browse here is almost invariably time well spent.

WHITTLE LE WOODS
(LANCASHIRE)

Smith, Hodgkinson, McGinty
The Auction Centre,
Preston Road
0257 261055
General sales every Thursday, plus intermittent sales of antiques.

WIDNES
(MERSEYSIDE)

Simms Cross Curios
92 Widnes Road
051 423 5581
General antiques, collectors' items and small furniture, to pre-war.

WIGAN
(LANCASHIRE)

John Robinson Antiques
172–176 Manchester Road,
Higher Ince
0942 47773
Mid-range and shipping furniture and general trade antiques.

John Roby Antiques
12 Lord Street
0942 30887
Furniture, to pre-war and shipping, plus general antiques, bric-a-brac and collectors' items.

WIGTON (CUMBRIA)

Jackson Antiques
71 High Street
069 73 45034
Furniture, decorative items and general antiques.

WORKINGTON (CUMBRIA)

Black's
5–5a Senhouse Terrace
0900 62923
Secondhand furniture, house

clearance basics and some general antiques.

WORSLEY (LANCASHIRE)

Ambassador Houses
273 Chorley Road
061 794 3806
A comprehensive range of antique, shipping and secondhand furniture, plus jewellery, porcelain and collectors' items.

YEALAND CONYERS (LANCASHIRE)

Finch Antiques
15–17 Yealand Road
0524 73 2212
Furniture, lighting accessories, pictures, books and antiques.

NORTHERN IRELAND

Northern Ireland offers the junk-buying potential you might expect in a province which has enjoyed both agricultural and industrial prosperity in the past.

Farmhouse pine and kitchenalia are still in plentiful supply, and the robust mahogany and gleaming brassware which characterised the lifestyle of the Victorian middle classes can still be found in abundance. While many areas of mainland Britain have been largely 'combed out' by stock-hungry dealers and shippers, Northern Ireland has, to some extent, been protected by geography, though many shopowners echo the cry of their fellow traders elsewhere – 'There's a lot less of the stuff around than there was.' Fortunately, there is still much left, and often of good quality; after all, Northern Ireland fostered the sort of craft traditions which were necessary for, say, fitting out the first-class dining room of the Titanic, down to the linen napkins. The main antique buying areas are in and around Belfast and its hinterland, and on the beautiful north coast.

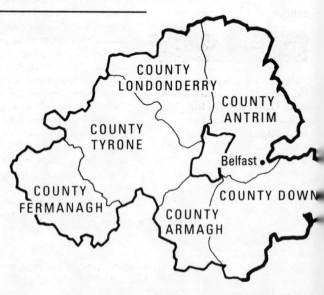

ANNAHILT
(COUNTY DOWN)

Period Architectural Features & Antiques
263 Ballynahich Road
0846 638091
Architectural and decorative items, including fireplaces, grates, stained glass and panelling.

ARMAGH
(COUNTY ARMAGH)

Hole in the Wall Antiques
Market Street
Established for 40 years, the main local source of general antiques.

BALLYCLARE
(COUNTY ANTRIM)

House of Antiques
38 The Square
09603 41818
Mid-range and shipping furniture, Georgian to Edwardian and some smaller antiques and collectables.

BANGOR
(COUNTY DOWN)

The main antique buying area in this seaside town is to be found in and around Grays Hill. Bangor was founded by St Comgall in AD 558.

The Emporium
18 Grays Hill
0247 270748
Mixed antique market with six dealers.

Golden Age
57a Grays Hill
0247 270938
Jewellery, small antiques and collectors' items.

McKee's
43 Belfast Road
0247 460134
Furniture and general antiques.

Memories
34 Grays Hill
0247 451677
Victorian to shipping furniture, general antiques and collectors' items.

This & That
43a Grays Hill
0247 451799
Porcelain, glass, linen, lace and general antiques.

BELFAST
(COUNTY ANTRIM)

Northern Ireland's seaport capital expanded at great speed during the 19th century, thanks to the wealth generated by the linen, shipbuilding and heavy engineering industries. It gained full city status in 1888, a monumental baroque city hall in 1906, and a university in 1909. Belfast's recent unfortunate history too often obscures the past achievements of its people, but there is much, both in the local architecture and the contents of its junk and antique shops, which evokes the discrimination and good taste of a sophisticated mercantile culture. Belfast produce, from pottery sinks and bedlinen to ocean-going liners, was famous throughout the Empire and the wider world. In a city accustomed to high standards of craftsmanship, even the junk often has its own distinctive quality.

Alexander the Grate
126–128 Donegall Pass
0232 232041

Fireplace fittings and accessories. The owner also runs **The Antique Market** complex *(Donegall Pass)*, where around 50 stallholders offer a wide variety of antiques and collectors' items on Saturdays.

Anderson's Auctions
28 Linenhall Street
0232 321401
Weekly general sales.

Balmoral Antiques
661 Lisburn Road
0232 665221
Shop and large store selling furniture and a range of general antiques.

Robert Brown
66 Donegall Pass
Secondhand furniture and general household goods.

Dunmurry Auctions
Barbour Gardens,
Dunmurry
0232 602815
Weekly general sales.

Gibson & Dodds, auctioneers
451 Donegall Road
0232 312882
Weekly general sales.

Oakland Antiques
137 Donegall Pass
0232 247372
Furniture, collectors' items and general antiques.

John Ross & Co., auctioneers
37 Montgomery Street
0232 325448
Weekly sales of general and household goods.

Sinclair's Antique Gallery
19 Arthur Street
0232 322335
Jewellery, silver, porcelain, glass, coins and medals and collectors' items.

BUSHMILLS
(COUNTY ANTRIM)

Dunluce Antiques
33 Ballytober Road
02657 31140
Smaller furniture, Georgian to pre-war, silver, glass, pictures, collectors' items, pottery and porcelain.

Causeway Books
110 Main Street
02657 32596
David Speers is principally a bookseller, but he also stocks some bric-a-brac and collectors' items.

CLAUDY
(COUNTY LONDONDERRY)

O'Hagan's
Bensara, 162 Foreglen Road
0504 338506
Storeroom adjacent to a private house selling a range of general antiques and secondhand furniture.

COLERAINE
(COUNTY LONDONDERRY)

The Forge Antiques
24 Long Commons
0265 51339
Mid- and upper-market general antiques, clocks, silver, jewellery, porcelain and pictures.

Serendipity
The Harbour
0265 834557

Jewellery and small collectors'
items.

COOKSTOWN
(COUNTY TYRONE)

Cookstown Antiques
16 Old Town
06487 65279
Smaller antiques and collectors'
items, jewellery, silver,
porcelain. Owner also has
premises in Portadown selling
furniture.

O'Donnel's Antiques
Loy Street
06487 63243
Small furniture, bric-a-brac,
collectors' items, general
antiques.

Saddleroom Antiques
4 Coagh Street
06487 62033
Furniture, collectors' items,
silver, porcelain and jewellery.

DONAGHADEE
(COUNTY DOWN)

Blackthorn Antiques
Manor Street
Mid-range to budget furniture
and general antiques.

Furney Antiques
3–4 Shore Street
0247 883517
Five showrooms of mid-range
furniture.

GREYABBEY
(COUNTY DOWN)

This is Ulster's best known
'antiques village' and there are a
number of mid- to upper-range
shops located on Main Street.
Three of those that sell across-
the-board stock are described on
the next page.

MEZZOTINTS

Those who believe that
image-making is a purely
modern phenomenon
should consider the
power that the mezzotint
had before the advent of
photography. The
mezzotint portrait, in
particular, was a
remarkably effective
means of conveying the
chosen characteristics of
the sitter: heroism,
authority, beauty, and
learning were some of the
many virtues which the
experienced mezzotinter
could project. First
developed by Ludwig von
Siegen in 1642, the new
technique of engraving on
to a metal plate allowed
form and tone to be
modelled realistically,
rather than suggested by
line. It was well suited to
the Baroque period, with
its fondness for well-fed
opulence and lavish
costume, and received a
boost in the 18th century
when a Dutchman, John
Faber, achieved runaway
success with his series of
prints called *Beauties of
Hampton Court*. Although
the French were inclined
to dismiss the technique
as *'la manière anglaise'*,
its earliest exponents
were often Dutch, Scottish
or Irish. Among these,
Dubliners Thomas Frye
and James MacArdell were
especially popular, the
former with his own
designs, the latter with
his reproductions of
Reynolds' paintings.

BB Antiques

Hoops Courtyard,
5–7 Main Street
0232 654145 (home)
Small furniture, textiles, lace
and linen, small antiques and
collectables.

Old Cross Antiques

3–5 Main Street
024 774 346
Silver, porcelain, small furniture
and a variety of other collectors'
items.

Priory Antiques

3–5 Main Street
024 774 346
Next door to **Old Cross**
Antiques (above). Victorian
and Edwardian costume,
textiles, linen, jewellery, silver
as well as small general
antiques.

LARNE
(COUNTY ANTRIM)

The Bric-a-Brac Shop

Riverdale
0574 275657
General bric-a-brac, pictures
and smaller antiques, plus
coffee shop.

LONDONDERRY
(COUNTY LONDONDERRY)

Foyles Antiques

Clarendon Hall,
North Edwards Street
0504 267626
A large selection of furniture,
collectables and general
antiques.

Richmond Antiques

6 Shipquay Street
0504 260562
Furniture, jewellery, porcelain,
silver, linen and secondhand
books.

The Saturday Market

Carlisle Road
Some general bric-a-brac.

Whatnots

22 Bishop Street
0504 265008
Bric-a-brac and collectors'
items.

LURGAN
(COUNTY ARMAGH)

Steven Russell

44 William Street
0762 327593
A comprehensive range of
furniture.

NEWRY
(COUNTY DOWN)

McCabe's Antiques Galleries

11–12 St Mary's Street
0693 62695
A long-established (1910)
furniture and general antiques
dealer with extensive
showrooms and warehouse.
Much material is rather
upmarket, but some mid-range
and cheaper items are also
available.

PORTADOWN
(COUNTY ARMAGH)

Moyallon Antiques

54 Moyallon Road
0762 831615
General antiques, pine and
country furniture, bric-a-brac
and ceramics.

PORTSTEWART
(COUNTY LONDONDERRY)

The Smithy

Cappagh, 182 Coleraine Road
0265 832209
General mid-range furniture,

also silver, porcelain and some bric-a-brac.

SAINTFIELD
(COUNTY DOWN)

Attic Antiques
90 Main Street
0238 511057
Selection of mid-range and general antiques. Owner plans a move to former premises *(90 Main Street)* during 1993.

Albert Forsythe
66 Carsonstown Road
0238 510398
Pine and country furniture.

STEWARTSTOWN
(COUNTY TYRONE)

Pat Smith Antiques
1–3 North Street
0868 73396
Fireplaces, beds and stained glass.

SCOTLAND

ORKNEY

Stromness

SHETLAND

Lerwi

HIGHLAND

Inverness

GRAMPIAN

Aberdeen

TAYSIDE

Dundee

CENTRAL

FIFE

Kirkcaldy

Stirling

Edinburgh

Glasgow

LOTHIAN

Kelso

STRATHCLYDE

BORDERS

DUMFRIES & GALLOWAY

Dumfries

Antique and junk buying in Scotland is much influenced by the prevailing local style, which in turn derives from varying historical social preferences.

Georgian Edinburgh, dominated by the professions, favoured the restrained mahogany look. Glasgow's ebullient Victorian merchants adopted a different approach, namely that one obligation of success was the cultivation of opulence. The citizens of Perth and Aberdeen held yet another view, and were more often concerned with quality and durability than with mere style. In the countryside, however, the individual preferences of the hierarchy of large estates usually prevailed – and the significance of this is still reflected today in the number of castles and stately homes that remain occupied, a fact that continues to astonish many visitors to Scotland.

ABERDEEN
(GRAMPIAN)

A cathedral city which also boasts a 500-year-old university, Aberdeen has been fortunate both in the wealth of its agricultural hinterland and its importance as a fishing port. The granite used to construct many of its buildings was widely exported – it paved the streets of London, for example. The city's prosperity today owes much to the continued exploitation of North Sea oil. Among the notable items to look out for while shopping in the city are examples of good provincial silver and, as with any international port, the occasional exotic curio.

Aladdin's Cave
37a Skene Square
0224 631944
General household and secondhand goods.

Jimmy Benzie
651 George Street
Long-established (1953) source of collectable items and smaller antiques. Glass, porcelain, brass and copperware, silver, pictures and prints.

Gray's Antiques
41a Justice Street
0224 646038
General antiques and shipping furniture. Adjoining premises sells jewellery (0224 625909).

Ingram's
486 George Street
0224 640342/3
A mix of secondhand and new household basics and electrical goods.

Instant Neighbour Project
The Gallowgate
0224 624228
Charity shop stocking low-priced furniture and general basics.

John Milne, auctioneers
9 North Silver Street
0224 639336
Weekly household and general sales.

Mr Reynolds
162 Skene Street
0224 644811
Mid-range furniture and general antiques with some cheaper items, such as a cane umbrella stand at £15.

Elizabeth Watt
69 Thistle Street
0224 647232
Bric-a-brac and smaller items of furniture, both antique and reproduction. Undertakes restoration.

ABERDOUR (CENTRAL)

Antiques & Gifts
26 High Street
0383 860523
Porcelain, jewellery, glass and collectors' items.

ALFORD (GRAMPIAN)

Gordons of Alford
Main Street
09755 62404
A premier North-East venue for bric-a-brac, furniture, Victoriana, clocks and general antiques.

ALYTH (TAYSIDE)

J & J Howe
24 Commercial Street
09283 2594
Auctioneers with weekly sales.

ANSTRUTHER (FIFE)

Anstruther's Attic
25 Shore Street
0333 311077
Small general antiques, bric-a-brac and collectors' items.

Bygone Days
18–22 Cunzie Street
0333 311970
A mix of furniture, mid-range to budget, bric-a-brac and general antiques crammed into two showrooms.

Scorpion Antiques
27 High Street
0333 311948
Books, bric-a-brac and general antiques.

ARBROATH (TAYSIDE)

Yesteryear
33 Millgate
0241 75226
General antiques and collectors' items.

AUCHTERARDER (TAYSIDE)

Antiques & Things
44 Feus
0764 63375
A mix of general antiques and smaller items, including golfing materials.

Old Abbey Antiques
4 High Street
0764 64073
Mid-range furniture, silver, pictures, porcelain, collectors' items and general antiques.

Ross Antiques
54 Townhead
0764 62750
Furniture and general antiques.

K Stanley & Sons
Regal Buildings, Townhead
0764 62252
Former cinema filled with furniture and decorative items.

Times Past
Broadfold Farm
0764 63166
Diversifying farmer with sheds full of stripped pine.

AULDEARN
(HIGHLAND)

Auldearn Antiques
Dalmore Manse, Lethen Road
0667 53087
Victoriana, furniture,
kitchenalia, architectural items.
One mile from village.

AULDGIRTH
(DUMFRIES & GALLOWAY)

Allanton House
Auldgirth
038 774 509
Summer B&B with room set
aside for selling furniture,
collectors' items, bric-a-brac.
Open any time. Ring to check.

AVOCH (HIGHLAND)

Highland Antiques
The Old Post Office
0381 21000
Furniture, paintings, books and
general antiques.

AYR (STRATHCLYDE)

Big Alec
29 South Harbour Street
0292 261007
General household and
secondhand goods.

Callan, auctioneers
22 Smith Street
0292 267681
Weekly mixed sales.

Heirlooms & Collectables
92a Sandgate
0292 286006
Art nouveau, art deco and
general collectors' items.

Rafferty Antiques
39 New Road
0292 265346
Mid-range general antiques.

BALFRON (CENTRAL)

Amphora Galleries
16–20 Buchanan Street
0360 40329
Mid-range furniture, general
antiques and decorative items.

BANCHORY
(GRAMPIAN)

Bygones
6 Dee Street
033 02 3095
Collectors' items, bric-a-brac,
small furniture.

BANFF (GRAMPIAN)

DK Antiques
50 Bridge Street
0261 812610
Porcelain, glass, collectors'
items and smaller antiques.

BANNOCKBURN
(CENTRAL)

Old Mill Antiques
Old Murrayfield, 1a Main
Street, Bannockburn Cross
0786 817130
Much reproduction furniture,
but also original fireplace grates
and accessories.

BEAULY (HIGHLAND)

Ian Marr Antiques
3 Mid Street
0463 782372
Some high quality stock,
particularly Scottish silver, but
also a good mix of general
antiques and collectors' items.

BIGGAR (STRATHCLYDE)

Carlo Pedreschi
176 High Street
0899 20466
Art deco, art nouveau and

general antiques. Prices start at around £10.

BLAIRGOWRIE
(TAYSIDE)

The Architectural Recycling Company
Craighall, nr Blairgowrie
0250 874749
Architectural antiques and re-useable building materials.

Roy Sim
The Granary Warehouses,
Lower Mill Street
0250 3860
General mid-range antiques, including furniture, silver, clocks and fishing items.

BONAR BRIDGE
(HIGHLAND)

Strath Enterprises
Dornoch Road
08632 643
Former local postman, now in the house clearance furniture business. Makes frequent forays to remote villages in best Highland travelling shop tradition with a lorry full of 'but and ben' household basics.

BRECHIN (TAYSIDE)

Pretty Old Things
15 Church Street
Under new management, but continuing with similar stock of smaller antiques and collectors' items.

BRIDGE OF EARN
(TAYSIDE)

Imrie Antiques
Back Street
0738 812784
A large stock of general antiques and shipping goods.

BRODICK
(STRATHCLYDE)

The Village Studio
Kames Cottage, Shore Road
0770 2213
On the Isle of Arran, supplying islanders and visitors with collectors' items, bric-a-brac, jewellery and smaller antiques.

BUCHLYVE (CENTRAL)

Amphora Galleries
Main Street
0360 40329
Off-shoot of the Balfron shop selling furniture and decorative items.

BUCKIE (GRAMPIAN)

Cluny Auctions
8–9 Cluny Terrace
0542 33318
Holds regular fortnightly sales.

The Curiosity Shop
Low Street
General antiques, bric-a-brac and collectors' items.

Alan Duncan
Drybridge, by Buckie
0542 32271
Stripped pine, bric-a-brac, general antiques.

BURNTISLAND (FIFE)

Ailsa's
113 High Street
0592 872689
General antiques and bric-a-brac.

CAMPBELTOWN
(STRATHCLYDE)

Annie's
Long Row
0586 552889

A general hardware shop which sells furniture from premises located at the rear of the shop once a month.

Nouveau Antiques
25 Long Row
0586 554931
Mid-range furniture, metalware, bric-a-brac, general antiques and a variety of collectors' items.

CARNOUSTIE
(TAYSIDE)

Lilljoy's Antiques
95 Dundee Street
0241 55750
A range of furniture, shipping goods, fireplaces and smaller general antiques and collectables. Closed on Tuesday.

CASTLE DOUGLAS
(DUMFRIES & GALLOWAY)

Bendall's Antiques
221–3 King Street
0556 2113
General antiques, furniture and shipping goods. Also owns Osborne's in Kirkudbright. Closed Thursday pm and Saturday.

Gelston Auction Service
St Andrews Street
0556 35921
Weekly general sales.

CERES (FIFE)

Ceres Antiques
19 Main Street
033 482 384
Mid-range antiques, collectors' items, porcelain and glass, with

FURNISHING TASTES OF THE SCOTTISH HOMEMAKER

All those Glasgow merchant villas, Edinburgh lawyers' town houses, Aberdeen professional residences and lairds' country piles had to be furnished and equipped, and it was often done with little expense spared. The quality of much of the furniture which is put through many Scottish auctions – or at any rate those items manufactured before the last war – is usually very high. Much was locally produced; Dundee, for example, turned out excellent flatweave carpets, while many brickworks and ironfoundries manufactured decorative and architectural items like garden ornaments and neo-classical firegrates. As habitual travellers, Scots could also be remarkably cosmopolitan in their tastes, importing ideas (like the Eastern-inspired Paisley design) as well as actual objects, such as Delft pottery, Chinese camphorwood boxes, African and Indian big game trophies and French clocks. Again, the results of all this can often be found in the country's auction rooms, antique shops and even junkyards. Inevitably, much that travelled into Scotland in previous centuries has travelled out in the last forty years, courtesy of a thriving tourist trade and an active antiques shipping sector. Even so, there is still a remarkable amount left.

nearby shop specialising in linen, lace and textiles.

Steeple Antiques
38 Main Street
033 482 553
General furniture, bric-a-brac and collectables.

COATBRIDGE (STRATHCLYDE)

Michael Stewart Antiques
Hornock Cottages,
Gartsberry Road
0236 422532
Mid-range furniture, including shipping items and smaller goods. Ring for appointment.

COLDSTREAM (BORDERS)

Coldstream Antiques
44 High Street
0890 2552
Main showroom with mid- to upper-range furniture and general antiques. Warehouse to rear often has cheaper goods.

COLLESSIE (FIFE)

Collessie Antiques
The Glebe
033781 338
Three miles from Auchtermuchty. Mid-range general antiques, porcelain, paintings and decorative items. Open Friday, Saturday and Sunday pm.

COMRIE (TAYSIDE)

The Coach House
Dundas Street
0764 70765
Pottery, porcelain and decorative items. By appointment in winter. Closed Wednesday.

West Perthshire Auctions
Dundas Street
0764 70613
Household and general sales held fortnightly.

CRIEFF (TAYSIDE)

Strathearn Antiques
2 Comrie Street
0764 4344
General antiques and small collectables; coins, medals, porcelain, jewellery, books.

CUPAR (FIFE)

Carolyn Scott
St Mary's Farm, by Cupar
0334 55677
A steading full of large decorative antiques, garden furniture and architectural items. Viewing only by appointment.

DALKEITH (LOTHIAN)

La Ronde
Eskbank Toll
031 663 2881 (home)
Porcelain, pictures, jewellery, small decorative items. Eminently rummageable.

DENNY (CENTRAL)

Century Antiques
Viewfield, 74 Glasgow Road
0234 823333
Some general mid-range antiques, but mainly clocks and associated items. Open by appointment.

DINGWALL (HIGHLAND)

Dingwall Antiques
6 Church Street
0349 65593
Good selection of books, both

secondhand and remaindered, plus pictures, bric-a-brac and collectors' items. The weekly auction sales on Friday at **Dingwall Auction Mart** *(0349 63252)* are a popular local event and also worth attending for the occasional bargain buy.

DOUNE (CENTRAL)

Jimmucks
The Square
0786 841066
Most rummageable shop in town, with wide selection of collectors' items, kitchenalia, metalware, etc.

DUMFRIES (DUMFRIES & GALLOWAY)

The local red sandstone was quarried to build much of south-west Scotland's major town, and was also used to construct Princetown University.

Cairnyard Antiques
Cairnyard, Beeswing
0387 73218
Furniture and general antiques, including clocks. Five miles south-west of Dumfries.

Dix Antiques
100 English Street
0387 64234
Small antiques and collectors' items, plus a further store with general antiques. Closed Thursday.

Gibson, auctioneers
Irving Street
0387 53670
Weekly general sales.

Thomson, Roddick & Laurie
60 Whitesands
0387 55366

Antique and general sales in both Dumfries and Annan.

Thornhill Galleries Antique Centre
47–48 Drumlanrig Street, Thornhill
0848 30566
Nine dealers trading in general antiques and collectables; furniture, pictures, porcelain, silver, jewellery and linen.

Unit 49
Heathhall Industrial Estate
0387 52466
Stripped pine furniture.

DUNBAR (LOTHIAN)

Cromwell Antiques
113 High Street
03683 305
General antiques, bric-a-brac, collectors' items, porcelain and jewellery.

DUNDEE (TAYSIDE)

Dundee was once a great East-coast mercantile port, but is now better known as the home of Captain Scott's ship, the *Discovery*, and the scene of the 1879 Tay Bridge disaster, which was immortalised in verse by William McGonagall, an aspiring local poet. The town's junk and antique shops cater largely for the resident student population and summer visitors, as well as for those from the more prosperous hinterland.

Anderson's
73 Albert Street
0382 453418
General antiques.

Angus Antiques
4 St Andrew's Street
0382 22128

Collectors' items, toys, advertising ephemera, medals, militaria and teddy bears.

Cornucopia
15 King Street
0382 24946
General antiques and collectables.

Dens Road Market
Dens Road
0382 451164 (enquiries)
Every weekend.

Double Ms
61 Albert Street
0382 455059
House clearance goods.

Doultons
186 Hilltown
0382 204186
Secondhand furniture and general household goods.

Fentons, auctioneers
84 Victoria Road
0382 26227
Household sales on Thursdays.

Kingbuyers
201 Princes Street
0382 45511
Secondhand furniture and house clearance lines.

Marshall & Johnston
7 Blinshall Street
0382 24931
Auction sales held fortnightly.

Robert Curr & Dewar, auctioneers
Ward Road
0382 24185
Weekly household sales.

Westport Gallery
3 Old Hawkhill, 48 Westport
0382 22033
Two shops selling old and new

furniture, jewellery and decorative items; a warehouse in Brewery Lane sells antique and shipping furniture.

DUNFERMLINE (FIFE)

Once the royal capital of Scotland, Dunfermline produced at least two exports of note last century. One was damask linen, which adorned the dining tables of Victorian Britain. The other was Andrew Carnegie, who gave New York its Carnegie Hall and helped to educate the world with his public library endowments.

The Bargain Shop
40 Campbell Street
0383 621878
General secondhand furniture and house clearance lines, with another branch at Inverkeithing.

Dunfermline Auction Co.
Loch Street,
Townhill
0383 729899
General household furniture and effects every Tuesday, antique sales quarterly.

Felix Hudson Ltd
2 Queen Anne Street
0383 724311
Clocks, watches, barometers, collectors' items, porcelain, glass and general antiques.

DUNKELD (TAYSIDE)

One of at least three Scottish towns which lays claim to the title of 'Gateway to the Highlands', Dunkeld was a popular and prosperous Victorian tourist destination. The young Beatrix Potter's family was one of many which had a summer retreat in the area. It was near here, while

watching Millais cast his line on the Tay, that she thought up the character of Mr Jeremy Fisher.

Dunkeld Antiques
Tay Terrace
0350 728832
Converted church filled with general antiques and decorative items, boxes, trunks and books.

Rectory Antiques
High Street
0350 727401
General antiques and collectors' items.

DUNOON (STRATHCLYDE)

Fyne Antiques
Summerville Place, Sandbank
0369 6646
Furniture, pottery and country items.

Cunningham, auctioneers
Bencorrum Villa,
17 Bencorrum Brae
0369 4102
Mixed sales about every six weeks.

DUNS (BORDERS)

Bygones
5 Market Square
0361 83229
Mid-range Victorian and Edwardian furniture, bric-a-brac, metalware and general antiques.

EAGLESHAM (STRATHCLYDE)

Eaglesham Antiques
73 Montgomery Street
035 53 2814
Smaller antiques and collectors' items.

EDINBURGH (LOTHIAN)

Best known worldwide for its international arts festival, Edinburgh has long been popular with junk collectors, Sir Walter Scott amongst them. Inevitably, rummaging for junk is a well established Edinburgh pursuit, and genuine bargains are still being picked up. St Stephen's Street, once a bargain hunter's mecca, is now largely supplanted as the major buying area by Causewayside and Buccleuch Street, to the south of the university area. More shops can be found in and around the Grassmarket, in the heart of the Old Town. Dedicated rummagers invariably end up at the open-air lane sales, to the rear of Lyon & Turnbull's George Street auction rooms, or the fortnightly household sales held by Phillips. Sam Burns Yard, to the east of the city, is another alfresco experience not to be missed, although the emphasis is increasingly on secondhand and salvage.

Adam Antiques
23c Dundas Street
031 556 7555
Buys, restores and sells mid-range furniture.

Another Time, Another Place
7 East Fountainbridge
031 669 3082 (home)
Mix of low-cost smaller goods and bric-a-brac.

The Antique Pine Shop
91–111 St Leonard's Street
031 667 9160
Expanding business, expansive owner, friendly service. Former publican Rolly Carter now sells cheap and mid-range

wardrobes, chests and fireplaces to students and younger home-owners.

Bacchus
95 West Bow
031 225 6183
One of several in the Grassmarket area with broad mix of smaller stock.

Barnardo's
18–22 Gorgie Road
031 337 7563
The city's leading charity shop for household furniture.

Barony Street Warehouse
24a/24b Barony Street
031 556 3134
Secondhand and house clearance specialists. Good for basic flat furnishing. Removal negotiable as part of the deal.

Paddy Barrass
15 Grassmarket
031 226 3087
Period costumes, linen and lace. Popular with students at the nearby Art College.

Laurance Black
45 Cumberland Street
031 557 4545
Mostly quality stock, well laid out. Scottish pottery, glass, treen, slipware, delft tiles, all reflecting the owner's refined aesthetic tastes (he worked with the Fine Art Society for several years). Prices can be moderate, starting at around £10.

Joseph Bonnar
72 Thistle Street
031 226 2811
Renowned for its stunning window displays, the softly lit interior is equally impressive. An essential visit for those with a serious interest in good antique jewellery and bijouteries, the atmosphere – like Asprey's – can be reverential. But junk-hunters should not be put off. Joe Bonnar started business at a market stall and can still offer surprising bargains.

Bourne Fine Art
4 Dundas Street
031 557 4050
Smart pictures and decorative porcelain upstairs, cheaper frames and prints in the basement.

The Bric-a-Brac Shop
109 Dalry Road
Cheap and cheerful bits and pieces.

Sam Burns Yard
Prestongrange, nr Prestonpans
0875 810600
A legend in its own time as a source of much cheap furniture for Edinburgh flatland. Not the place it once was for amazing Victorian mahogany bargains, but it still stocks some good solid pieces sold on the pile-it-high-and-sell-it-cheap principle. Nine miles east of city centre on coastal road. Wellington boots recommended.

Byzantium
9a Victoria Street
031 225 1768
High-spec upper-floor conversion of a Victorian church where nine dealers offer a variety of (mostly smaller) goods. The complex includes a well-run cafe.

Car Boot Sales
Bristo Street Car Park,
nr George Square
Held on most Sundays. Much on offer is trader-tat, but some

furniture and bric-a-brac can usually be found.

Charities Aid Shop

131 Dalry Road
031 337 3131
Smaller goods and clothes, with occasional furniture.

Cinders

3 Trinity Road
031 552 0491
Recently abandoned St Stephen's Street for larger premises on north side of town. Specialises in fireplaces and grates, but now also stocks furniture and general antiques.

Classic Telephones

7 West Crosscauseway
031 668 2927
Reconditions and sells pre-war and 50s telephones. Also stocks anything to do with the history of telecommunications. A good nostalgia trip for techno-freaks.

Collector Centre

63 Viewforth
031 229 1059
What it lacks in floor space (300 square feet) it makes up for in shelves, all well-laden with bric-a-brac, kitchenalia, silver and plate, books, boxes, militaria and pictures.

Collectors' Shop

49 Cockburn Street
031 226 3391
Ephemera of all sorts, with the exception of postage stamps, plus small items of silver,

BUILDING SPECIAL COLLECTIONS

A branch of collecting that has become especially popular over the past few years is the single-theme speciality. The computations for this are limitless, involving not simply such obvious areas as pottery cats or pigs, or specific denominations of stamps, but also the occasional inspired subject which suggests itself almost by accident. One distinguished Edinburgh architect has, almost literally, been building up a unique collection over the years and has even demonstrated that it can be done without spending a single penny. His chosen theme resulted from visits he made to cleared building sites, a fairly routine occurrence for an architect. Wandering through the rubble, his attention was attracted by the imprinted names on the old bricks that were scattered around. Virtually every site he visited, it seemed, had bricks of a different identity, a clear indication that brick production in the past was often a local affair, with medium-sized brickworks being scattered throughout industrial Britain. Soon, every site visit would produce another brick for the collection. Fellow architects, hearing of this interest, would add to the collection and dinner guests would appear on the doorstep clutching their kiln-fired rarities. Bricks are now piled up in the garden, and have begun to take over in his basement. As for display, the answer, he says, is quite simple. When he has enough he'll simply hire a cement mixer and build a wall.

jewellery, coins, medals and
militaria.

James Cook
2 Summer Place, Inverleith
031 556 7857
A cabinetmaker supplying the
professional antique trade, the
owner also carries his own
restored stock, which often
overspills onto the pavement.

Court Curio Shop
519 Lawnmarket
031 225 3972
Small shop, small stock, mostly
silver and jewellery.

Crawford's Saleroom
250–252 Leith Walk
031 554 6407
Better quality secondhand and
a few sub-stylish items like
Lloyd Loom chairs.

Curtain Trading Company
57 Causewayside
031 662 0255
Revamped rehangs, cleverly
presented. Most curtains
reconditioned secondhand, but
also some cotton-print Indian
imports.

Dick's
13 St Stephen's Street
The peerless Bobby Dick, noted
for his homburg and laconic
style, died last year, but his
nephew is continuing the
tradition of one of the last of
Stockbridge's junk emporia.

George Duff
254 Leith Walk
031 554 8164
Mid-range antique and shipping
goods.

Dundas Street Gallery
23 Dundas Street
031 556 0234
Framing is now the mainstay,
but cheap pictures and prints
are still available.

Dunedin Antiques
4 North West Circus Place
031 220 1574
The upmarket ethos is geared
to the New Town smart set, but
some interesting budget items –
like a cast-iron fireplace – can
sometimes be found in the
basement showroom.

Edinburgh Architectural Salvage Yard (EASY)
Unit 6, Couper Street, Leith
031 554 7077
Highly organised architectural
salvage stored on two levels.
Everything from plain Belfast
sinks and chimneypots to
carved stone and stained glass.

Edinburgh Coin Shop
2 Polwarth Crescent
031 229 2915
General ephemera, jewellery,
clocks and antiques, in addition
to coins and medals.

Donald Ellis Antiques
9 Bruntsfield Place
031 229 1819
Mix of low-cost and mid-range
furniture and general antiques.

Tom Fidelo
49 Cumberland Street
031 557 2444
Paintings, prints, objets d'art,
decorative pieces, occasional
theatricana.

Dokter Finlay
161 Gilmore Place
031 229 1764
The mis-spelling presumably
circumvents any medical ethics
problem. Customers include
flat-renting nurses who work at
the nearby hospitals. House

clearance, secondhand bric-a-brac and electrical.

Georgian Antiques
Poplar Lane,
10 Pattison Street, Leith
031 553 7268
50,000 square feet crammed to the gunnels with – for the most part – fine furniture. Much high-quality, but some eminently affordable.

Gifford Park Antiques
94 Buccleuch Street
031 667 3258
General mid-range antiques and bric-a-brac.

Gladrags
17 Henderson Row
031 557 1916
Period clothes, lace, linen, costume jewellery and accessories.

Hand in Hand
3 North West Circus Place
031 226 3598
Edinburgh's longest established (1969) specialists in period costume and accessories, well known for Paisley shawls. Also stocks lace, linen, embroideries and soft furnishings.

Tim Hardy
110 Grassmarket
031 225 9953
General antiques, decorative items, kitchenalia and collectables.

Homeworthy
6a Middlefield, Leith Walk
031 554 6407
Secondhand basics.

Mrs Humphrey
48 Thistle Street
031 226 3625
After almost 50 years in the business – most of it in the Grassmarket area – Mrs Humphrey continues with the same mix as before. All kinds of less expensive glass and porcelain, up to the 30s, etchings, curios, commemorative items. In a street of well-polished oak and mahogany, her stock provides an interesting contrast and frequent bargains.

Alan Jackson
67 Causewayside
031 667 0616
Original owner of **Jacksonville** (below) which he has since sold on. Now sells virtually anything and everything from smaller premises.

Jacksonville
108a Causewayside
031 667 0616
Now relocated from nearby old wash-house and under new management, but much as before, with secondhand and budget antique furniture, architectural salvage and some bric-a-brac.

Joys
39 Candlemaker Row
031 225 3432
Typical Grassmarket rummage.

Just Chairs
36 Dundas Street
031 557 5092
Dining chairs, desk chairs, comfy chairs and others.

Just Junk
87 Broughton Street
031 557 4385
Former restaurateur now serving up varied menu of everything from tailor's dummies to old trunks, chests, bentwood chairs and fireplaces.

Kaimes Smithy Antiques

Kaimes Junction,
79 Howdenhall Road
031 441 2076
Across-the-range furniture,
clocks, bric-a-brac, collectors'
items and general antiques.

Lamont

54 Candlemaker Row
031 225 8524
General antiques and bric-a-
brac, pictures, prints and books.

Laub Antiques

141 Buccleuch Street
031 668 4312
Seven-day trading in a mix of
low-cost and mid-range
furniture.

Loads of Tat

38 Argyle Place
031 226 4860
Splendidly eclectic range of
junk – a wonderful rummage.

London Road Antiques

15 Earlston Place, London Road
031 652 2790
Newly opened in 4,000 square
feet of former foundry
premises. Specialises in mid-
range pine and general
furniture.

Lyon & Turnbull, auctioneers

51 George Street
031 225 4627
Still with more than a hint of
Dickensian charm, Edinburgh's
oldest established rooms have
an eclectic throughput. The
monthly antique sales can
command high prices; the
household sale, which runs
concurrently, provides beds and
basics. More basic still, the
thrice-weekly lane sales are an
institution; old lawmowers,
dog-eared Reader's Digests,
ladders, carpets, sheets and
blankets are all here, plus,
inexplicably, the occasional
prize piece. A Wednesday
saloon sale of household goods
is held in a back hall and
occasional police lost property
sales further along the lane.

William MacIntosh & Co.

499 Lawnmarket
031 225 6113
General antiques, architectural
fittings, lighting and brassware.

William MacAdam

86 Pilrig Street
031 553 1364
Stocks the useable and the
unusual, particularly glass.

Jean Moran

145a St Leonard's Sreet
031 667 1699
Mix of general furniture, bric-a-
brac and pictures.

J & L Newton

108 Causewayside
031 668 4363
Decorative items, pine, pictures,
kitchenalia and occasional
statuary pieces. Closed Monday.

North Edinburgh Action Group

368 Leith Walk
031 555 1224
Charity shop selling donated
house clearance basics at
minimal cost.

Now & Then

9 Crosscauseway
031 668 2977
Leading city specialists in toy
trains and cars. Also carries a
varied general stock.

Off-beats

152 Albert Street, Leith Walk
031 555 2366

General household basics, some reconditioned.

Omnia
4 Teviot Place
031 225 5298
Bric-a-brac and furniture.

Out of the Nomad's Tent
21 St Leonard's Lane
031 662 1612
An opulent assortment of kelims, carved wood and general Eastern treasure. Some old, some new, all well chosen.

Oxfam
204–206 Morningside Road
031 447 8454
One of several Oxfam outlets in the city and large enough for the occasional item of furniture.

Phillips (Scotland)
65 George Street
031 225 2266
Specialist sales predominate, but general household items can be picked up at the fortnightly 'Victorian' (loosely applied) sales. Bargains can even be found at the monthly antique sales, though record prices can also be set.

Pine Country
14 Springvalley Gardens, Morningside
031 447 5795
Large showroom with old and newly crafted pieces above a workshop and stripping area.

Quadrant Antiques
5 North West Circus Place
031 226 7282
General mid-range antiques and decorative items available from both shop and pavement.

Margaret Reid
58 St Stephen's Street

Porcelain, collectors' items and smaller furniture.

James Scott
43 Dundas Street
031 556 8260
When a hotel or church closes down, the contents often end up here. Stock is varied, always interesting, often cheap, especially when it arrives in bulk. Also stocks a range of smaller items, such as jewellery and watches.

Scottish House Auctions
8c Loaning Road, Restalrig
031 659 6634
Occasional house clearance auctions in premises roughly two miles east of city centre.

Daniel Shackleton
17 Dundas Street
031 557 1115
His enthusiasm undiminished after 25 years in the business, Dan Shackleton knows a good picture when he sees it – and he's seen a few. Those in the upstairs showroom can be priced in the thousands. Downstairs, however, the stock-in-trade is much as it has always been; prints, engravings, original book illustrations and the like from around £20.

This & That Antiques
22 Argyle Place
031 229 6069
Furniture, porcelain, bric-a-brac, pottery, silver. Closed Monday to Wednesday.

The Thrie Estaits
49 Dundas Street
031 556 7084
Decorative and collectors' items, including pottery, sculpture, pictures and glass, plus some furniture.

The Thursday Shop
5 Clermiston Road, Corstorphine
031 334 3696
Despite the name, open five
days per week for the sale of
jewellery, collectors' items, bric-
a-brac, pictures and antiques.

Top Brass
77 Dundas Street
031 557 4293
Declares all stock as authentic –
original light fittings, door
furniture, fireplace accessories.

Trinity Curios
4–6 Stanley Road
031 552 8481
Stock geared to the needs of
young flat-furnishers.

Unicorn Antiques
65 Dundas Street
031 556 7176
Wonderfully compact, with not
an inch of space wasted. Sells
anything which can be fitted in.
Brass window and door
furniture, pictures, bric-a-brac,
glass, jewellery.

West Bow Antiques
102 West Bow
031 225 3335
Friendly service and assorted
stock of porcelain, pottery,
brass, furniture and general
antiques.

Wild Rose
15 Henderson Row
031 557 1916
General antiques, collectors'
items and bric-a-brac, glass,
jewellery.

ELGIN (GRAMPIAN)

West End Antiques
35 High Street
0343 547531
Clocks, watches, jewellery,

silver and bric-a-brac.

ELIE (FIFE)

Malcolm Antiques
5 Bank Street
0333 33016
Clocks, curios, collectors' items.

FAIRLIE (STRATHCLYDE)

EA Alvarino
86 Main Road
0475 568613
Victorian and Edwardian clocks,
bric-a-brac, collectors' items
and smaller antiques. Closed
Monday.

FALKIRK (CENTRAL)

James Finlay
178 Grahams Road
0324 20264 (home)
General antique and shipping
dealer of 25 years standing.
Usually carries a good selection
of comprehensive stock. Open
Wednesday all day, Saturday
pm or by appointment.

FOCHABERS (GRAMPIAN)

Antiques Etcetera
18 The Square
0343 821269
Mid-range small furniture,
paintings and bric-a-brac.
Closed Wednesday pm.

Granny's Kist
Hadlow House, 22 The Square
0343 820838
Victorian and later vernacular
antiques; tools, kitchenalia,
collectors' items and furniture.

Pringle Antiques
High Street
0343 820362
Furniture, general antiques and

collectable items in a converted church.

FORRES (GRAMPIAN)

Forres Sale Room
Tytler Street
0309 72422
Mixed sales every Thursday evening.

Michael Low Antiques
45 High Street
0309 73696
General antiques and smaller items and collectables. The business has been reduced to a single shop and no longer stocks furniture.

FORTROSE (HIGHLAND)

Black Isle Antiques
Fortrose
0381 20407
Owners currently searching for new premises, which will either be in Fortrose or nearby Cromarty. In the meantime, will sell by appointment. Stock generally smaller items: silver, porcelain, glass.

FRASERBURGH (GRAMPIAN)

John Anderson, auctioneers
33 Cross Street
0346 28878
Weekly general sales at the nearby village of Strichen.

FREUCHIE (FIFE)

Freuchie Antiques
Oxley House, Main Street
0337 57348
Small collectable items, postcards and ephemera. Opening times vary. Ring to check.

FRIOCKHEIM (TAYSIDE)

Barclay's Antiques
29 Gardyne Street
02412 265
General antiques, furniture, clocks, jewellery, silver, china and collectors' items.

GARTMORE (CENTRAL)

Robert & Vashti Lewis Antiques
Blarnaboard Farm, Drymen Road
087 72374
A comprehensive range of farm, vernacular and kitchen-related items, plus some general antiques. Just beyond village.

GLASGOW (STRATHCLYDE)

Wealth and confidence were the hallmarks of 19th-century Glasgow. The remnants of this dynamic culture survive in the architecture of the city centre and, to some extent, in the stock carried by local antique and junk shops. While the very best furniture – say a piece by Mackintosh – will now be quickly recognised, the influence was pervasive, and can even be seen in the ubiquitous mass production of the 1930s. Buying patterns in Glasgow differ from those in Edinburgh, thanks largely to the frenetic post-war redevelopments which wiped out many of the low-rent retail outlets. Trading now tends to take place in larger market complexes. Even so, a few shops have survived, and these can certainly be worth a visit.

Adams Furniture
1155 Argyle Street
041 204 2563

Flatfillers and secondhand basics shop.

Albany Antiques
1347 Argyle Street
041 339 4267
Antique furniture and shipping goods, 1800–1930, £25–£1,000.

All Our Yesterdays
6 Park Road
041 334 7788
A spectacular array of jewellery, porcelain, bric-a-brac, walking sticks, mirrors, furniture and more besides. Essential visiting.

Bath Street Antiques Gallery
203 Bath Street
041 248 4220
Located between Christie's and Phillips, the dozen or so dealers here cater largely for the mid- to upper-range buyer, which is not to say that an assiduous search won't produce a bargain.

The Barras (including Quinn's Antique Market)
Saltmarket
041 552 7258/1245
One of Glasgow's most popular weekend events, the Barras is one-stop shopping with a difference and Quinn's has much rummageable potential.

Cathcart Bazaar
698 Cathcart Road
041 423 8535
A mix of smaller secondhand goods.

Christie's (Scotland)
164–166 Bath Street
041 332 8134
Regular specialist sales, including collectors' items.

Allan Clark
16 Stevenson Street

041 632 9098
Low-cost secondhand basics.

Arthur E Collins & Sons
114 Trongate
041 552 0489
Weekly auctions held on the premises.

The Den of Antiquity
Langside Lane, 539 Victoria Road, Queens Park
041 423 7122
The major component of the West of Scotland Antiques Centre, taking up just over half of the total 10,000 sq ft. Stocks mostly mid-range and cheaper furniture. Open seven days.

Finnie Antiques
98 Torrisdale Street
041 423 8515
General antiques and decorative items.

First Choice Removals
Off Argyle Street
041 637 2161
Not a retail outlet, but owner is prepared to sell by appointment from his warehouse off Argyle Street to trade or 'serious' buyers. Ring above number stating requirements.

The Glasgow Furniture Saleroom
325–359 Eglinton Street
041 429 1373
General secondhand basics and flat fillers.

Great Western Saleroom
29–37 Otago Street, Kelvinbridge
041 339 3290
Auctions held fortnightly.

Heritage Antiques
Walker Street, Paisley
041 889 3661

Off the High Street. General antiques, mid-range and shipping furniture and smaller items.

Heritage House
Yorkhill Quay
041 334 4924
An expanding sector of the business, now with 15 dealers in 90,000 square feet of former dockside warehousing. Goods on offer cover the whole gamut – jewellery, bric-a-brac, oriental rugs, furniture, architectural salvage, decorative items, general junk.

Home Store
Wellmeadow Street, Paisley
041 848 1390
Secondhand basics and general household items.

Housewise
52 George Street, Paisley
041 887 7503
Basics and flatfillers.

PHOTOGRAPHS

For the Victorians, photography was the perfect fusion of art and science. William Fox Talbot, a physicist by profession, was as committed to it as the artist David Octavius Hill, whose massive oil painting of Scotland's dissenting clergymen was produced with the help of calotype portraits. The calotypes of Fox Talbot, Hill and Adamson, and the images produced by such successors as Julia Margaret Cameron and Frank Meadow Sutcliffe open a window on to a century. For the first time people were able to see with their own eyes the true appearance of well-known individuals such as Tennyson, Carlyle and Queen Victoria, as well as accurate representations of cities such as Venice, alpine landscapes or Chinese street scenes. Photography was also used from the earliest times to communicate powerful journalistic messages, notably the shocking scenes of the Crimean War and the American Civil War. Examples in these categories are bought and sold for enormous sums, yet the vast majority of Victorian photographs can still be bought for remarkably low prices, particularly that perennial favourite, the portrait carte de visite, usually depicting demure young ladies attired in their Sunday best, or mustachioed young beaus looking vaguely ill at ease. The best buys of all, however, are probably the large album photographs that were originally acquired by middle class overseas travellers, visiting the tourist traps of their day. Italy and Greece were particular favourites, although many of the best photographs were taken at popular resorts in the British Isles. The artistic quality of some of these photographic prints can be superb. Among the more notable are those of photographers such as George Washington Wilson and John Valentine, who supplied the tourists of Victorian Deeside with some spectacular images which, today, can be picked up for as little £2 or £3.

Caroline Kerr Antiques
103 Niddrie Road, Queens Park
041 423 0022
A broad range of decorative furniture – some budget and smaller items. Open Tuesday, Wednesday and Thursday.

Kerr & McAlister
Queens Park Auction Rooms,
140 Niddrie Road
041 473 4271
Weekly auction sales.

King's Court Antique Centre
Units 1–6, King's Court,
King Street
041 552 7854
Adjacent to high-tec St Enoch shopping centre and the Dickensian Paddy's Market (below). Nine dealers selling mix of general antique and other secondhand items. Open Tuesday to Sunday.

Ivor Lovatt
100 Torrisdale Street
041 423 6497
Long-established family firm in large premises next to Queen's Park Station. Sells a mix of Victoriana, general antiques and shipping goods. Closed Saturday.

J McGinn
37 Merchant Lane
041 552 3076
Secondhand basics.

Robert McTear & Co.
Royal Exchange Saleroom,
6 North Court, St Vincent Place
041 221 4456
Weekly sales are held on the premises.

James Mangan
187 Maryhill Road
041 332 3122

General secondhand goods.

Mercat-Hughes Antiques
85 Queen Street,
Royal Exchange Court
041 204 0851
Collectors' items, silver, jewellery, ceramics and smaller furniture at across-the-board prices. Open Monday to Friday.

Nice Things Old & New
1010 Pollockshaws Road,
Shawlands
041 649 3826
A mini-emporium, just nine feet wide, in an area which, according to the owner, is no longer what it was. Established more than 30 years ago, the shop has successfully retained a reputation for stocking the interesting and unusual and often at rock-bottom prices. Open afternoons.

Nithsdale Antiques
100 Torrisdale Street, Queens Park (also 79 St George's Road)
041 424 0444
General antiques and shipping items.

Paddy's Market
The Briggait
A do-your-own-thing affair, weather permitting, where anybody can sell anything and many do. Quality varies from the awful to the possible.

Robert Paterson & Son, auctioneers
8 Orchard Street, Paisley
041 889 2435
Sales every second Tuesday.

Phillips (Scotland)
207 Bath Street
041 221 8377
Monthly general sales, as well as antique and specialist sales.

Renaissance Furniture Store
103 Niddrie Road
041 423 0022
General antiques and decorative items.

Frank Russell & Sons Antiques
Unit 4, 1 Rutherglen Road
041 647 9608
0236 736385 (home)
Essentially a trade and shipping dealer. Viewing can be arranged by appointment. No regular hours.

Secondhandjoe's
176 Allison Street
041 422 1544
Cheaper furniture, electrical goods, household basics.

Victorian Village
53 and 57 West Regent Street
041 332 0808
Mid-range antiques and specialist items in a market of 10 dealers. Furniture, bric-a-brac, militaria, jewellery, period clothing and sports-related collectables.

Virginia Antiques Gallery
31–33 Virginia Street,
041 552 5840
Off Argyle Street. Mixed market of more than 60 traders, about 20 of whom sell a broad range of antiques and collectors' items. The building was once the dealing hall where merchants bought and sold tobacco shipments from Virginia. Open all week.

West of Scotland Antique Centre (WOSAC)
Langside Lane, 539 Victoria Road, Queen's Park
041 422 1717

Yet another in the one-stop shopping genre, this one dominated by the **Den of Antiquity**. Other dealers offer a mix of general antiques, pine and furniture.

Yesteryear
158 Albert Drive
041 429 3966
Furniture, general antiques and collectables.

GLENLUCE (DUMFRIES & GALLOWAY)

Glenluce Antique Centre
Dervaird Farm
05813 540
Across-the-board range from bric-a-brac at £1 to Charles II furniture in the low thousands. On A75 14 miles from Newtown Stewart.

GORDON (BORDERS)

Black's Auction Centre
Gordon
0573 410230
Household and general auctions every third Wednesday. On right, just north of village crossroads.

GOUROCK (STRATHCLYDE)

Bygones
59 Shore Road
0475 31114
General antiques and collectors' items.

GREENLAW (BORDERS)

Collectors' Corner
3 The Square
An extraordinary concoction of old books, bric-a-brac, metalware, treen and antiquities – it is also the headquarters of

'Dr Bearnardo's Rest Home for Teddies'.

Greenlaw Antiques
Greenlaw
036 16 220
Main showroom in former town hall at village centre. There is a further shop nearby and a warehouse at the west end of the village. Together these offer a mix of secondhand, bric-a-brac and antique goods, with occasional architectural items. Excellent potential for cottage furnishers.

GREENOCK
(STRATHCLYDE)

Loraine, auctioneers
26 West Stewart Street
0475 23150
Weekly general sales. Phone for details.

GUARDBRIDGE (FIFE)

Circa Antiques
9a Main Street
0334 838896
General antiques, Victoriana and collectors' items in a small village near St Andrews.

GULLANE (LOTHIAN)

Gullane Antiques
5 Roseberry Place
0620 843326
General antiques and collectors' items, including jewellery, glass and porcelain.

HADDINGTON
(LOTHIAN)

The main county town of East Lothian, Haddington retains many fine buildings from its heyday as a bustling local centre. Its people have a strong sense of history: the restoration of its medieval church, wrecked by Cromwell, has been achieved within the last 25 years, as has the establishment of a museum in the house of Jane Welsh Carlyle, wife of Thomas, the 'Sage of Chelsea'. The antique trade is supplemented by four busy charity shops.

Antiques & Things
36 Market Street
062082 2206
An extensive mixed stock of furniture, books and general collectors' items. Closed Monday to Thursday.

Elm House Antiques
The Sands, Church Street
062082 3413
Porcelain, Scottish pottery, tea caddies, small items of mid-range furniture. Appointment advised.

Leslie & Leslie, auctioneers
77 Market Street
062082 2241
Sales of household furniture, general goods and antiques held about four times a year. The firm also has a shop at 77 Market Street selling mostly reproduction brass and furniture, but some older items.

HAMILTON
(STRATHCLYDE)

Hamilton Saleroom
19–21 Wilson Street, Burnbank
0698 421886
General secondhand and household furniture.

LS Smellie & Sons, auctioneers
Lower Auchingramont Road
0698 282007

Household and general sales held weekly.

plus the occasional garden or architectural item.

HELENSBURGH
(STRATHCLYDE)

Lindsay, auctioneers
31 East King Street
0436 72314
Monthly general sales.

The Time Before
67–71 East Princes Street
0436 71510
General antiques, jewellery, bric-a-brac and collectables.

HOUNDWOOD
(BORDERS)

Houndwood House Antiques
Houndwood
08907 61232
Country house 13 miles north of Berwick-on-Tweed selling a comprehensive range of furniture, pictures and collectors' items, including some in the affordable bracket. Owners are in residence and opening hours are flexible.

INNERLEITHEN
(BORDERS)

Collectables
Main Street
General antiques, bric-a-brac and collectors' items.

INVERARY
(STRATHCLYDE)

Cottage Antiques
Inverary
0499 2407
Tucked away beside the distinctive 18th-century church is a mix of mid range and reproduction furniture, pictures, bric-a-brac and collectors' items

INVERKEITHING
(FIFE)

The Bargain Shop
3 Boreland Road
0383 416727
General secondhand furniture and household items. Good flatfillers. Same business also operates in Dunfermline.

INVERNESS
(HIGHLAND)

Capital of the Highlands, say some, while others – usually West Highlanders (*see* Oban) – suggest that Inverness was merely a garrison town which grew. Whatever the historical truth, it presents something of a challenge for the junk buyer, with limited – if good – outlets. Occasional fairs in Eden Court Theatre help to top up local requirements, but the demographic background gives the impression that there isn't a great deal around. The outlying countryside, after all, was thinly populated, and usually by crofting families with few possessions. Yet there are finds to be made. At the height of the stalking business last century there were between twenty and thirty taxidermists, for example, producing mounted stags' heads, and a visit to the silver collection in the museum illustrates the calibre of local silversmithing.

The Attic
Riverside, 17 Huntly Street
0463 243117
Recently extended range of furniture, general antiques and collectors' items.

Fraser's, auctioneers
28–30 Church Street
0463 232395
Mixed sales held fortnightly on
Thursdays and Fridays.

Jackie Stewart Antiques
33/39 Townhead
0294 74074
General antiques, with a
specialist line in maritime items.

**Jedburgh possesses one of the
most complete of the famous
Borders abbeys, as well as the
house where Mary Queen of
Scots slept, which is now the
town museum.**

The Mini-Market
The Building,
Exchange Street
0835 64210 (home)
A mix of new and secondhand
goods, plus the occasional
budget antique.

Turner Antiques
34–36 High Street
0835 63445
Extensive mid-range antiques,
pictures, porcelain and
collectors' items in shop and
upper showrooms, plus
rummageable warehouse with
secondhand furniture and some
cheaper goods to rear.

Robert Hendry, auctioneers
167 Mid Street
05422 2535
General sales every two to
three weeks, plus about eight
antiques sales per annum.

Honor Horne Antiques
3a Abbey Court
0573 224805
Small furniture, porcelain, bric-
a-brac, pottery, silver, pictures,
collectors' items and furniture.

Whites
3 Oven Wynd, off The Square
Secondhand furniture, bric-a-
brac and household items.

Gardner's Antique Shop
Wardend House,
Kibbleston Road,
Kilbarchan
05057 2292
Extensive selection of general
antiques in rural setting, 12
miles east of Glasgow city
centre. Open six days a week
(seven days to trade).

Marjorie & Sandy McDougall
10 The Cross, Kilbarchan
050 57 2229
On Glasgow's rural fringe, well
known for stylish bedroom
items from brass beds, Paisley
shawls, linen, lace and smaller
items of furniture. Quality and
presentation is good, and there
are also affordable buys – a
Victorian pillow case with
hand-crocheted edging at £14,
for example. Open Thursday to
Sunday.

Mossat Antiques
Bridge of Mossat
097 55 71300
General antiques and collectors'
items.

KILLEARN (CENTRAL)

Country Antiques
Main Street
0360 70215
An interesting selection of bric-a-brac, smaller antiques and collectors' items being sold by the local laird's wife.

KILLIN (CENTRAL)

Maureen Gauld
Cameron Buildings,
Main Street
056 72 475
Stock includes a mix of mid-range smaller antiques, silver, jewellery and collectors' items. Closed in winter.

KILMACOLM (STRATHCLYDE)

Kilmacolm Antiques
Stewart Place
050 587 3149
The emphasis is on mid-market and quality, but some less expensive jewellery and collectors' items are often available.

KILMARNOCK (STRATHCLYDE)

MacInnes Antiques
5c David Orr Street
0563 26739
General antiques, furniture and collectors' items. Phone in advance because stock is only shown by appointment.

QS Antiques
Moorfield Industrial Estate,
Troon Road
0292 74377
A varied stock of shipping goods, mid-range furniture, architectural fittings, collectors' items.

KILMICHAEL GLASSARY (STRATHCLYDE)

David Murray Antiques
Rhudle Mill
054 684 284
Furniture, decorative items,

MODERN MINIATURES

People buy old things for many reasons, but one practical consideration is an appreciation of quality and durability. This invites the assumptions that craftsmanship is a thing of the past and that only the rich can afford to buy new furniture of a quality that is comparable to the furniture made a few generations ago. Although this is true up to a point, there are one or two reassuring exceptions. An area that has seen a particularly impressive revival of craftsmanship is that of miniature-making. Almost anything can be miniaturised to the 1/12 scale that is generally favoured. Working glass plate cameras, Aga cookers, lawn-mowers, fishing rods with functioning reels, foundry-cast fire-grates and accessories, light fixtures with functioning 'grain of wheat'-sized bulbs, light switches, books, newspapers, carpets and even embroideries with up to 7,000 handworked stitches per square inch.

bric-a-brac, collectors' items as well as architectural fittings. A broad range for browsing in a spectacular rural setting.

KINCARDINE O'NEIL (GRAMPIAN)

Amber Antiques
1 Southside, Old Turnpike
033 984 277
General collectors' items, pictures, porcelain, silver, books and jewellery, particularly amber.

KINGHORN (FIFE)

Pend Antiques
53 High Street
0592 890207
Victorian and pre-war furniture, textiles, pictures, bric-a-brac and collectors' items.

KINGSTON ON SPEY (GRAMPIAN)

Collectables
Lein Road
034 387462
General small antiques and furniture, boxes, bric-a-brac and jewellery, with specialist line in militaria.

KINGUSSIE (HIGHLAND)

Mostly Pine
Gynack Cottage,
54 High Street
0450 661838
Mid-range pine and country furniture, decorative and collectable items.

KINROSS (TAYSIDE)

Miles Antiques
16 Mill Street
0577 864858

Furniture, decorative items and general antiques.

The Portcullis
76 High Street
0577 862276
General antiques and collectors' items.

KIRKCALDY (FIFE)

The Golden Past
90 Rosslyn Street
0592 53185
Victorian and Edwardian antiques and collectables.

Methuselah's
124 Commercial Street
0592 643088
General antiques and furniture, with a strong emphasis on art deco and post-war collectors' items and a range of memorabilia.

KIRKUDBRIGHT (DUMFRIES & GALLOWAY)

Chapel Antiques
Chapel Farm,
Ringford
0557 22281
Comprehensive selection of antiques and collectors' items. Shipping furniture to silver. Two miles outside town, off the A75.

Osborne's
41 Castle Street
0557 30441
Converted church with a range of furniture and general items.

KIRKWALL (ORKNEY)

Kirkwall Auction Mart
By St Magnus Cathedral
0856 2520

Intermittent general sales.
Phone for details.

LADYBANK
(FIFE)

Ladybank Auctions
Kinloch Street
0337 30488
Weekly auctions of general and
household goods.

LAIRG
(HIGHLAND)

Duka Antiques
Lairg
0549 2240
A fair stock of mid-range
furniture and general antiques,
including occasional items
which were made by estate
joiners for the local mansions
and shooting lodges at the turn
of the century.

LANGHOLM
(DUMFRIES & GALLOWAY)

The Antique Shop
High Street
03873 80238
Porcelain, silver, pictures, glass
and jewellery in shop, with
furniture, books and shipping
goods in nearby trade
warehouse.

Charity Shop
Langholm
Behind Town Hall. Clothes,
costume jewellery, bric-a-brac
and smaller items.

LARGOWARD (FIFE)

Lathallan Antiques
Wester Largoward
0333 36499
A range of smaller antiques,
silver, porcelain and collectors'
items.

LARGS
(STRATHCLYDE)

Narducci Antiques
11 Waterside Street
0475 672612
Warehouse stocked with
shipping goods and general
antiques. Appointment advised.

LERWICK
(SHETLAND)

Shetland Marts
33 South Road
0595 2369
Intermittent general sales.
Phone for details.

LEVEN (FIFE)

**Robert Dowie,
auctioneers**
Station Road
0333 23438
Fortnightly general auction
sales.

LINLITHGOW
(LOTHIAN)

**Antiques & Collectors
Fair**
Burgh Halls
036085 201
Regular fair held on the first
Sunday of each month.

Heritage Antiques
222 High Street
0506 847460
Small antiques, jewellery,
porcelain, silver, collectors'
items.

LUNDIN LINKS
(FIFE)

Bits 'n' Bobs
19 Leven Road
0333 320266.
Small general antiques and a

variety of interesting collectors' items.

MELROSE (BORDERS)

Serendipity
Abbey Street
089 682 3312
Bric-a-brac, furniture, books and useful household items.

Waverley Antiques
Scott's Place,
089 682 2415 (home)
General antiques, collectables and decorative items, including jewellery, kitchenalia, garden furniture, pictures, prints and textiles. Eminently rummageable.

MOFFAT (DUMFRIES & GALLOWAY)

TW Beatty
22 Well Street
0683 20380
Large shop and warehouse with an extensive range of furniture, pictures, porcelain, metalware, glass and general antiques.

MONTROSE (TAYSIDE)

Trade with the Baltic ports gave Montrose a cosmopolitan air which it has never quite lost. In the 17th century the town had one of the largest fishing fleets in the whole of Scotland, and Montrose salmon was much appreciated by the rich merchants of Venice. It also had its famous sons and daughters; generations of the Coutts family, for example, who provided provosts for the burgh and bankers for the king; and the celebrated beauty, Lola Montez, who also had royal connections – she was mistress of Bavaria's mad King Ludwig.

Aladdin's Cave
50 Castle Street
0674 7720
General secondhand goods.

Harper-James
25–27 Baltic Street
0674 671307
Mid-range furniture, porcelain and smaller antiques. Also does restoration and upholstery.

Taylor's, auctioneers
11 Panmure Row
0674 72775
Popular fortnightly auctions with a broad mix of antique and household goods.

MUSSELBURGH (LOTHIAN)

Monkton House Antiques
Old Craighall
031 665 5753
Specialist in mechanical antiques, musical boxes, pianolas etc. On west side of town. Ring for appointment.

NEWTONMORE (HIGHLAND)

The Antique Shop
Main Street
0540 673272
Smaller furniture, bric-a-brac, collectors' items, jewellery, silver, books.

NEWTON STEWART (DUMFRIES & GALLOWAY)

Brown's, auctioneers
Newton Stewart
0671 3185
Monthly sales conducted at Carsluith Village Hall nearby.

Pathbrae Antiques
20 Albert Street
0671 3429

Porcelain, silver, jewellery and collectors' items.

NORTH BERWICK
(LOTHIAN)

Fraser's Antiques
129 High Street
0620 2722
Furniture, porcelain, silver, collectors' items.

OBAN
(STRATHCLYDE)

Major embarkation point for the Isles, including Mull, Iona and Rhum. Oban also boasts its own version of the Colosseum, MacCaig's Folly. It has been claimed that Oban is the true spiritual capital of the Highlands, despite its incorporation into the Glasgow-dominated mega-region of Strathclyde.

Oban Antiques
35 Stevenson Street
0631 66203
Furniture, general antiques, books and collectors' items.

PEEBLES
(BORDERS)

A thriving county town, whose past residents included the novelist and adventurer John Buchan, the African explorer

SCOTTISH SILVER

Scotland's silversmiths were working in many of the country's smallest burghs as far back as the 16th century, when the Elgin silversmith Walter Hay was fined for supplying communion tokens to non-locals. The first identified silversmith was Henry the Bald, who worked in Perth in the 12th century, although there was already an established tradition of Celtic and earlier silverworkers going back several centuries before that. The 18th and 19th centuries were particularly busy times for local smiths, most of whom made a lucrative living from the growing demand for fashionable tableware. There were – and are – noticeable differences between the tastes of the average Scottish and English household. In England, where baroque sumptuousness and Huguenot influence had prevailed, there was a tendency to favour more decorative styles. Scots, on the whole, had a natural predilection for restraint, and an innate sense of practicality. Design was often simple and disciplined, and the satisfaction of owning silver lay as much in the feel of the piece and the attractiveness of the metal as in the artistry of its production. Teaspoons are particularly popular with today's collectors, but other collecting themes can be based on place of origin – Dundee, for example, with its lilypot hallmark – or on specific workshops, such as that of Keay of Perth. Prices can be low – less than £10 for a pleasing example with a couple of time-honoured dents. Rare pieces, however, can command high bids in the saleroom – perhaps as much as £500 for a good early Wick tablespoon.

Mungo Park, and the publishing brothers Robert and William Chambers.

Lawrie & Symington, auctioneers

South Parks, Caledonian Road
0555 2281
Monthly general sales at above address.

Cobweb's Antiques

66–68 High Street
0721 29709
A mix of mid-range and cheaper furniture, collectables and bric-a-brac.

PERTH
(TAYSIDE)

Perth is the capital of one of Scotland's wealthiest counties, and is well supplied with antique shops of all descriptions. Many cater for a discriminating collector clientele with stocks of good provincial silver, Monart glass, jewellery and fine pictures. Others deal in more general stock, with definite junk-buying possibilities. Given the town's compact size, most could be covered within the day.

Robert Ainslie Junior

80 Perth Road,
Scone
0738 52438
A mid- to upper-market mix, with a few cheaper buys. The shop is located two miles north of the centre of town.

Ainslie's Antique Warehouse

Unit 3, 13 Gray Street
0738 36825
Operated by the brother of the shop listed above. The stock includes general antiques and shipping pieces. Hours are irregular, either weekends or by appointment.

Antiques & Bygones

Tighvallich, Dunkeld Road,
Bankfoot
0738 8745
Stock includes oil lamps, tools and instruments, scales and balances. About nine miles north of centre by A9. Trades seven days a week.

AS Deuchar

10–12 South Street
0738 26297
Furniture, china, metalware, pictures and prints and general shipping goods. Closed Saturday.

Atholl Bank

Main Street,
Bankfoot
0738 87253
Specialising in smaller antiques and porcelain.

JG Henderson

5 North Methven Street
0738 24836
Long-established (54 years) dealer in small collectables. Jewellery, silver, glass, porcelain, coins, medals and banknotes. Closed Wednesday.

Lindsay Burns, auctioneers

6 King Street
0738 3388
Fortnightly household sales. In addition, quarterly antique sales include pictures, jewellery, porcelain etc. as well as furniture.

Love's Auction Rooms

52–54 Canal Street
0738 33337

Household and general sales weekly. Mixed antique sales quarterly. Three collectors' sales a year.

Ian Murray's Antique Warehouse
21 Glasgow Road
0738 37222
A decommissioned train shed stacked with mid-range and shipping goods provides a setting for some excellent rummaging. One of the six resident dealers, Graham Proudlock, carries interesting ironware and decorative architectural pieces.

Tay Street Gallery
70 Tay Street
0738 20604
Mostly mid-market furniture, pictures and prints. Closed Wednesday and irregular hours otherwise.

J Wilman
93–5 Canal Street
0738 38007
Eminently rummageable backyard stores of mostly secondhand and shipping-grade furniture, with a showroom of mid-range and collectable goods.

PITTENWEEM
(FIFE)

Pittenweem Antiques
15 East Shore
0333 312054
Much quality stock, but also less expensive smaller items.

PORTREE
(SKYE)

Ar Bhute Beagh
2 Wentworth Street
0478 2443

A range of small general antiques, bric-a-brac and collectors' items.

PORTSOY
(GRAMPIAN)

Other Times Antiques
13–15 Seafield Street
0261 42866
General antiques and collectors' items up to 1950.

PRESTWICK
(STRATHCLYDE)

Yer Granny's Attic
176 Main Street
0292 76312
Furniture, Victoriana, bric-a-brac, linen and stained glass.

RAIT (TAYSIDE)

Rait Village Antiques Centre
Rait
0821 670205
A large converted farmstead, rather than a village, midway between Perth and Dundee on the A85. Around half a dozen dealers offer everything from top-of-the-range period furniture to rummageable finds, including teddies, dolls and Paisley shawls.

ST ANDREWS
(FIFE)

Bygones
68 South Street
0334 75849
Furniture, bric-a-brac, silver, collectors' items. Closed Thursday.

MacGregor Auctions
56 Largo Road
0334 72431
Fortnightly general sales.

Magpie
28 Bell Street
0334 72487
Small antiques, jewellery and collectors' items.

ST BOSWELLS
(BORDERS)

Christcott's Antiques
The Crescent
0835 22045
Small furniture, bric-a-brac, jewellery, collectors' items.

Mainstreet Trading, auctioneers
Main Street
0835 23978
Frequent sales of furniture and household effects, decorative items, stable and farm accessories, architectural items.

Mr Casey's
Weirgate Brae
089 682 2017 (home)
Small country antiques, Victoriana, tiles, linen, collectors' items.

SALTCOATS
(STRATHCLYDE)

Narducci Antiques
57 Raise Street
0294 61687
Shipping and general antiques, mainly for trade and export.

SCALLOWAY
(SHETLAND)

The Sea Chest
Scalloway
059 588 326
Reputedly Britain's northernmost antique shop, with a cosmopolitan stock which reflects the local seafaring tradition – teaware from Japan, clocks from Pennsylvania, as well as the customary Scottish fare of wally-dugs, spinning wheels and jug and ewer sets.

Shetland Marts, auctioneers
33 South Road, Lerwick
0595 2369
Intermittent general sales.

SELKIRK
(BORDERS)

Heatherlie Antiques
6/8 Heatherlie Terrace
0750 20114
Furniture, bric-a-brac and general antiques, with cheaper secondhand furniture and basics in the adjacent store.

SORBIE
(DUMFRIES & GALLOWAY)

RG Williamson & Co.
Old Church
098 885 275
General antiques and furniture, some modern.

STIRLING
(CENTRAL)

Elizabeth Paterson Antiques
52 Spittal Street
0786 50648
Oriental porcelain and a range of furniture, including pine.

Stewart's Saleroom
Dunbarton Road
0786 73414
General secondhand goods.

STRATHBLANE
(CENTRAL)

Whatnots
16 Milngavie Road
0360 70310

General mid-range antiques and shipping goods, furniture, clocks, silver, jewellery, paintings and horse-drawn vehicles. Ten miles north of Glasgow.

STROMNESS
(ORKNEY)

West Mainland Mart
Ferry Road
0856 850288
Intermittent general sales.

THURSO
(HIGHLAND)

Thurso Antiques
Drill Hall, Sinclair Street
0847 63291

Porcelain, jewellery, collectors' items, pictures, coins, fiddles, pictures.

WALKERBURN
(BORDERS)

Townhouse Antiques
8 Peebles Road
089687 694
General antiques, furniture, textiles, porcelain and collectors' items.

WICK
(HIGHLAND)

Paterson's Auctions
Harbour Place
0955 5874
Intermittent general sales.

MAPS

The maps on the following pages show the towns featured in this guide. The main roads and motorways are also shown, to assist orientation, as are the outlines of the counties of England, Wales, Northern Ireland and Scotland.

All towns are listed in the index and gazetteer between pages 310 and 320. Beside each place name (with its county in brackets) is a page number indicating where it appears in the guide and also reference to the town's location on these maps.

To find a town, look at the map number (number M1 to M7) and the letter, a, b, c or d, that appears after it. This letter indicates the quarter of the map in which the town can be found – a = top left, b = top right, c = bottom left and d = bottom right. For example, the map reference for London is M3c, indicating it can be found on Map 3 in the the lower left quarter.

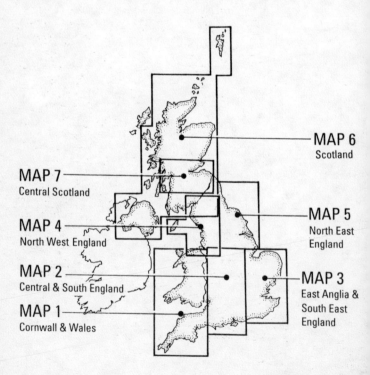

MAP 6
Scotland

MAP 7
Central Scotland

MAP 5
North East England

MAP 4
North West England

MAP 2
Central & South England

MAP 3
East Anglia & South East England

MAP 1
Cornwall & Wales

MAP 1
ornwall & Wales

MAP 2
Central & South England

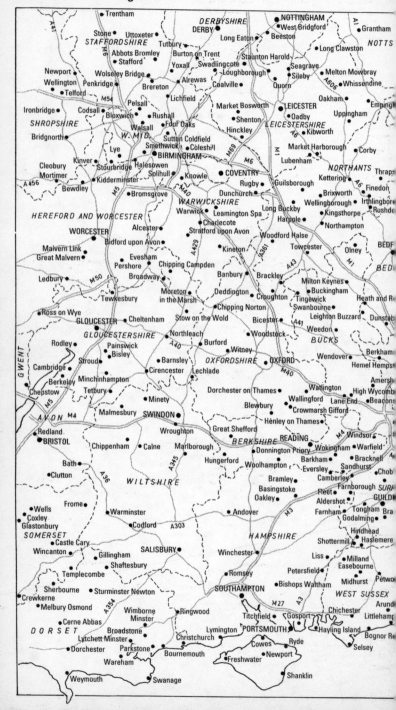

MAP 3
East Anglia & South East England

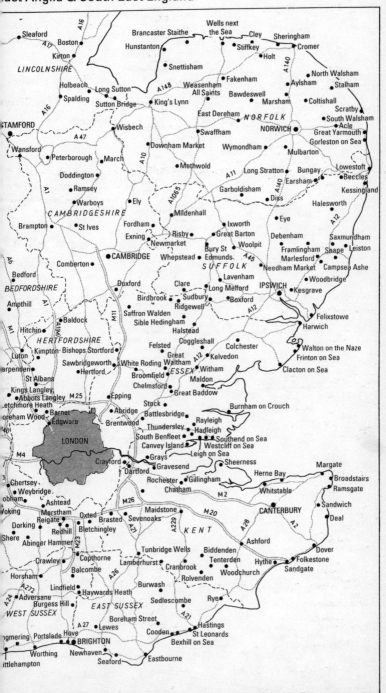

MAP 4
North West England

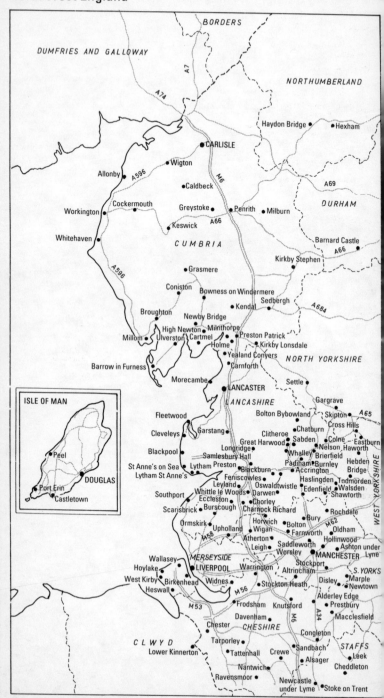

MAP 5
North East England

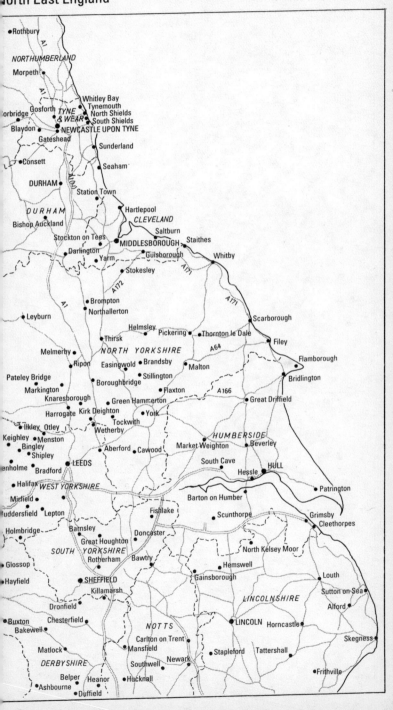

MAP 6
Scotland and Northern Ireland

NORTHERN IRELAND

Bushmills
Portstewart
Coleraine
Londonderry
LONDONDERRY
Claudy
ANTRIM
Larne
Ballyclare
Bangor
M2
TYRONE
Cookstown
Stewartstown
BELFAST
Donaghadee
Greyabbey
Lurgan
Saintfield
FERMANAGH
Portadown
Annahilt
Armagh
ARMAGH
DOWN
Newry

SHETLAND
Lerwick
Scalloway

Stromness
Kirkwall
ORKNEY

Thurso
Wick

Lairg
Bonarbridge

Kingston on Spey
Portsoy
Fraserburgh
Dingwall
Fortrose
Elgin
Buckie
Banff
Avoch
Forres
Fochabers
A98
Beauly
Auldearn
Keith
INVERNESS
GRAMPIAN
HIGHLAND
Kildrummy
Alford
ABERDEEN
Kingussie
Kincardine O'Neil
Banchory
Newtonmore

TAYSIDE
Brechin
Montrose
Alyth
Friockheim
Dunkeld
Blairgowrie
Arbroath

CENTRAL
FIFE

EDINBURGH
GLASGOW
LOTHIAN
M8

S T R A T H C L Y D E
BORDERS

Campbeltown

Moffat
Langholm
DUMFRIES & GALLOWAY
NORTHUMBRIA
Auldgirth
DUMFRIES
Newton Stewart
Castle Douglas
Glenluce
Kirkudbright
CUMBRIA
Sorbie

Portree

MAP 7
Central Scotland

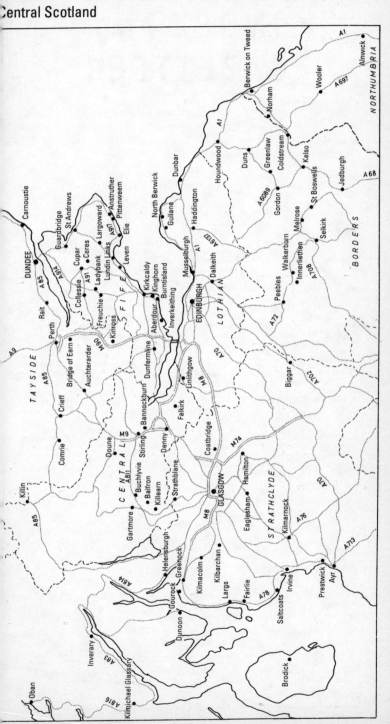

INDEX AND GAZETTEER

This index to the towns in the guide lists place names in alphabetical order, followed by the county (in brackets), then the page number or numbers where the town appears. The index also gives map references (Map 2a, etc) to the maps on pages 303 to 309.